*cpl*
PRESS

# THE UK
# GREEN
# GROWERS
# GUIDE

by

Steve Lisansky PhD
Alison Robinson BSc
Jim Coombs PhD

© **CPL Scientific Limited 1991**

Published in the United Kingdom by:
CPL Press, a division of CPL Scientific Limited, Science House, Winchcombe Road, Newbury, Berkshire  United Kingdom
Telephone 0635 524064, Fax 0635 529322

Written by:  S.G. Lisansky PhD, A. Robinson BSc, J. Coombs PhD

The company acknowledges with thanks the assistance of Christina Humphrey and Elinor Coombs in the preparation of this book.

Cover and symbol design:  J Coombs
Cover and symbol artwork:  Sue Lisansky Illustrations, Reading, Berkshire UK
Cover set by:  CPL Press, Newbury, Berkshire UK
Printed by:  J.W. Arrowsmith Limited, Bristol UK

This book is one of a number of publications by CPL Scientific Limited on agriculture, food, waste treatment and biotechnology.

ISBN 1 872691 10 2

# Table of Contents

## Part I  The Green Scene

## Part II  The Products and Where to Get Them

## Indexes

# Key to product uses

 Houseplants

 Orchards

 Flower & Vegetable Gardens

 Forestry

 Horticulture

 Arable Farming

 Glasshouses

 Animal Husbandry

## Key to Product Sections

 Insect Control

 Silage

 Disease Control

 Fertilisers

 Nitrogen-fixing Seed Treatments

 Other Products

 Products for Animals

 Chemical Products Accepted by Some Green Growers

# PART I

# The Green Scene

# 1 Why Do We Need Green Products?

This is a book about choice. Unlike many recent publications containing the word **GREEN**, this book is not a description of threats to the global environment, nor does it tell you what to do for the future good of mankind. Rather, it is a source of information. It will enable you to make up your own mind about the type of inputs you want to make into your home, garden, orchard or farm. It will inform you about those organisations which promote alternatives to the current widely accepted growing practices based on synthetic chemicals. And it will tell you all about the alternative products available.

Putting into practice the principles of green growing can be a lengthy and complex process. From the viewpoint of the actual growing, it may require modifications to every aspect of what we do, from digging the soil, through choosing which plants to grow and which weeds to encourage, through where and how we compost and re-use that part of the crop we discard. Many of these techniques and principles are well covered in other books. From the philosophical viewpoint, green growing is often tied up with whole sets of ideas about growing, folklore, the world, the greenhouse effect and many other environmental issues that may not touch directly on how we keep caterpillars off our cabbage. Some groups, like those doing biodynamic farming, require knowledge of and obeisance to the phase of the moon and other natural phenomena not yet proven to have any direct effect on pests or yields. Everyone concerned with their environment and with the food they eat would like to see all reasonable aspects of green growing implemented. However, in practice many ordinary gardeners and farmers either can't or won't be able to do this.

What they need is specific green products that replace the chemicals they're trying to avoid. This includes fertilisers, pest and disease control agents, and products for animal husbandry

The UK Green Growers Guide will enable both gardeners and farmers to understand the way in which the alternatives to conventional chemical inputs work. It tells you where to obtain the products and indicates the extent to which these may be used in the home, garden, orchard, horticultural holding or farm. It deals with products that are NOT

SYNTHETIC CHEMICALS or DRUGS, yet in many cases can replace such compounds. These products can be beneficial in both the growing of plants and in animal husbandry. The Guide will help you *reduce* your use of chemicals as pesticides, fertilisers, nutrient supplements, etc. in growing things.

The UK Green Growers Guide has been published in response to a wide and increasing concern about the longer-term effects of synthetic pesticides, fertilisers and other chemicals on the environment and human health. It fills a key need for better information concerning the options available to those wanting to meet the growing demand for organic or conservation grade methods. At the same time, general attitudes concerning animal well-being are also changing. Many people are turning to vegetarian diets due to uneasiness about how animals are reared; whilst even meat eaters want to see an end to inhumane methods of intensive husbandry and drug-induced rapid growth.

The products listed in the UK Green Growers Guide are available now. Demand for them has been increasing and many are set to find new markets. There is a sound reason, based on scientific evidence, for this prediction. Prolonged use of synthetic chemicals, at higher concentrations as resistance develops, has revealed many unsuspected deleterious effects. There is a continuing need to re-evaluate what we know about these chemicals and their compliance with statutory requirements, regulations and codes of practice within the industry. Such re-evaluation, especially where it leads to withdrawal of synthetic pesticides or drugs, will increase the need for and use of the products in the UK Green Growers Guide.

Growing things with chemical inputs has now become "conventional" agriculture. Justification for this, cited by government spokesmen, agricultural economists and many farm organisations is the increased yields this method provides. Chemical farming has brought Europe from food deficiency (overcome by imports) to surplus and to food mountains with massive support costs under the Common Agricultural Policy. The surplus now exists on a global scale, with most developed countries taking agricultural land out of production and waging increasingly acrimonious arguments about international trade, agricultural subsidies and the future of the General Agreements on Tariffs and Trade (GATT). Using less land will result in ever greater chemical inputs by the large, 'efficient' few, who will obtain a increasing share of the income while smaller farmers income will decline in a downward spiral. Adoption of Green Growing principles may represent not only a viable option, but ultimately the only option.

The potential for alternative systems, such as organic and conservation grade, has been recognised by the Commission of the European Community and to a lesser extent by the UK Government. Research and Development of these systems is accepted as a legitimate and useful expenditure and is being promoted within the Community at this time. Adoption of such systems will reduce the rate at which the environment is being degraded by loss of topsoil, contamination of ground water and generally decreased fertility. Produce grown by alternative systems can attract significant premiums (see chapter 2), reflecting market demand, which will help to maintain farm incomes. For the home grower, there is the satisfaction of knowing that one is both producing a better quality product and doing less damage to the wildlife in one's own and everyone else's garden.

It is often suggested that lower inputs, as in organic or conservation grade growing, means lower yields. However, this may not be so. Many studies have been carried out where little difference has been detected between yields produced with chemicals and those produced by alternative systems. Indeed, in some cases, increased yields have been recorded from organic systems. Conventional analysis stresses the additional labour required while taking little notice of the environmental benefits obtained. There is no reason why alternative systems should not match chemical systems in yield, if adequate nutrients are supplied and pest control can be achieved with products like those in the UK Green Growers Guide.

These products are the result of the search for alternatives which can achieve the beneficial effects of synthetic chemicals and reduce the risk of total crop failure without the need for backbreaking pest and weed control. It is, of course, still early days. The *"agrobiological"* equivalents of many agrochemicals have yet to be discovered. Even so, the range of products both worldwide and in The UK Green Growers Guide is considerable with new entries to the market anticipated. Many of these new products reflect the emphasis placed on the application of biology to industry during the 1980s - biotechnology.

Our objective in producing the UK Green Growers Guide is to provide a complete compilation of all the non-chemical (agrobiological) products available in the UK that can help reduce chemical dependency in growing. If you know of any others, please tell us for the next edition.

Some products in the Guide are presently only available in bulk, usually to professional growers. Smaller manufacturers may have difficulty in providing individual gardeners with small orders. Some agrobiological products, unlike most chemicals, have short shelf-lives. They need to be bought and used fresh like food from supermarkets and before their expiry dates. At present, the small markets for these products make it uneconomic for manufacturers to consider selling them in refrigerated cabinets in garden centres. As demand rises, producers will find it increasingly profitable to distribute their products more widely. So if there's a product in this Guide you can't find, ask the manufacturer. Even if it can't be supplied now, if enough people ask, perhaps it will be available in the future.

# 2 The Growing Business

Most people are fortunate in that they can indulge in the cultivation of plants and the raising of animals as pets without having to concern themselves with the detailed finances of what they are doing. In fact, the cultivation of vegetables and plants in the home garden is a peculiarity of the British, involving one of the largest of the leisure markets with sales through specialist garden centres, DIY stores and food supermarkets running into hundreds of millions of pounds each year. However, for a small proportion of the population (around three percent or less) growing is not for fun, but is a business. Like any other business, it is based on balance sheets related to inputs and outputs: crops, time and labour, chemicals and finance. The return on effort can be measured by the output of saleable product in the same way that the return on capital employed can be measured by interest earned through investment or profit derived through business activity and acumen. In Europe however, over the last two or three decades, the business of growing has differed from most others in that it has expanded in an uncontrolled way through subsidies under the auspices of the Common Agricultural Policy (CAP). Most forms of business have to identify a product niche, manufacture the product and then market it in competition with other suppliers at a price dictated by the laws of competitive supply and demand. If the product is in surplus, the price will fall and if demand ceases, the business will adapt its products or fail. This is not so for agriculture; for several decades the CAP has provided an assured market at guaranteed minimum prices with produce entering intervention stores when supply exceeds demand. The cost in financial terms has been large, up to billions of pounds each year. In addition, there has been a second price to pay, the cost to the environment.

The payment of guaranteed prices, with no limit set on quantity of production, has encouraged the continued growing of the same crop, such as wheat, on the same land for many years. The extent of and the yields produced by this monoculture have been raised by the intensive use of mechanisation. Increased efficiency can be achieved through the use of ever larger machines which in turn require ever larger fields - leading to 'improvement schemes', land drainage, hedge removal and ditch filling. This, combined with liberal application of powerful, cheap chemicals and fertilisers has given Britain to a generally prosperous farming community and a depleted landscape. As with everything else, there were degrees of richness among the farming community and degrees of degradation to the land. It is fashionable, but not always true, to link the two as cause and effect.

Since Britain joined the European Community, as a result of farmers' efforts, we have moved from food imports to food surpluses. Now these surpluses are becoming too costly, so the politicians want to reverse the process by the introduction of quotas, decreasing farm gate prices and reduced guarantees and subsidies. At the same time, Government-backed agricultural research budgets have been slashed and the balance re-directed towards food, nutrition and basic science rather than the short-term needs of the farmer, while, at the same time, EC-backed set-aside schemes pay farmers not to use their land.

The change in emphasis has been rapid and farmers are now suffering significant losses. These losses are in part financial and in part social and political. From the financial viewpoint, many farmers are having to reassess their whole business strategy. Encouraged by the potential income from acquisition of new technology and larger machines, many borrowed heavily from banks, increasing their fixed overheads. Now, their income is reduced while prices fall, leaving them with only one apparent option to keep their balance sheets in the black, that is, to increase the yield per hectare of land to cover these mounting fixed costs. Conventionally, yield is measured in terms of weight of product produced each year from each unit area of land. This is recorded in terms of tonnes of wheat, or whatever, per hectare.  The ultimate maximum yield fixed set by a combination of our climate, the quality of soil and the genetic make-up of the crop. As far as climate is concerned, what matters is the soil temperature, the amount of water or rain and the amount of sunshine. As far as soil is concerned, its fertility reflects both the level of nutrients and its structure, which governs a soil's ability to hold water and air and to allow roots to penetrate. Adding massive quantities of nutrients to the soil is a low cost, short-term way of increasing yields which can be sustained only by the additional input of myriad chemical pesticides, herbicides and fungicides.

A simplistic view is that as prices fall income can only be maintained by pushing yields ever higher by using ever more inputs. One alternative is

6

to replace the measurement of yield in crop weight per hectare with yield in monetary returns per hectare; this leads to the concept of crop diversification. For the average farmer, diversification usually means growing 'alien' crops for non-food use, or trees for energy or cosseting herds of deer, or more drastically departing into the realms of holiday homes, adventure games and golf. These may make money and keep the bank manager happy, but they are not farming in the true sense of the word.

The same trends which have turned their financial world upside down have also totally reversed the social standing accorded to farmers. Once one of the mainstays of the social structure in village life, along with the priest and schoolmaster, farmers are now critically hammered for destroying the countryside and the wildlife in it. However, in general, the average farmer is no keener to see wildlife disappear than the rest of us. It is easy to overlook the fact that much more damage has been done in the past by industry and more recently by urban sprawl and the provision of motorway and road networks. As in other walks of life, the basic question is one of need, opportunity and compromise.

Farmers want reliable incomes that others on salaries take for granted and for this they require reliable products to ensure good harvests with markets available for the resulting products. As a group, farmers are environmentally aware and choose to use products that are the most effective and cause the least damage. Even the less scrupulous farmer is constrained by law. On the other hand, the major source of information made available to the farmer comes from the manufacturers of agrochemicals. Many of these companies are now, and over the last few years, attempting to improve their image and to raise the level of responsibility in the way their products are used. Some are even researching, promoting and marketing agrobiological products such as in this Guide. Substitution of agrobiologicals for agrochemicals does occur, but the rate of change is slow. Change is limited in part by what farmers will accept and in part by lack of accurate information on the alternatives.

Organic farming provides less than 1% of total production in the UK and is still considered to be in the realm of the eccentric by the majority of farmers. Some farmers have turned to organic methods of production to satisfy consumer demand for residue-free food. Some have been attracted by the concept on the basis of philosophical considerations, others through concern about the overuse of chemicals and others may have just been looking to put their 'toe in the water' and try it out.

There can be a firm financial basis for turning at least part of a farm over to alternative husbandry systems. A combination of premium payments, reflecting what the consumer in the shop is prepared to pay, and careful management can result in improved farm income as data from both Organic Farmers and Growers and other, completely independent, sources has shown. The problem remains that alternative farm methods require more attention to detail and the replacing of chemical remedies with extra thought, planning and effort. Where such attention is lacking, and no simple remedy is available, then yields may be too inconsistent for the peace of mind of both the farmers and the nation. If everyone switched over to organic production methods our food supply would be at risk. However, at present, two-thirds of the organic food consumed in Britain is imported and with demand for chemical-free food predicted to rise there is room for many more farmers to turn to organic farming.

Opportunities for a successful business without chemicals are not restricted to arable farmers. Increasing consumer awareness of about health and nutrition has created a demand for lean meat which has been met by selective breeding often combined with the use of growth promoters in animal feed. These growth promoters are mostly antibiotics that adjust the balance of bacteria in the gut and increase growth at stages in the animal's life that produce more lean meat. The use of antibiotics in this way is in itself controversial as there may be residues in the meat. However, recent developments in biotechnology have allowed farmers to alter the microfloral populations in the gut of animals directly by administering doses of beneficial bacteria or yeasts; 'probiotics'.

Pressure on all producers to reduce agrochemical use can be expected to increase. Understanding by farmers and consumers of each others' needs is likely to lead to a wider acceptance of an integrated farming system that uses biological and chemical products together to provide nutrients and protection for crops and livestock, justifying the belief that Green Growing can be the growth business of the future.

Organic farming gives lower yields per hectare for milling wheat, milling barley and potatoes than if the crops are grown by a conventional farming system. Field beans show a slightly higher yield per hectare than if conventionally grown as the beans are legumes and so can give good yields even with low nitrogen inputs.

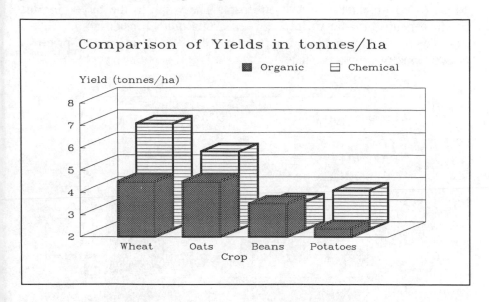

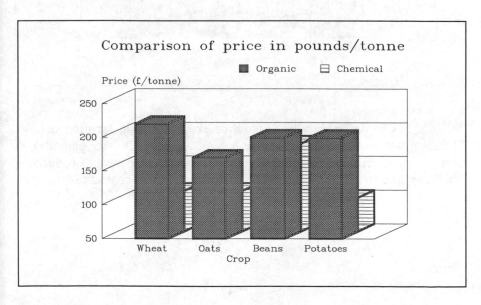

Organically grown produce commands higher prices from the consumer partly to cover higher production costs. The value to the buyer for the produce being organic varies between crops quite considerably. All the organic crops shown have a premium of 40% or more the price of conventionally grown produce.

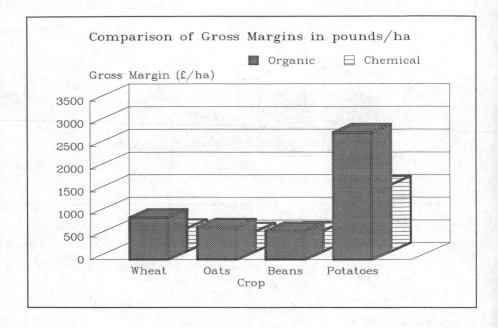

Despite lower yields in non-leguminous crops, organic farming obtains higher gross margins per hectare for all crops than are gained byu conventional farming systems.  This is because organic produce is obtaining higher prices that more than covers the extra cost of productions

# 3 Growing Food - Is There a Need For Chemicals?

*"With an estimated 1.3 billion people to be added to the human family in the remaining years of this century, this will require an increase in food production of 3-4% annually...Agricultural policies in practically all countries have focused on output growth. Despite this, it has proved far more difficult to raise world agricultural output by a consistent 3% per year in the mid-1980s than it was in the mid-1950s...Moreover production records have been offset by the appearance of linked economic and ecological crises: industrialised countries are finding it increasingly difficult to manage their surplus food production, the livelihood base of millions of poor producers in developing countries is deteriorating, and the resources base for agriculture is under pressure virtually everywhere."* Our Common Future - World Commission of Environment and Development, 1989.

This report states that an annual increase in world food production of 3% is needed just to keep up with population growth. Appeals for famine relief in one country or another throughout the world are a regular feature of our nightly news. In February, 1991, harvests in Ethiopia and the Sudan were known to have failed and famine relief workers were saying that 27 million people were in danger. One million people in Ethiopia alone were expected to die. The famine was described as *"unprecedented, and worse than 1984-85."* Where will this food come from? How can developed nations even contemplate reducing food production when the worldwide need is so great and shows no sign of abating?

However, many authorities believe that the real problem is not the absolute amount of food in the world, but its availability to the people who need it. Some advocate sending American and EC surpluses to the hungry. This is an excellent plan and it will clearly feed the famished for a short time. The longer-term solution is to avoid future hunger and famines by making sure poorer countries can grow enough food. The way to do this is give them enough technology and money to get going, and to advise on the sensible use of all available inputs, better varieties, green products and, where warranted, some chemicals.

The main methods used to increase food production have been:

to improve crop yields by selecting varieties that are disease-resistant and which allow more than one crop to be obtained;

to use more chemicals including fertilisers, pesticides and growth promoters to improve growth and reduce losses due to pests and diseases - in the past 35 years fertiliser use has increased nine fold and the use of chemical pesticides has risen 32 fold;

to increase the use of irrigation - in the past 35 years irrigated land area has doubled.

Agrochemical use has also increased to make full use of varieties that have been bred for their higher yields. In the UK, yields per hectare of cereals rose by 55% from 1966 to 1986. Use of fertilisers and lime peaked in 1984 with the UK farmers spending a record £954 million pounds to fertilise the soil. The use of nitrogen on all crops increased by about 80% between 1970 and 1986. Since 1984, expenditure has fallen due to reductions in use combined with a gradual decrease in the real price of fertilisers beginning in the mid-1970s.

Pesticide use rose by 40% from 1970 to 1989 despite prices doubling during this time. Since 1985, expenditure on pesticides has fallen although prices have remained fairly static indicating an overall reduction in use. Agrochemical use can be expected to decrease further as the real price for cereals continues to fall making current use levels uneconomic.

These large increases in fertilisers and pesticide use have been made economically possible in many countries by government incentives. Government policies have placed a strong emphasis on the quantity of food produced; incentives to continue producing more food exist even in the absence of any demand for the product. For example, by keeping EEC intervention prices for cereals constant for ten years, farmers have had to increase production in order to increase their incomes in line with inflation. Livestock premiums have been paid for every animal, regardless of how many were being kept, encouraging growers to overstock their land. In hilly upland areas overstocking can cause serious soil erosion.

The combination of many years of intensive use of resources on land, chemicals, money, new seeds and new equipment, has led to surplus food in the EC and the US. Farming methods may need to become less intensive both to reduce pressure on resources and to conserve wildlife. Truly sustainable agriculture cannot be based on methods that deplete the soil of nutrients and degrade its structure.

Although some recent subsidy systems have stressed retiring land from production, such as the set-aside system operating in the UK, these may not necessarily have the desired effect as farmers will try to maintain their income by farming their remaining land even more intensively. This is less likely in Europe where land is farmed fairly intensively already, but it is quite common in the US where average yields per acre are relatively low and can easily be increased by using more fertilisers and pesticides.

Overproduction not only uses up costly resources, it creates food mountains and wine lakes which have to be maintained and paid for. Many people get very irritated at the thought of what seem like ridiculously high food prices combined with massive surpluses, high storage costs and occasionally very conspicuous destruction of the extra food. Politically and often economically it is more attractive to export surpluses. Unfortunately, the release of large quantities of food onto world markets can cause other problems especially for developing countries by depressing world prices and reducing their already small and vulnerable incomes. For example, rice and sugar are important export products for many developing countries, low prices on the world market caused by surplus EC sugar or surplus US rice means lower incomes for these countries. When famines occur, they can be alleviated in the short term by providing food aid, usually for free, but at the same time, the depressing effect this has on food prices does not encourage farmers in the developing countries to improve their own balanced food production. Instead farmers may concentrate on a single cash crop for export or switch land to other, non-food crops for sale to developed countries.

However, we should remember that the Common Agricultural Policy (CAP), so often a target of abuse from politicians and bar stool experts, has been one of the most spectacular successes of our era. Before World War Two, the UK and much of Europe was not self-sufficient in food, importing up to 60% of requirements. Hunger and privation, if not famine, were frequent occurrences even in the developed countries. Food prices, especially in Britain, were kept very low by importing food from the Empire produced using cheap labour; domestic producers could not compete and went through frequent boom and bust cycles as world prices, and their incomes, fluctuated wildly. The war showed how vulnerable Britain had become by nearly cutting off our food supply. At its end, Europe was in ruins and many were hungry if not actually starving. Although food became more available over the next decade, a long-term solution to Europe's food insecurity was essential. Following the formation of the Common Market, the CAP was designed and implemented to make Europe self-sufficient in food, to provide buffer stocks against crop failures, and to stabilise the food supply by stabilising the prices paid to producers. Of course this meant higher prices for consumers but it also meant there would always be something to buy.

In addition, promoting farming is not just about economics and food. In most of the EC, the rural, agricultural countryside is now part of our self-image, part of our man-made heritage. In the US, when farms disappear, shopping centres usually take their place. Inherited farmland may be valued, **and taxed**, at its value as developed land. This virtually forces its sale to developers just to pay the taxes even when the inheritors want to stay in farming. If this happened in Europe, our landscape would be demolished in a generation. By ensuring a livelihood to farmers, even to those whom the British disdainfully believe to be 'inefficient', the CAP has helped to preserve our countryside, our agricultural infra-structure and has provided us all with sufficient, if expensive, food. In the longer term, farmers must be the custodians of our landscape and will only be able to fulfill that role if they have sufficient income.

Part of the process of providing much more food from relatively little arable land involves the use of better strains and more inputs, and has brought us to our present situation of anxiety about chemicals. No one disputes that the movement to green growing will decrease productivity as yields decline and pests obtain a larger share of the crop. For some products, like natural fertilisers, there is a limit to just how much is available. While some growers can use manure, compost etc there simply will not be enough of these materials for every grower to have a good supply. For other products, like many of the alternative pest control products, additional skill, care and patience may be required to use them and many of these products are not as deadly as the synthetic chemicals they replace. Yields will almost certainly fall.

# Developing countries

The use of agrochemicals in many developing countries is low, partly because of their cost. Where chemicals are used they remain effective as pests have not yet become resistant and yields are a long way below their potential. An increase in food production in developing countries is essential: to feed their rapidly increasing populations; to improve their economies by reducing imports; and to provide employment so that the people can afford to buy the food. Careful use of agrochemicals as well as green products and environmentally sound techniques will allow most developing countries to increase their food production.

Placing the emphasis of production on food deficit countries will also reduce the need for agricultural inputs in the developed world. This will help us progress towards a more sustainable agriculture which will also reduce overproduction. This argument could be interpreted as suggesting that agrochemical use should be transferred from the developed to the developing world; that we should move our pollution somewhere else. In practice, eating tends to be most people's shortest-term requirement. Once there is enough to eat, other considerations can take precedence. We have to recognise that developing countries want to be as affluent as we are, and that the use of agrochemicals is at present one of the short-cuts to that objective. Agriculture everywhere should include the balanced use of organic wastes and fertilisers to maintain soil productivity and biological and chemical methods to control pests and diseases to ensure adequate food production with minimal environmental degradation.

# 4 Going Green
## The Options & The Organisations

Pollution and environmental damage have led some companies to paint their products with a convenient green wash. For even the nastiest of chemical cocktails, a green sales point has been found. Most claims could charitably be described as imaginative. *"This products has no known detrimental effect on the environment"* turns ignorance into a selling point. The lack of legislation on green matters has let companies introduce new logos and phases that imply everything but guarantee nothing. *"Contains organics"* sounds wholesome but is the product free of chemicals? - not at all. *"Bio-friendly"* sounds even better but means even less.

The absence of regulation and legal definitions means that although a company could, in theory, be prosecuted under The Trades Descriptions Act for falsely selling a product as organic or environmentally friendly when it wasn't, a conviction would be very unlikely at present. The legislation is coming and gradually confusion and mis-leading statements will disappear.

If you want to grow your plants and/or animals without chemicals or drugs, there are a few decisions you have to make first. If you want to sell what you grow, you should observe one or another of the standards outlined in the UK Green Growers Guide. Since, as explained elsewhere, the United Kingdom Register of Organic Food Standards (UKROFS) will become the dominate standard, adherence to UKROFS is probably the best long-term plan.

If you are growing for yourself, you may please yourself. You may choose to adopt one of the existing standards on the theory that someone has already worked and thought hard to create these standards so why invent your own? Alternatively you may select which methods and which products you consider to be the best for your purposes. A number of the following chapters provide guidance on how to think about these problems and which factors to consider in coming to conclusions. Understanding the problems and thinking through what you want to do is an important part of the process. It makes us conscious of how the plants and animals we eat are produced. That consciousness is almost bound to lead us to greener, safer and more humane methods of producing food.

Adherence to any of the published standards should begin with obtaining them in detail from the relevant organisation (addresses in the index). Most of the organisations concerned with green growing are organic and follow either Soil Association standards or those of Organic Farmers and Growers. The remaining green growing groups include the Guild of Conservation Food Producers and Free Range Production and others such as Farmhouse Chicken set up by ASDA stores. There is even a system for veganic gardening which uses no animal products (like bone or fish meal) and relies on the composting of weeds and other plant wastes as the main nutrient input to the soil. These groups have been set up to meet demand for food grown by environment friendly methods rather than for 'health' reasons. Although the main aims of all the organisations are similar, there is controversy amongst them as to the details of various practices and products.

# The Soil Association

International charity, established 1946 by Lady Balfour et al

Initial Aims: To coordinate and assist research work on the relationships between soil, plant, animal and man with specific emphasis on nutrition and health; to collect and distribute information to the general public.

Current Aims: To encourage production of pure, tasty and nutritious food without damaging the environment; to educate the public and bring awareness of organic farming as a way forward that allows agriculture to work in harmony with the environment.

The Soil Association has been in the forefront of the development of standards for organic agriculture. Its standards are based on guidelines from the International Federation of Organic Agriculture Movements (IFOAM). They have been adopted by most organic associations and were used as the basis for both the United Kingdom Register of Organic Food Standards (UKROFS) and the proposed EEC regulation discussed in chapter 13. The standards are formulated by six technical committees made up of representatives from the various sciences and commercial interests.

The standards put all products into one of four categories: recommended, permitted, restricted and prohibited. Recommended is

17

exactly that; permitted means not quite recommended but allowed sometimes with qualifications; restricted means special permission is required from the Soil Association Council before use due to incompatibility with organic principles; prohibited is, of course, forbidden. Synthetic pesticides and soluble fertilisers are not allowed.

Organic systems are designed *"to produce food of optimum quality and quantity..to employ practices which coexist with, rather than dominate, natural systems, sustain or build soil fertility, minimise damage to the environment, and minimise the use of non-renewable resources."* Conversion to organic systems can take several years and must follow an agreed plan.

Use of the Soil Association symbol requires complete adherence to the standards.

# History of the Soil Association

The Soil Association was established in 1946 as a registered company with charitable status by a group inspired by the book *"The Living Soil"* written by Lady Eve Balfour. The book addresses the link between health and nutrition and the effect of the soil in providing nutrients to plants and animals. The hypothesis, based on observation, is that food grown in an organic way promotes health in humans. This requires a mixed system where the optimal use is made of all materials and microbial activity in the soil is maintained at an optimum level.

To test this 'closed cycle' hypothesis, The Haughley Research Trust was established by Lady Balfour in 1939 and several years were spent in preparation for the first trial, with 200 acres divided between three farming systems. The Soil Association funded the research by buying the farmland involved and returning the purchase price as a grant. A trial was carried out from 1948 until 1969 when it ceased. A difference of opinion occurred with some members favouring using the farm to prove that organic farming could be productive rather than to continue research on the closed cycle concept.

In 1971 the Soil Association moved into a new era of development with the realisation that proving that organic farming was better for the soil and our health was no longer the most important aim. With conventional farming running into trouble with problems caused by the loss of soil structure and pests becoming resistant to chemicals, the emphasis of the group changed to proving that organic farming could be profitable and to organising the availability of 'poison-free' food. This lead to the Soil Association standards and logo which is now widely recognised.

Farmers, growers and manufacturers can use the Soil Association symbol on their goods if the standards have been observed.

Advisory services are provided to farmers and gardeners for organic growing via British Organic Farmers and The Organic Growers Association set up in 1980 and 1983 respectively. These are membership organisations run by elected committees of farmers and growers dedicated to supporting the needs of members before, during and after conversion to organic systems. They also aim to promote organic farming as a viable alternative to conventional systems. The organisations offer training courses, conferences and seminars for their members as well as representing them politically. Some of their most important work is involved in helping the grower find a suitable market for the produce without which they could not survive.

The current work of the Soil Association includes the promotion of organic agriculture by educating the public about the benefits of organic farming to the environment and human health. Much of this work is done via publication of books and leaflets about environmental or health issues such as pesticide residues, problems of chemical spray drift and pollution. It has lobbied the Government for changes to agricultural policies that encourage organic farming practices rather than create a market where farmers find it difficult to compete. Its current campaign is to convert 20%

of British agriculture to organic methods in the 1990s, an ambitious goal given the present figure of 1%.

## Sister Organisations

Irish Organic Farmers and Growers Association - IOFGA follow the Soil Association standards and operate in Ireland which is not directly covered by the Soil Association.

British Organic Farmers and the Organic Growers Association - represent over 1000 organic producers in Britain. Coordinate training and circulates information about developments via a quarterly journal.

Organic Advisory Service - based at Elm Farm Research Centre offers a consultancy service, advisory farm visits and soil analysis. Carries out research in organic agriculture.

Henry Doubleday Research Association - formed by Soil Association member Lawrence Hills, the HDRA has demonstration gardens and sells a wide range of organic products. Members of the HDRA obtain free information and advice.

The McCarrison Society - formed in 1965 by a group of doctors and dentists concerned with the importance of nutrition to animal and human health the society is devoted to nutritional studies.

# The Guild of Conservation Food Producers (GCFP)

National charity, established in 1985 by W. Jordan Ltd, European Oat Millers Ltd, David Stickland & Sons and The Pure Meat Co.

Initial and Current Aims: To meet demand for food grown by an environmentally sympathetic way that provides adequate food supplies and pays attention to animal welfare.

Conservation Grade was conceived a relatively short time ago as a transitional stage for growers wishing to convert from chemical to organic growing. It has always been recognised that going 'cold turkey', withdrawing suddenly and completely from chemical use, was difficult both technically and economically. Conservation Grade was designed to assist in that conversion by allowing the temporary use of only those chemicals that were deemed the least harmful and least dangerous. Transitional stage growers who followed Conservation standards could also obtain at least a partial premium for their products.

Practitioners of the Conservation Grade evolved into the Guild of Conservation Food Producers (GCFP) and published their standards. Most of the Conservation Grade producers have probably decided to stick with the system as markets have been found for their produce and are unlikely to follow a further conversion to full organic practices. The standards make clear GCFP's origins saying, *"Conservation Grade farming seeks to combine the best features of both modern Conventional and Organic farming."*

GCFP's aim is to provide consumers with food which is the product of a 'traditional less intensive farming system'. GCFP defines Conservation Grade as, *"Farming using good husbandry, well established crop rotations, concern for the health and welfare of livestock, conservation of the natural environment and wildlife of the countryside together with use of carefully selected, researched and approved inputs, for crops and animals, to attain good yields of high quality foods."*

Conservation Grade farming is based on methods which result in, *"non-domination of the natural environment by use of carefully balanced inputs, maintenance or improvement in soil fertility, and reduced reliance on use of non-replaceable raw materials."* These goals are almost identical to those of the Soil Association. However, conversion to Conservation Grade can be immediate except in exceptional circumstances.

The grade permits what it describes as, *"...selected materials to ensure good yields and to maintain plant and animal health as well as to sustain the natural fertility of the soil..."*. It tries to be as unambiguous as possible, stating that, *"...unless a specific practice, treatment or product is listed in these standards then it is not allowed."*

GCFP suggests that the rigid exclusionary rules of organic farming dissuade farmers from taking it up. GCFP's own rules, being not so much more lenient as more rational, are intended to persuade conventional farmers that better, greener methods can be used without making them paupers. It also states that Conservation Grade cannot be thought of as 'low-input', because, *"such a farming system will, of necessity be 'low-output' which is neither economically feasible nor good farming practice."*

Use of the GCFP symbol requires both adherence to their standards and membership in the Guild. Members are concentrated in the south of England due to restrictions of markets and policing of the scheme. Conservation Grade meat is sold by the Pure Meat Company and ASDA.

The Guild are actively involved in the promotion of the use of straw composts to replace peat in many products and also in the use of recycled waste to reduce pollution caused by refuse dumps. Conservation of ancient buildings and barns is also important to the Guild so that the character of the countryside is preserved.

## Organic Farmers and Growers (OFG)

OFG is a national (farmer-owned) cooperative of organic farmers, established in 1975 by organic farmers with the aim of expanding the production of organic produce by providing advice on production of organic produce. As the name suggests, OFG is a group of organic farmers run essentially as an advisory, mutual assistance and marketing cooperative. Many products sold through OFG are produced in the UK and some, certifiably organic, are imported.

OFG's *"main objective is to expand the production of organic produce by providing complete professional advice for the viable production of members' organic produce."* OFG is a strong supporter of UKROFS, it has adopted the UKROFS standards and applied to be recognised as a producer. OFG requires a two year transition from conventional to organic growing. Their emphasis is on making organic growing economically successful and they cite examples showing this is possible. OFG is responsible for ensuring that produce from their members is of the organic standard required under UKROFS and they carry out farm and produce inspections. OFG members and non-members can obtain certification of farm holdings conforming to the UKROFS standard and products can be obtained from the company to ensure that prohibited substances are not used. Members receive advice from OFG on conversion, suitable products to use and on growing and marketing produce. A consultancy fee of £50 (+ VAT) is charged for an initial farm visit, organic conversion plan and the detailed organic standards (£12.50 by post). Meat produced to symbol approval standards is sold by Carousel Meat Packers.

## The United Kingdom Register of Organic Food Standards (UKROFS)

The United Kingdom Register of Organic Food Standards is described in detail in chapter 13 on green laws. Derived from a combination of standards from the Soil Association, Organic Farmers and Grower, and IFOAM and drawn together by a variety of interests including commercial companies it will eventually provide a legally enforceable system of organic production. UKROFS will probably replace the voluntary systems now operating as both The Soil Association and Organic Farmers and Growers are recognised by UKROFS as approved organic sector bodies. This means that their standards will have to be adjusted to comply with the UKROFS standards and the groups will be involved in regulating and policing the enforcement of the standards.

# Comparing standards

There are some differences between the organic standards of the Soil Association and Organic Farmers and Growers and those of the Guild of Conservation Food Producers. The Soil Association derives its emphasis from a desire to improve the quality of the edible food product by using good management, avoiding environmental damage and treating animals ethically. The GCFP puts its emphasis on working with the natural environment, following practices similar to those of the Soil Association and producing good quality food as a consequence of this behaviour. UKROFS was derived from the Soil Association standards and is similar in its principles. OFG, although adhering to UKROFS standards, was at one time involved in Conservation Grade Standards, and like GCFP, approaches organic growing from the viewpoint of the producer of the food rather than the eater.

Conservation Grade allows the use of some non-biological fertilisers that are forbidden in organic production. GCFP also allow the use of some chemicals for pest control where a suitable product exists (one that degrades to leave little or no residue in the crop, livestock or soil). Organic farming forbids all such substances as well as wormers or vaccines unless there is a specific problem. Vaccine use is encouraged in Conservation Grade on a *"prevention is better than cure"* basis and certain wormers are permitted to maintain stock in *"prime condition and good health"*. Organic farming permits the use of probiotics with special committee approval but no probiotics are allowed in Conservation Grade.

Despite the organic system being based originally on mixed farming principles, the Soil Association has approved the continual production of arable crops to help meet the high demand for organic cereals, a practice contrary to original principles. Organic cereal farmers have been encouraged by premiums of 112% on wheat whilst premiums have been around 10-15% for organic meat. This may be due to a greater demand for organic produce from vegetarians than from meat eaters, a not wholly unexpected situation. Some of the organic movement have joined the Conservation Grade in consequence.

Differences of opinion between Conservation Grade and organic systems stems from the different aims. The Guild aim to have a minimal effect on the environment but realize that all agricultural systems will affect the soil and related flora and fauna. Organic groups aim to provide food that is more healthy by maintaining the cycle of nutrients and interactions of soil, plants and animals by permitting the use of products from only biological sources and protection of the environment has come as a secondary aim now considered to be of equal importance.

Choosing between these various standards is for once, a pleasure; in effect, almost choosing between the greater of two goods.

The differences in detail amongst the standards of the Soil Association (SA), GCFP, UKROFS and OFG can be illustrated by a few comparisons of permitted substances.

# Probiotics

SA      Probiotics are permitted as feed additives if they are 'naturopathic', meaning that the product has not been chemically processed or added to. Specific approval of the SA committee is needed.

GCFP    Probiotics are not permitted under any circumstances. The addition of bacteria to the gut is thought to upset the natural balance and may cause discomfort. GCFP principles advocate balance in all systems and they argue that tipping the balance positively in favour of beneficial microbes destabilises the established system which may react by swinging in a negative direction.

UKROFS  The use of non-food ingredients intended to increase growth or production by modifying the gut microflora is prohibited. This includes antibiotics and probiotics as both modify the microflora. The presence of more beneficial flora is thought to increase the efficiency of digestion and tend to increase feed intake which in turn increases production. However, probiotics are permitted for therapeutic treatment if they could save the animal's life, reduce suffering or treat a condition with no known alternative. Therefore, probiotics could be used to cure scours in young animals but not to prevent it.

OFG     Probiotics are neither specifically permitted nor prohibited. The products are considered fairly new and are still being evaluated.

# Silage additives

SA        Molasses is the only additive that is permitted. Biological silage additives can be used only with specific permission from the SA committee. The standards are unclear as to whether such restricted 'biological' additives include those with enzymes or bacteriophages.

GCFP      Molasses, enzyme activators and microbial cultures are permitted. Chemical additives, acids, are not.

UKROFS    No silage additives are permitted.

# Stored products

SA        Chemical pesticides in stored products are prohibited; no mention is made of biopesticides which may be permissible.

GCFP      No products are allowed at all except for vermin control.

UKROFS    No mention of biopesticide products, which may be permitted.

## Green Supermarkets

Many supermarkets have shown willing in the race to green consumerism. They have been faced with demand for organic food which, unlike most of their other supplies, is seasonal and is in relatively short supply. Supermarkets need guaranteed supplies and organic food is more difficult to supply this way. Most supermarket chains sell organic produce in selected trial stores usually to Soil Association standards. The first was selected Safeway stores in 1981 and in all Safeway stores in 1985. Organic beef was introduced at the beginning of 1990 and was followed by organic lamb in June 1990. Safeway also stock a range of organic wines. The Safeway chain hope to improve the availability of organic produce by supporting the producers by providing a market for their produce.

Gateway stock organic fruit and vegetables in 160 of their stores and one organic wine is available. Other organic groceries available include rice cakes, rice, cookies, oat flakes, raisins, muesli and soya milk.

Asda stores have a range of organic fruit and vegetables at over 70 stores with 8-12 organic products available at any one time. The produce are packed on pulp-fibre board trays with film wrap that is free of plasticisers. Asda also stock two organic wines, two organic cheeses and organic bread, marmalade, flour and cornflakes. A number of conservation grade cereals are also sold and Asda is the only store other than the Pure Meat Company to stock conservation grade meat. Asda have also set up and control their own poultry production system in Ireland. It includes a traditional feed ration and freedom to roam around in straw litter. The poultry are sold under the name of Farmhouse Fresh Chicken and are available in 150 stores.

Tesco started trialing a range of organic produce at eight stores in 1988 and in 1989 extended the number of stores to fifteen. Organic produce is packed in recycled cardboard trays with cellophane made from wood pulp which are both biodegradable. Tesco tries to ensure that the inks used on the labels lend themselves to easier recycling.

# 5 Make Up Your Own Mind

Companies do not set out to produce agrochemicals which are dangerous (if used as instructed), nor does the Government permit food containing harmful contaminants to be sold; yet problems exist with land, water and food becoming contaminated. The questions that need to be answered relate to the extent of such problems. Do they really matter and can anything be done to overcome them?

To protect the consumer procedures, of testing, trials and registration have been set up and in broad terms these work and are effective. Nevertheless, residues of the persistent insecticide DDT (now banned in most countries) can be detected almost anywhere in the world, increasing levels of pesticide residues are being detected in water supplies and in many areas established farm practices are being changed to reduce such contamination of land and water. At the same time products which have in the past been permitted for use in the home or garden are being withdrawn, whilst others are no longer approved for use with certain crops or on farms.

The history of agrochemical production and use is one of continuing improvement and increase in knowledge. Fundamental to the whole question of agricultural improvement has been the increase in yield which has transformed European agriculture from the days of potato famines, through the era of imports to self-sufficiency and over the last decade to one of surpluses. This enables a change in perspective. In times of need the tendency is to accept what is available and, if additional chemical inputs reduce hunger and increase choice, quality and shelf-life, these are welcomed with open arms. Now, from the secure position of overproduction of food, retrospective analysis may suggest that farming went *the wrong way*. The price of self-sufficiency has been chemical dependency, destruction of the environment (hedges, diversity of wildlife, etc), mineralisation of soil (with loss of organic matter) and contamination of the environment with man-made chemicals (known as *xenobiotics* from the Greek *xeno* strange and *biotica* = of living things), which are not readily biodegraded and hence accumulate.

Within the agrochemical industry enormous sums of money, running to perhaps hundreds of millions of pounds per annum, are spent on researching, developing, testing and marketing agrochemicals. Obviously the aim of this industry is to trade profitably. However, it is also in the interest of both individual companies and the sector as a whole, that products are safe. Quite apart from the damaging publicity and possible lawsuits most major companies have ethical policies and want to produce products which are both effective and safe. The most difficult question to answer, though, is:

## What is safe?

In fact there is no simple straightforward answer. For every compound there are questions of mode of action, persistence, method of application, type of soil, target pest and interaction between this and other life forms reflecting the complex ecology of the total environment in which it is used. An accurate assessment will certainly require training in chemistry, physiology and ecology and, depending on the use, may extend to many of the other more specific -*ologies*, covering insects, fungi, weeds and mammals. Institutions such as the research centres of industrial companies, government departments and universities will employ or contain such a range of experts. However, such are the uncertainties of many aspects of the complex question of safety, that even the *experts* will not agree.

At the same time the perspective taken by the user, the agrochemical industry and the legislature will reflect their individual interests; the production of better crops, the profitable sale of a product or the safety of the public. All these differ from those of YOU *the man or woman in the street*.

No doubt this book will be read by farmers, horticulturalists, gardeners and other users of agrochemicals, as well as employees of the agrochemical industry, those involved in testing and legislation and those with the view that all chemicals are harmful. Each will have their own views of what should or should not be permitted and their own views of what actions need to be taken to ensure that their food is safe. Here, an attempt is made to provide guidelines which will enable you to evaluate your particular viewpoint, without the need to obtain the long list of -*ologies* indicated above.

Indeed it is information and accumulation of knowledge which has led to the changes in perception of the need for and methods of use of chemicals. In the early days the objective was to find a chemical which was more effective and more selective at killing pests than blanket poisons such as cyanide, nicotine, arsenic, copper and so on. Testing was carried out to see that these new compounds were effective at low doses (for economic reasons as lower doses would increase the cost-effectiveness of the treatment) whilst at the same time they did not pose a direct threat to the user in handling and application. This view missed at least four important considerations; persistence in the environment, the development of resistance which would lead to the need to increase application rates, the knock-on effect within the environment as a whole and the fact that the chemical might have other unsuspected effects on metabolism or physiology of plants or animals other than the targeted pest. The realisation that such problems can arise did not evolve over night, but represents the gradual accumulation of all sorts of information from many sources over the last thirty years or so. The realisation that there was *something rotten in the States of America* (with apologies to W Shakespeare) was highlighted in the early 1960s by Rachel Carson in her dramatic denouncement *Silent Spring*. This highlighted the environmental impact of certain chemicals and started the fashion of knocking agrochemicals, but at the same time initiated some of the *extremist* views which have served to cloud the issues. For instance publicity was given at one time to the fact that the Great Lakes on the US/Canada border were dead, at a time when some 100,000 tonnes of fish were being caught commercially. Nevertheless this book brought the concepts of the environment and ecology to the notice of politicians and the public and the situation has been improving ever since; perhaps not at the rate that some people would like, but certainly massive changes have occurred in policy and in public knowledge.

To a great extent these changes reflect developments in two areas of science. The first is the understanding of the mechanisms of life at all levels, including genetics, molecular biology, the immune system and the way in which specific compounds (molecules) can be tailor made to interact with receptors to cause very specific changes which can be used to control, amongst other things, pests and disease. The second concerns the development of sophisticated, sensitive and accurate methods of detection and analysis which can be used to monitor and police the release and distribution of environmental pollutants. This, coupled with a much greater environmental awareness, has led to changes in legislation aimed at improving the quality of the atmosphere (reduction in acid rain, reduction in carbon dioxide levels, stopping the release of CFCs), fresh water bodies and the seas (stopping discharge of industrial wastes and sewage sludge into rivers and seas). However, in a way land has been served less well. Legislation has improved the ways in which radioactive, hazardous and toxic wastes are disposed of, whilst strengthening the control of leachate and gas emissions from landfill sites. These are the obvious things. Less obvious are the long term impacts of continued deliberate spraying of the land with agrochemicals and fertilisers. In fact at the legislative end of the scale it is concern about water quality and crop surpluses which has led to suggestions for legislating on, or taxing of, chemical inputs to farming, rather than concern about the impact on the land and wild-life itself. Conversely, it is the destruction of the natural environment and killing off of the innocent by-standers by non-selective spraying which concerns the environmentalists; whilst concern about residues in food has led to an increasing emphasis on the lower-input or organic systems described elsewhere in this book.

This section examines the various facets of the concept of safe pest and disease control in plant production and animal husbandry, ranging from home to farm use.

# 6 Why Use Any Inputs in Growing?

The reason for introducing any input into the growing or husbandry system, be it farm or garden, is to direct the natural population of plants and animals to give you more of what you have decided to produce and to produce better quality. Exactly what is meant by quality will depend on the product and reason it has been grown. Fortunately there are many opportunities to both define and judge quality through the many local, regional and national horticultural and agricultural shows held each year. Seldom do these consider the means by which the object on show has been produced, whether it is the largest pumpkin or onion, the sweetest apple, the most massive bullock or perfect fleece. However, quality is recognised, judged and rewarded. The winning products will have been cossetted and pampered well beyond that which is realistic or viable economically for a commercial venture. So the commercial grower will use lower inputs and the casual gardener may use few if any, unless faced by a sudden outbreak of a particular easily recognisable pest. In every case a judgment has to be made between the effort and cost required and the result anticipated or desired.

Inputs (whether agrobiological or agrochemical) may be introduced into growing systems for one or more of the following reasons:

1. To protect plants or animals from disease, or to control disease or pests, or to cure existing disease. The distinction between prevention, control and cure is important since some products may be over used when disease is not present (just in case) even when the risk of infection or of yield loss is low.

2. To increase the growth rate (or modify the growth pattern) of a plant or animal for purely cosmetic reasons; that is to make it look better to the judge at the local produce show, to impress the buyer in the supermarket, to make the product (such as peas of carrots) fit the machinery of the processor or canner or to meet other marketing needs. In these cases neither the yield nor the nutritional value of the products is improved in any way.

Such inputs may either be nutritional supplements (including plant fertilisers), growth modifiers or compounds that kill (biocides), distinguished as herbicides, fungicides, insecticides and so on depending on the nature of the targeted pest. As far as nutrients are concerned, the actual elements required by plants, or food required by animals, are similar in nature whether derived from an organic or an inorganic source. In contrast, if the objective is to kill, then there are differences between the agrochemical and the agrobiological compound. As far as agrochemicals are concerned to achieve these objectives the products are designed specifically to interfere with the normal metabolism of animals, plants, bacteria and fungi, etc. Agrobiologicals, in contrast, are usually components of the natural ecosystem, where introduction of the organism alters the balance of nature increasing the degree of competition against the pest.

## Reasons for concern

By definition, chemicals designed as pesticides are expected to kill living organisms. The degree of concern can be reduced as the degree of specificity is increased. However, to make more specific products targeted at a particular pest increases costs and reduces the volume of sales of any particular product. To use an analogy with the pharmaceutical industry, the volume of sales of general pain killers (analgesics) such as aspirin or paracetamol are much greater than those for products used to treat specific illnesses such as cystic fibrosis. The choice of compound is a result of choice between a number of conflicting options which can best be considered in terms of the balance between risk and benefit. The problem is that most people (gardeners, horticulturalists and farmers alike) are not capable of assessing the risks, nor in many cases are the real benefits known. This is due in part to the complexity of risk assessment, an art rather than a science, and in part to the way in which information within the pesticide industry and government circles is handled. Indeed, in contrast to the United States where *Freedom of Information* is the rule, in the UK some aspects of trials and government studies may fall under the aegis of the *Official Secrets Act*.

At the same time there is increasing concern about the dependence of modern agriculture on pesticides and about the risks posed to wildlife and potentially to man. It is claimed, with some justification, that the continued use of pesticides is essential to maintain food supplies and at the same time much care is taken by manufacturers through existing regulatory mechanisms to ensure their safety in use and to minimise adverse environmental effects. The view taken by the agrochemical industry and some governments is that because of the stringent tests to which these chemicals are subjected and the guidance given to users, the increasing quantities applied give no grounds for anxiety and in any case the high cost of pesticides discourages excessive application.

Even when used according to manufacturers' instructions and government approvals there is still the inherent concern that since pesticides are by design biologically active they will always pose some threat. Irrespective of the stringency of tests there is always the possibility of unforeseen or unforeseeable effects. All responsible growers and manufacturers believe that they should be used with care, in the minimum quantities needed for effective pest control, using the least hazardous compounds commensurate with the desired effect. However, to achieve this ideal situation would involve a change in a number of current practices involving preventative use where present considerations of cost-benefit override risk-benefit assumptions and more chemicals are used, 'just in case', than are actually needed.

**The objective should always be to minimise pesticide use, using the minimum number of compounds and selecting those which achieve the required result with the least detrimental effect on the environment and the highest degree of overall safety.**

## Use of chemicals should be restricted to the curing of ills rather than the increasing of profit.

To make the right, logical choice it would appear as irrational to eschew all conventional agrochemical products as to blindly apply each and every compound which came to hand. What is required is an informed choice. In turn, this will vary depending on the framework in which it is made.

You may decide, if you are a commercial producer, to take advantage of the premiums available for Organic or Conservation products. In the same way if your concern is about possible pesticide allergy you may decide to use no agrochemicals. Or your concern may mainly be for the *good of the environment*. Whatever your reason for interest in agrobiologicals you can take a stance which may vary from pale lime green to the deepest forest green. The choice is yours - scientifically there is no right or wrong in this area, but rather a spectrum of perception from the dedicated intensive farmer to the most radical environmentalist. Here, we would like to indicate how agrobiological products may be integrated anywhere within this spectrum of personal views, to clarify areas of confusion and to provide technical rather than emotive concepts.

## Choosing your green inputs

The choice of pesticides compatible with *Green Growing* depends really on only two considerations. These are selectivity and persistence. What one would ideally like is a pesticide which is very effective against the pest it is intended to control, is completely harmless to all other living things and breaks down very rapidly after application leaving no harmful residues. However, such compounds do not really exist and indeed some aspects of this idealised concept are in conflict with the objectives of the agrochemical manufacturer looking for a prolonged effect to control emergent weeds, secondary infections or bursts of pest activity. On the other hand, the selectivity of many modern pesticides has been increased enormously compared with traditional blanket poisons. This is especially true for herbicides, fungicides and insecticides designed for use in crop protection, where the ability to distinguishing between a specific crop and competing weeds is great; although this is one area where emerging resistance is an increasing problem.

Selectivity may depend on the nature of the chemical or be increased by using a specific method of application, formulation or timing the application to hit a particular stage of development. Both considerations of economics and technical constraints make it difficult to market highly specific solutions to many control problems. However, such limitations are greater for agrochemicals than for agrobiologicals.

Because of the high cost of development and registration of a new pesticide, the tendency is to select chemicals which control a wide range of pests. In the same way, the user will find it cheaper to make a single application of chemicals to cure as many ills as possible. Hence, conventional broad spectrum products are preferred as being more cost-effective. This is the reverse of the environmentally desirable aim of selectivity, which can be met by the use of biological or mechanical methods of control, but at higher cost. In the same way, persistent chemicals are economically preferable due to the prolonged beneficial effect, but this economic benefit goes against the environmental goal. The actual persistence of both chemical and biological pest control products ranges from hours to years and depends on both the chemical structure and on a wide variety of chemical, photochemical, biological and physical factors including soil type, pH, temperature, moisture etc. Some of the problems in terms of risk-benefit analysis can be understood by consideration of chemical based pesticides: the organochlorine compounds such as DDT are very persistent but have low mammalian toxicity, whereas some organophosphorus compounds break down very quickly but are highly toxic to mammals as well as insects. Therefore using these compounds exposes either a few people to a high risk (organophosphorus) or many to a low risk (organochlorines). However, the problem is not that simple, since the acute effects of high exposure (i.e. death) are well understood and can be guarded against by suitable protection in manufacture and use, whereas the effects of a slow build-up of low levels of persistent compounds are not obvious and may be unexpected. For instance the build-up of DDT through the food chain resulted in thinning of the shells of eggs of birds of prey. Other potential long-term risks include changes in the genetic make-up of organisms which may be carcinogenic (cancer producing), teratogenic (causing abnormalities in embryonic development such as occurred with thalidomide) or mutagenic (resulting in changes in enzyme levels, metabolic pathways and so on which may or may not cause changes in appearance).

It is obvious that such effects are brought about by the use of pesticides since the development of strains of pests resistant to a given agrochemical product is a result of changes (mutation) in a given enzyme. An example of this sort of effect would be the evolution of the so-called super-rat resistant to warfarin. However, this is only one example of what now amounts to thousands of individual cases of pest or disease resistance, ranging from the resistance of various forms of malaria to many of the products used for prevention it to the pyrethroid-resistant whiteflies found in many commercial glasshouse systems. However, such resistance is not restricted to human or animal disease and animal pests, but extends into the plant kingdom. Here, an emerging problem has been the emergence of weeds of the cereal crops such as wheat, barley, oats and rice.

# 7   Why Worry?

On the surface there would appear to be no reason for concern since in the UK, as with the rest of the industrialised nations of the world, the use and selection of pesticides is controlled by law and monitored by government agencies. The reassurance this should give one is tempered by the wide country-to-country variation in the products which are approved, the approval procedures, the extent of policing and the penalties for failing to comply. At times such variations would appear to be almost random, at other times it might be thought by the cynical that legislation on the grounds of safety might be a neat way of getting around some of the various international trade agreements or reducing international competition.

At the same time there are uncertainties in testing procedures and the influence of conscious or even unconscious *vested interest* is difficult to avoid in a real world. Any trial in a court of law which involves the opinion of scientists appearing as *expert witnesses* is sure to produce two opposing scientists equally convinced of their own infallibility. At the same time, the scientific and technical literature is largely based on groups with conflicting theories attempting to strengthen their own perceptions, striving to get them accepted as *text book facts*. So what chance is there for truly impartial analysis of the risks and benefits.

For this reason, the fact that a given compound or product has been approved for use in any particular country does not mean that it will be found acceptable for use by Green Growers. How then does one choose what to use in order to reduce the risk to oneself and to the environment?. To make this choice it is necessary to consider the circumstances under which risks really exist, the nature of the risk, the size of the damage or other consequences of something going wrong and the ease with which it can be corrected. These alternatives can be illustrated by considering some well known disasters.

The consequences of wide spread use of DDT have already been mentioned above; what was not mentioned was that spraying with DDT totally eradicated malaria in some countries by killing the mosquitoes responsible for the spread of the disease. Since eradication programmes ceased, the disease has come back with tragic consequences. However, the number of birds of prey have increased. The tragedy of Bhopal or the disaster at Seveso and the contamination of the Rhine following the disastrous fire at Sandoz' plant in Basle all involved accidents in production plant or storage areas; all are well known and do not need further description. Similar man-made disasters include the Spanish cooking oil scandal, the mix-up of a chlorinated fire retardant with an animal feed additive in the US which led to almost every one in the state of Michigan ending up with varying levels of polychlorinated biphenol (PCB) contamination in their bodies and associated neurological and skin disorders. Less publicised but more frequent are accidents, often killing tens of individuals in developing countries, resulting from inadequate handling, transport and storage of insecticides, whilst paraquat remains a cause of both deliberate and accidental deaths. Each of these cases are different in scale, in terms of the impact on people and/or the environment and in the extent to which the reason it happened depended on accident, ignorance or misinterpretation of technical or scientific data.

In order to establish the framework within which agrochemical products acceptable to Green Growers may be chosen it is necessary to consider the nature of risks, what may be regarded as safe, and the choice of actual chemicals as listed in the standard.

## Levels of risk

The various types of risk or danger inherent in the use of chemicals designed to kill can be categorised on the basis of those which can arise from accidents, those which are due to mistaken legislation and those due to errors in science. The dangers inherent in the use of pesticides may be summarised as follows, starting with the clearest and most obvious risks (those associated with the undiluted concentrate or manufacturing process) running through to those which may be based on flimsy evidence and supposition that everything is potentially harmful.

There is a particular danger to persons manufacturing, storing, transporting, or coming into contact with many agrochemical products in concentrated form. Similar dangers apply to people preparing products by dilution prior to use. Common sense, care and use of the right protective clothing as well as proper storage in the original container, safe disposal of any diluted solutions and the empty containers according to manufacturers' instructions should prevent harm. However, accidents do happen. Individual incidents may be reported. However, there are no real records of the extent of accidental injury or deaths attributable to agrochemical mis-use. In recognition of this a three year study into the long-term effects of pesticide poisoning was launched by the Health and Safety Executive in early 1991, in response to public and official concern. The study involves a Green Card system by which General Medical Practitioners (family doctors) can report pesticide poisoning cases to the West Midlands Poisons Unit. This should provide a better understanding of incidents, including the often quoted, but not always substantiated, damage to people, bees, fish, pets and other animals as well as country gardens as a result of faulty apparatus, wrong dilution or drift from aerial or other large scale spraying.

In general, the consequences of accident, drift or misapplication (departure from manufacturers' recommendations) are instantaneous and the effects may be predicted from data published by manufacturers and appropriate regulatory and advisory bodies as discussed below.

Incorrect application can also damage the very crop, plant or animal which, it was hoped, would be protected. This may be the result of incorrect doses, application to a susceptible variety, or overuse of the chemical during periods of drought, frost, high temperature or other extreme weather conditions. In the same way, agrochemicals may affect other components of the living world; for instance killing earthworms, ladybirds or food plants preferred by specific species of butterflies. This eradication of useful insects, killing of soil algae, bacteria and fungi, destruction of earthworms and so on can be likened to the concept of *Collateral Damage*, brought to everyone's attention during the Gulf conflict.

The extent of such problems reflects both the nature of the chemical and the method and efficiency of application and in particular the extent of runoff from the crop to the soil, which again will reflect the extent of ground cover by plants at the time of application. The degree of harm will also reflect the dose rate and the rate of breakdown of the compound used, as well as its specificity. Here, many of the highly specific agrochemicals despised by the Green Movement may be much less damaging than traditional remedies such as Bordeaux mixture. In fact, liberal application of this copper-containing product to vines in the Bordeaux region itself has resulted in areas where the soil is so toxic little will grow.

So far what has been discussed has been related to the legal use of approved products. Many instances of real tragedies arise from deliberate illegal use or misapplication such as the game keeper who baits eggs or the carcasses of dead birds or small animals with pesticides with the deliberate intention of killing foxes, birds of prey and scavengers such as crows. However, even when used in an approved manner the wider long-term consequences of any application remain uncertain. The tests carried out during development of a new product aim to establish that the novel product is effective against the target organisms, that it does not offer a threat to humans, their pets or other animals (including bees) which are deliberately husbanded and that run-off or contamination of water will not damage fish. Where some such effects are detected, the product may still be eventually approved and sold, with the side-effect problem solved by suitable labelling of the package. Warnings, such as the following, are common on many products. The fact that a package contains one or more of the following statements may cause the Green Grower to automatically reject the product.

*Toxic to fish*
*Use on non-crop plants only*
*Do not graze cattle after application*
*Do not feed produce once sprayed to animals*
*Not to be used on food crops*
*Long term persistence*
*Not suitable for use on organic soils*
*Can injure the crop if misused (i.e. phytotoxic)*
*Toxic to bees*

The problem in adopting this attitude is that a number of the Green products, based on agrobiologicals, listed in the directory section of this book will also bear such warnings. This reflects the fact that anything designed to destroy life can damage organisms other than the target ones and these side effects are often unpredictable. Any product may alter the ecological balance in a given area to change the nature of dominant species, which in turn may create the need for further pesticide use. This effect may be increased in those areas where hedges have been removed because absence of hedges increases the possibility of drift of spray and reduces natural protection for animals and insects etc. Problems are also accentuated where the same crop is grown year after year in the same place, or animals are kept constantly on the same ground. This leads to build-up of associated pests which can only be controlled by application of ever increasing and more complex use of chemicals. Many of the problems can be reduced by moving things around, using suitable rotations in farming, varying the position of various vegetables in the home garden and moving free range animals from field to field, leaving periods of non-use or fallow land.

Hence it may be more important for the Green Grower to adopt acceptable management practices, using appropriate inputs, than to reject chemicals out of hand. The question then is one of deciding what are the acceptable inputs. There is concern about the long-term effects of residues resulting from build-up in the soil at the site of application or elsewhere, due to run-off from saturated zones. In the same way, residues may occur in food products or animal feed. Such residues may be derived from the applied chemical or result from trace impurities which vary with the chemical route used in synthesis, the quality of the starting material and the efficiency of manufacture. Such impurities may be biologically harmless and merely cause taints; on the other hand they may be undetectable to the consumer while representing a low but real risk. This is an unquantifiable area since most of the people who have caused these problems are not around by the time the long-term effect is seen whilst the ever increasing accumulation of knowledge causes shifts in what is regarded as acceptable. Registration, approvals and conditions of use are regularly updated as evidence of problems emerge. However, again there are differences in opinion. For instance, over the last year a compound known as ALAR, used on apples, came under attack in the United States - but the fears were regarded as groundless in the UK.

Plants and microorganisms are capable of adapting to survive the presence of harmful chemicals through development of resistance. In part, the evolution of resistant strains is due to selection. Some individuals will have a natural resistance, or be less susceptible to a given treatment. These will survive, whilst the less tolerant individuals will be eliminated, so gradually the characteristics of the population change. Since some agrochemicals can affect the genetic makeup of organisms, causing mutations, it is also possible that new resistant races will evolve. In either case the rate at which such resistance emerges depends on the number of generations subjected to such selection pressure. Hence, resistance is much more likely to arise in microorganisms or insects and similar pests where the life cycle may be measured in weeks, days or even hours, than in large mammals where each generation develops over several years. However, small rapidly-breeding animals, such as mice and rats, have also developed resistance.

As far as humans are concerned it might appear unthinkable to use a chemical which resulted in the death of large proportions of the population, leaving a resistant population. In fact this has occurred in the past with disease, where visits of European explorers to the New World, Australasia and the Pacific Isles resulted in decimation of the population with childhood diseases such as measles. Agrochemicals are less likely to have similar effects on the human population, unless they resulted in sterility or inheritable mutations. The possibility that agrochemical residues contribute to deaths through cancer, cardiovascular and autoimmune diseases may be real. However, in general these are diseases of the elderly and hence show up after children have inherited the unmarred genetic material of their parents.

Irrespective of the mechanism of change and development of resistance what the user sees is a need for more frequent applications of more potent compounds at higher doses. To the manufacturer this may not be a bad thing as sales will increase in volume and products aimed at solving special problems can be sold at a higher price. The use of products known to induce resistance could be questioned on this basis. However, if they offer the only cure to a serious problem, their use may be the lesser of two evils. The most important thing is that the use of compounds known to induce resistance should be restricted to such emergencies and they should never be used for cosmetic or preventative reasons.

The only sure way to guard against all these hazards is not to use chemicals at all. However, present high population densities require highly productive agricultural systems to meet the nutritional requirements of the population at reasonable cost and at the same time the commercial grower requires a reasonable return for his investment of time. Hence, the first way to look at chemical applications is from the viewpoint of the grower.

# 8    The Growers' Needs

Growers have turned to chemical inputs partly as a substitute for human effort, a need to increase yield and a desire for an increased standard of living. The desire for a better life extends from the farmer who wants a higher income and hence has to aim for a higher profit margin, to the member of the public who wants to be able to purchase any of a wide variety of foodstuffs of high quality all year. To a large extent, the increased use of pesticides reflects changes in agricultural practice and in particular the reduced use of labour, the reduced use of rotations for disease control and new systems of husbandry in which the main criterion of success is the yield in terms of weight produced per unit of land area. At the same time, there has been an increase in specialisation in production, not only in the division between arable farming and animal production, but also in the production of specific crops in particular regions. As a result, the continuous cultivation of large areas with single crops (monoculture) requires the use of pesticides which become the only way of controlling outbreaks of disease. In particular, the extensive use of herbicides is one of the main factors which makes this possible. However, this is not the only reason for making inputs to the growing system.

In some circumstances the use of chemicals may be an absolute necessity for weed or pest control. In these circumstances, if no chemicals are used, the crop or animal may be completely lost or not grow sufficiently to produce an economic yield. This category of chemicals includes those which are required by law to control specific diseases, accidental import of insects etc. The farmer or importer has only two alternatives; to use the chemical or to abandon that crop, animal or type of produce. There is a parallel between the curative use of such inputs and the selective use of antibiotics or surgery to treat a life threatening disease.

Less direct is the use of inputs as a preventative or protective measure, prior to any obvious symptoms. Such prophylactic use has its parallel in human health in terms of immunisation against diseases such as polio or rubella. The population and most individuals benefit enormously since the disease can be more or less eradicated. However, a small risk exists and some individuals may die as a consequence of such programmes. It is a question of choice, with the choice depending on the amount and quality

44

of information available to the grower. In choosing to be protected, there must be a reason to suppose that it is needed and a belief that infection would occur if action were not taken. This assumption may be based on the fact that the disease or pest has occurred locally, or previous experience suggests that it might, or it may be based on Government warning schemes.

It is only a question of degree to move from such preventative measures to what might be called 'insurance' spraying. The application is made on a speculative basis against a low level of risk, justified on the basis of *"let's spray just in case"* or *"let's spray twice to be sure"* or *"let's double the dose to make certain"*. An extension of this attitude is to spray the crop to make it look better, that is, for cosmetic reasons or to enable the product to meet standards set by a packer or canner and attract a premium. From here it is but one small step to using chemicals (such as artificial plant growth substances, artificial animal hormones or products such as bovine somatotrophin (BST)) in order to increase growth rate to an unnatural extent. Here a parallel exists in the world of sport. The runner who takes a few glucose tablets in order to increase blood sugar, or the American footballer gulping oxygen is acceptable; but the use of muscle-building steroids is not.

If you decide to be a Green Grower then you may decide that only cure and prevention of known problems are justified. If you were looking for a premium on a commercial basis you would do so on the basis of organic quality rather than yield or appearance. The problem here is that the average shopper has become used to the size, colour and absence of blemishes produced by agrochemically-based horticultural and orchard practices. As a result, much organic produce (fruit and vegetables) looks small, mis-shapen and diseased when lined up on the shelf next to standard products.

We would not recommend the total avoidance of chemicals but. The real objective should be moderation and balance, based on scientific principles rather than historical convention or folklore, in effect, a rational view of what is wanted and needed. Indeed, this attitude by one author of this book contributed to the establishment of what became the Conservation Grade.

Even in conventional, intense, agrochemically-based production systems there are changes taking place with moves towards consideration of the environment, rather than maximisation of yield. This is also an area receiving research inputs from the Commission of the European

Communities and many National Governments. The concepts of increased rotation and integrated pest control combined with lower inputs are both becoming more fashionable and attracting the attention of the law makers in Brussels.

The primary objective should be to choose varieties with natural resistance to their major pests, to remove weeds by mechanical means and to adopt good practice and to stop the introduction of wind blown seeds from non-productive areas (although this can raise problems with less responsible neighbors). Rotations are also important. However, these are much easier for the home gardener than for the farmer trying to match production with market demand.

The concept of integrated pest management is one in which the opportunities for disease to develop are minimised by cultural practice and pesticides are used sparingly, but in a directed way. Again this is an area where the individual will have to decide what is the risk and what is an acceptable level of damage or loss. Often the crucial information enabling the level of pest or disease attack at which spraying is necessary to be correlated with potential loss of crop yield is lacking.

The results of chemical inputs on yield in farming will follow the law of diminishing returns. This means that for every further input the proportional benefit is less, until a plateau is reached which reflects the point at which limitations are set by the genetic characteristics of the crop combined with environmental factors such as temperature, light and carbon dioxide availability which (with the exception of glasshouse crops) cannot be influenced by man. However, it is not as simple as this, as climatic conditions or high level of attack by a specific pest may cause catastrophic losses.

In general the most important inputs are nutrients. This is true of both plants and animals. With plants, both major nutrients (NPK) and trace elements may be provided by either synthetic products, by organic fertilisers (blood, bone, hoof, seaweed extract, etc) or by well rotted manure or sludge-based compost. Fertility can also be improved by the growing and subsequent ploughing in of nitrogen fixing plants. For the arable farmer, especially those producing grains, broadleaf weeds are the next most important area of concern, so a safe herbicide is needed. Risks from fungi come next, with insect problems of less significance. In contrast, the home gardener or horticulturalist will be more able to deal with weeds by mechanical means and will find major problems are mildew and insects such as aphids.

Well fed, comfortably housed animals free from stress may go through their lives without the need for treatment for serious disease. However, parasites of various types (especially worms) may make regular treatment necessary, either from the viewpoint of common sense or under Agricultural Regulations. Good management should avoid problems, where they do occur professional veterinary advice should be sought. What the Green animal husbander must do is to ensure the animals are well treated, eschewing any form of intensive (battery) or restrictive housing and allowing the animals a measure of freedom within an environment which is as natural as possible. This includes the provision of a natural diet. Again there are opportunities for choice here. Some of these have been discussed in the chapter on the various types of organic production. What should be avoided are synthetic concentrates and formulations as well as products fortified with antibiotics or other chemical products. There have been cases where unsuspecting farmers have fed their animals on unwarranted (and possibly illegal) formulations simply because they do not understand the terms used to describe the ingredients and have been convinced by pushy sales people that the product has especially beneficial properties. The Green Grower should ask to have the origin, nature and purpose of feeds and feed additives explained and if not convinced, most public libraries will have a reference section where such things can be checked. Problems of regular use of antibiotics and recycling of wastes and residues through the food chain, as well as using intensive rearing practices, have been highlighted by increasing incidence of *Salmonella* infection and the evolution of mad cow disease (bovine spongiform encephalopathy, BSE).

These particular problems are subject to legislation and precautions can be quickly adopted, including wholesale destruction of crops or infected animals. No one knows what the next man-made disaster of this type will be. However, the greater the adoption of Green Growing principles the less likely it is to occur.

The provision of a good natural diet for cattle extends to silage. There are three options: rely on natural organisms; buy in living cultures and microbial growth promoting additives; or add chemical preservatives. Again the Green Grower can choose between the first two of these alternatives, depending on the shade of green they want to achieve.

However, the use of synthetic chemicals such as propionic acid should be avoided as should the use of ammonia or alkali-treated straw. Obviously, to produce an organic meat will require that the plant material going into animal feed has been produced through an organic system.

The production of true organic food is clear cut and represents an ideal situation in respect of hazards from pesticides. However, true organic farming limits the total production possible as well as yields per unit area, and hence financial returns. One has to have a particular form of dedication to produce wholly organic products and most of the organisations and associations giving approval to products recognise this, sometimes bending the absolute concept to enable practical implementation.

The most important thing for the Green Grower to recognise is that there is no scientific justification for not using judicious amounts of certain fertilisers in the right form in order to maintain soil fertility and pH. It is unlikely that such use would affect the nutritive or health value of the food. However, the use of fertilisers increases both crop growth and succulence (and the appeal of the crop to insect and fungal pests) and also increases competition from weeds, thereby creating the need to control both pests and weeds by the use of pesticides. This generates a conflict between the desire to Grow Green and to protect a crop. It has been suggested that this conflict can be resolved if safe compounds are used. The problem then revolves around the questions of what is safe? and what claims can validly be made for the produce?

# 9 What is a Safe Product?

The definition of a safe product to be used as an input for animal or plant production systems differs according to the viewpoint of those involved. The 'establishment' of agrochemical companies and government bodies associated with pesticide control will have one view. The Green Grower may have another. Due to the publicity given in the past to the effects of compounds which proved dangerous or had unsuspected side effects - DDT, DNOC, 2,4,5-T, paraquat, parathion, mercury, lead, cadmium etc., the public has become more knowledgeable and now expresses concern over the continued use of toxic compounds subject to the poisonous chemicals acts, such as heavy metals (organomercury compounds) as well as organophosphorus or organochlorine based compounds.

Considerable legislation and a number of official bodies and trade organisations have been built up to serve the pesticide industry. The objective of these organisations is to improve the safety of pesticide use, to monitor new products and advise the practitioner on their use. At the same time, similar procedures exist to monitor the use of pesticides, accidents, levels in food stuff and the impact on the environment.

Hence, it might be impertinent to suggest that Green Growers are not happy with these established views and, knowing more (or being better informed), wish to employ a new, more stringent, set of constraints to pesticide use. However, for some people their own perception of the inherent qualities of risk and benefit will make them happier to exceed what is required by law. It has been suggested that the law is an ass and anyway, *"big business is just out for profit"*. Such suspicions are enhanced by the way some business sectors have leapt on the green bandwagon whilst only making token concessions to improving the environment. In the same way, the official handling of both the questions of *Salmonella* in eggs and BSE infection in animals has not reassured the public.

The perception of risk and benefit is a judgement issue, influenced by economic and financial criteria as well as by a desire for maximum yields and blemish-free crops. The idea is to reduce the risks to a minimum even if this results in some loss of benefit. Green Growers have an additional worry that chemicals may affect soil microorganisms, earthworms, nitrogen-fixing bacteria and soil fungi and have a deleterious effect on soil organic matter.

The objective of both industry and government regulatory bodies is to ensure safety in the use of pesticides. This can be achieved in two ways: *'safety of the product'* and *'safety of the method of use or application'*. This is illustrated by the fact that in most developed countries a large number of compounds are subject to regulation and/or restriction under various laws. Use of these compounds may be, for example, restricted to trained users wearing extensive safety and protective clothing sometimes including a full respirator. Some products can only be used by authorised contractors, i.e. they are in fact extremely hazardous, but *'safe'*, because of the precautions taken. Obviously, such substances cannot be regarded as safe for Green Growing.

Developing new pesticides is still a process of trial and error. New compounds are screened for their effects on representative organisms. Effective compounds are then tested to establish any health, environmental or other effects which might limit their use. The 'hit-rate', the number of new commercial products per compound tested may be as low as 1 in 10,000 to 100,000, and the costs will be $25m to $100m before any income from sales is derived by the manufacturer. New compounds will need sales of around $50m **per year** in order to recoup the expense of research and testing. It must be in the interests of the chemical companies to have their compounds regarded as safe.

Due to the fact that much of the information used to determine the safety of pesticides from the official viewpoint is not available to the public it is very difficult to answer the question *What is safe for the Green Grower?*. The reason for doubt stems from the multiplicity of choice concerning levels of accepted hazard and the nature of the hazard. As previously discussed, a safer compound will be one which is selective and rapidly broken down. These properties reflect the chemical nature, formulation, distribution method and means of application as well as the extent to which instructions are obeyed. However, in spite of uncertainties there are some basic scientific assumptions which lie behind industrial and government decisions.

For an input to be effective, whether the desired effect is improved growth or destruction of the target, the first need is uptake. Where animals are fed, uptake is not a problem, although formulation may be needed to make deadly poisons attractive or even to get animals to consume a healthy diet. With plants, fungi and disease organisms the problems are somewhat greater. Not all chemicals are taken up by the target organisms. A compound has to get into the living cell in order to work, which means it has to penetrate the cell membrane. This is more likely if the compound is soluble in oil than if it is soluble in water. However, many pesticides are spread as a water solution hence, solubility in water is also an advantage. In general, sodium ($Na^+$) and potassium ($K^+$) salts are more soluble than free acids. Hence, compounds may be formulated as salts or esters to increase ease of distribution. The fact that a given compound is a salt or ester may not make any difference to its safety, although the hormone type herbicides may be preferable as salts, rather than as esters since the former are less volatile, and greater volatility can increase the chance of spread to non-target organisms. Since the active ingredient in many pesticides is more soluble in oil than water it may be dissolved in an organic solvent to which a surfactant is added to form an emulsion for spraying. As the surface of many plants and insects has non-wetting characteristics, spray could form droplets and run off. In some formulations separation occurs, water runs off and the oil carrier and pesticide remains in contact with the leaf. This is suitable for systemic compounds which will be carried around the plant after uptake. For contact pesticides, even spread is more important and formulations can include compounds to enable wetting and adhesion. in some cases it is the various compounds added to make the active ingredient work that cause more damage than the ingredient itself. In particular the fact that formulations in the concentrated state contain both organic solvents and surfactants may make them dangerous to skin and particularly to eyes due to irritation and dissolution of fat or oil rather than specific hazard from the active ingredient. The fact that a given formulation carries a warning about skin contact does not necessarily mean that it cannot be considered safe.

Uptake into the cell reflects the balance between lipophilic (oil soluble) and hydrophilic (water soluble) characteristics. Selectivity may be obtained by exploiting differences in this property; chemicals will interact in different ways with the surfaces of target as compared to non-target species. Some compounds are taken up unchanged; others are metabolised to a more active form during uptake. Hence, the compound may be more toxic when absorbed than on application. Again, distribution around the plant may be in either xylem (passive flow with the water stream) or

51

phloem (active) and this will alter the distribution and potency of the chemical.

Most of the above comment applies to sprays since over 75% of pesticides are applied in this form. However, other formulations include powders, granules or vapours. These variations generally reflect attempts to make the product more effective and safer to use.

The effectiveness of a compound will relate to its toxicity at a given concentration at a given location within the target organism. Low doses will have less effect and high doses will be a waste of money. In some cases, low doses can be dangerous since they may allow resistant strains to evolve. Once it has been decided to use a given compound, the manufacturer's recommendations must be followed precisely as they are based on scientific principles and tests. The attitude that *'we will not worry about using this chemical because we are only using a low dose'* should be discouraged. Extrapolation should not be made from one situation to another i.e., a dose which is effective in one set of circumstances may not be in another. The actual dose received will be a function of both concentration and time.

Residues can contaminate soil for a long time. Once a chemical reaches the soil the active concentration and apparent life (or availability) depends on a number of factors which lie outside the applied concentration and rate of breakdown. In the soil, it is in contact with charged particles which will affect the ability of the plant to absorb them, the effects they have on other organisms and the rate at which they are leached from the soil. In particular, the soil particles will contain negatively charged clay particles and humic acids derived from the breakdown of organic matter. The proportion of negative charges carried on the organic portion is greater than on clay particles which in turn will be greater than in sandy soils. Consequently, the effects of interaction between positively charged pesticides and the soil will be much greater in (negatively charged) organic soils such as those developed by application of Green Growing principles. The acidity of the soil is also important since acidic soils will increase the degree of binding (they are more able to donate $H^+$ ions to basic substances).

The water content of the soil is a significant factor in determining the speed and extent of breakdown of chemicals in the soil since the applied chemical will partition between soil particles and the surrounding film of moisture. In solution, the chemicals will become available in an active form and may be taken up by plants or may be broken down by microorganisms. In general the neutrality of the soil is due to cations such as calcium which interact in an exchangeable way with the negatively charged soil particles. Pesticides with cation characteristics can replace the soil cations and become bound with a variable intensity which depends on their chemical structure and the pH of the soil water. Part of the applied chemical will remain in solution; as this solution is depleted, active chemicals may pass from the bound form on the soil particle into the soil water and be taken up. If the chemical has a low solubility the actual amount in free solution may be low. As a result the rate of penetration through the soil will also be low. This can make the herbicide selective against shallow-rooted plants.

Very strong cations, such as paraquat may be bound irreversibly to the soil and consequently rapidly inactivated. In contrast, hormone weedkillers, such as MCPA, are strongly acidic and will not be complexed, remaining in solution in the soil water to be carried down into the soil or leached away. Such pesticides which remain in solution are more likely to be broken down by bacteria in the soil and hence hormone weedkillers show short lifetimes as active ingredients in the soil. Some apparently persistent compounds may only persist since they are bound to soil particles from which they are released very slowly into solution. Others, such as the organochlorine pesticides, are very persistent because they are not broken down either by organisms or by natural forces like sunlight.

# 10 How Chemicals Kill

To kill, pesticides interfere with cell metabolism. This interference includes effects on energy metabolism, cell growth and division, nucleic acid metabolism and protein synthesis and the processes which control cell growth. Other compounds kill by attacking membranes in such a way as to make them leak, or attack nervous, hormone or other control systems. The exact mode of some compounds is not known or is speculative. However, in general the targets are as follows:

## Energy metabolism

All living organisms respire to release energy in the form of an electron flow which in turn is coupled to the formation of Adenosine Tri-Phosphate (ATP, a high energy intermediate of metabolism). Organisms can be killed by substances which interact with the enzymes of respiration or which uncouple electron flow from ATP synthesis. Respiration is similar in most organisms and many of the classical poisons such as cyanide, arsenic, mercury etc. interfere with this process. Thus, targetting must be based on selectivity in uptake or selective metabolic steps such as conversion of a non-active precursor to an active form specific to that particular pathogen or pest.

Plants differ from other organisms in that they obtain their energy from light by the process of photosynthesis. This also involves an electron flow which is coupled with ATP formation; different specific compounds are capable of uncoupling photosynthesis. Hence, it is possible to be selective towards plant metabolism. However, dangers may arise (e.g. with paraquat) since the chemical may have a different and unsuspected effect when it comes into contact with animal tissues.

## Cell division, nucleic acid metabolism and protein synthesis

Growth may be stopped by interfering with cell division or conversely plants may be killed by compounds which promote rapid, unnatural cell

54

division and elongation. Such compounds may interfere with nucleic acid metabolism. The problems with some such compounds is that interference with nucleic acid metabolism may increase mutation rate and hence the rate of development of resistance. They may also cause abnormal cell division, chromosome damage and potentially be carcinogenic.

## Metabolic regulation and control

Both plants and animals are regulated by hormones, chemicals which, at very low levels, influence cell metabolism. However, plants and animals differ significantly in the nature of the active groups which result in growth or metabolic responses. In animals these are steroids; in plants a number of different classes are known including auxins, gibberellins, abscisic acid, cytokinins etc. Auxin is indole acetic acid (IAA) and the most widely used weedkillers such as 2,4-D and MCPA are stable analogues of this. Gibberellins, commonly GA3 and GA7 are used to control bolting and to swell fruit. Cytokinins, commonly benzyl adenine are used as growth regulants.

In animals a second level of control exists through the nervous system. The problem here is that there is a similarity between the mode of action of transmission of nervous signals in most animals. Some chemicals, the organochlorine compounds in particular, show high specificity towards insects; however, their persistence in the environment and *'collateral damage'* to birds of prey, has made them no longer acceptable. In contrast, the organophosphorus compounds which have the advantage in that they break down rapidly, are more dangerous to all animal life: early compounds of this type were very toxic (and were developed as nerve gases for war purposes). However, more recent compounds are less deadly.

## Membrane disruption

Plants and animals consist of up to 80% or even 90% water retained within the cells due to the nature of the membranes. Destruction of these membranes can be used as a very effective means of attack. This may be very general as with some antibiotics, the effectiveness depending on binding to specific components of the cell wall, giving high selectivity.

# Interference with behaviour or feeding pattern

Insects use chemical messengers (pheromones) as a means of communication and for reproductive purposes. Use of artificial compounds can result in confusion, preventing mating and/or feeding, providing an effective means of control.

# Unknown and multiple effects

Although the above list gives some target objectives, in many instances the effectiveness results from a number of effects or the actual mechanisms may not be clear. Compounds are usually found to be effective through selection trials, and the mode of action is discovered afterwards. Since many of these modes of action are common to both target and other species, some methods of selection for specificity are needed. These may depend on metabolic differences, or the application is such that the target gets a higher dose, or may result from the fact that only the target organism can metabolise the compound to an active form. The safer compounds are those which break down quickly or are adsorbed onto soil particles and have a very specific mode of action or a low mammalian toxicity.

## *Even a safe compound may be dangerous if*:

The manufacturer's recommendations are not followed

It has unexpected side effects

It accumulates along the food chain, and then has unexpected side effects

It is not as specific in its mode of action as predicted

The manufacturing process for material cleared from one source differs in batches or production from another source, resulting in unusual levels or types of impurities.

As far as Green Growers are concerned problems can be kept to a minimum if chemicals used are restricted to those which are known to have the following characteristics:

Low mammalian toxicity

Rapid breakdown or are both non-systemic and applied early

A long trouble free history

Even when such acceptable products are used, care should be taken to reduce the chance of harmful residues in the harvested crop by strict adherence to harvest intervals, timing of spraying and so on.

# 11 Choosing Pesticides and Fertilisers

## Weedkillers

The first types which might be considered are those which have a very high mammalian toxicity (e.g. DNOC, Dinoseb, Paraquat etc,). These are highly poisonous and their use entails a risk to the user; considerable damage can be done to wildlife caught in the spray at time of use. However, they are very rapidly inactivated, do not leave residues, do not have long term environmental effects, do not accumulate along food chains, and treated areas can be occupied by animals after a short period (say 10 days). However, the high toxicity may make them unsuitable for Green Growers.

The second group are the urea derivatives, carbamates and triazines which interfere with photosynthesis. These do not affect animals or insects in the same way, have a low mammalian toxicity, do not build up along food chains or build up in soil in the free form and do not appear to have adverse effects on insects, earthworms etc. However, they may also interfere with cell division and may be mutagenic. A number of these compounds are aromatic and chlorinated.

However, the same applies to all members of the carboxylic acid herbicides which act as plant growth stimulants due to their similarity to indole acetic acid or auxin. In the pure form these do not affect animals although problems have arisen with 2,4,5-T, due both to the presence of dioxin and some evidence of abnormal effects on cell division; such effects have also been claimed for 2,4-D. They may also cause taints in animals which eat treated crops due to low levels of chlorinated phenols in some batches. They have low mammalian toxicity, break down in soil, and in fact it can be shown that treated soil adapts to the presence of such compounds, since the rate of breakdown increases with time of use as bacteria evolve the capacity to deal with them. However, this may reflect the fact that these compounds stay in solution due to charge effects as discussed above, whereas other compounds may appear to persist as they are complexed on soil particles.

# Fungicides

The traditional compounds such as Bordeaux mixture (copper sulphate) and lime sulphur can lead to problems due to the formation of persistent stable residues which remain in the soil for a long time and can affect soil fauna, earthworms, fish and algae if they drain off. The literature contains the quote 'luckily they are being replaced by safer organic compounds'. However, at present the only fungicide considered acceptable by organic farmers is elemental sulphur. Some possible alternatives include benomyl and the related compounds carbendazim, thiabendazole and fuberidazole. In particular thiabendazole is used orally in humans and animals for round worm control and is said to be non-hazardous to wildlife. Captan and the related Folpet have very high LD50 values and are regarded as amongst the safest fungicides. Maneb and Zineb are also of interest as contact fungicides since they do not appear to pose an environmental threat, although they may be toxic to fish, and it is suggested that animals are not allowed to eat treated crops.

# Insecticides

Choice of an acceptable insecticide poses the greatest problem since there is a similarity between insect and animal nervous systems. Organochlorine compounds are now falling into disuse because of the problems with DDT and are being replaced by organophosphorus compounds (OPs). Many OPs are very dangerous and will destroy beneficial insects, cause human fatalities and pose a danger to domestic and wildlife. Again the more recent compounds developed such as malathion (which is used as a head wash for lice in humans) have a low human toxicity. The class of most interest to Green Growers might be pyrethroids. Pyrethrum is a natural contact insecticide which has the advantage of very rapid action against insects, very low human toxicity, and no residues. However, the natural product has very low persistence and hence insects can recover from attack: hence, the search for more stable artificial analogues e.g. allerthrin, bioresmithrin, etc. However, once again there are problems with these since the more stable compounds are produced by addition of aromatic groups and chlorine atoms (e.g. decamethrin) to produce products which are more stable, still show low mammalian toxicity, but are extremely toxic to many (sometimes beneficial) species of insects and to fish and other aquatic life.

Seed dressings In the past these have mainly been based on organomercury compounds, e.g. phenyl mercury acetate. It has been claimed that application levels are so low that they result in less than 1/10th ounce per acre. But in this case the problem is to wildlife which may eat seed or indeed seed may be fed by accident. Such alkyl mercury compounds are now banned in many countries. Aryl mercury compounds are less toxic to mammals and birds but can still cause problems when leached. If seed treatment is absolutely necessary some fungal attack can be prevented by use of fungicides such as benomyl, fuberidazole and milstem, which would appear to be much safer than the mercury compounds.

## Fertilisers

Fertilisers are added to replace soil nutrients which have been lost when produce is harvested, nutrients which have been lost as a result of climatic effects (rain, wind, temperature) or microbial breakdown (mineralisation). They do not differ from those elements or compounds which normally comprise plant nutrients. In the past, when farm yields were lower and rotation and mixed farming common, it was possible to meet most of the nutrient requirements of crops by application of organic residues and animal manures. At the end of the last century it was shown that the basic plant nutrient requirements for nitrogen (N), phosphorus (P) and potassium (K) can also be met by application of inorganic fertilisers.

Since then, use of such chemicals has made a major contribution to crop yields in most western countries. However, the use of these compounds can be associated with pollution of water ways by nitrate, with health hazards to babies, possibilities of formation of nitrosamines which cause cancer, changes in population of soil organisms, plant growth in lakes, etc. In particular, the use of inorganic fertilisers without addition of organic matter or attention to the details of ionic balance in the soil has resulted in the structural degradation of large areas of soil, which in turn has led to widespread criticism of the use of inorganic fertilisers.

It is also probable that the use of inorganic fertilisers has resulted in an increase in susceptibility of plants to disease due to the effect some formulations have in increasing the succulence of vegetative parts. In the same way application of high rates of nitrogen fertilisers can have an adverse effect on the natural soil microorganisms - such as destruction of beneficial organisms which cause increased pest resistance in plants and destruction of organisms which produce 'antibiotic' substances which inhibit growth of disease organisms in the soil. Another deleterious effect of application of inorganic fertilisers arises from the fact that their use permits continued growth of the same crop for many years in the same fields without rotation, building up reservoirs of pests and weed seeds whilst the natural organic content of the soil decreases. These are problems which can be reduced in impact if the correct management techniques are used. The essential points are as follows:

When nutrients are removed from the soil they may be replaced by addition of either organic or inorganic materials. However, the type of material added and the rate of application must be such that the level of organic matter in the soil, the pH and other important characteristics which contribute to the growth of a good microbiological and earthworm population, are maintained. This entails the incorporation of sufficient amounts of organic residues into the soil, coupled with the choice of synthetic or non-organic fertilisers which maintain the ionic balance of the soil. As a result both soil organic matter and soil pH are stabilised. In particular the inorganic materials should be provided in a form and at a rate compatible with the nutrient requirements of the crop and its particular growth pattern.

It may be difficult to see how the use of an inorganic chemical differs from the use of the same element supplied in an organic form, as long as the form in which the inorganic component is supplied is compatible with the soil system. Problems arise when the inorganic material elements are used in a chemical form which is not compatible with the environment or ecosystem, or when they are applied in excess.

In particular, it has been claimed that application of excess nitrogen fertiliser is the cause of increased levels of nitrate in natural waters. There is little doubt that this does come from the land. However, in the same way that different sources of nitrogen are not distinguished by the plant, different sources of nitrogen are not distinguishable as far as leaching is concerned. Hence, nitrate may come from fertiliser, or it may come from animal urine or faeces directly or indirectly applied to fields, or it may come from the bacterial decay of organic matter.

Cultivation increases the mineralisation of organic matter to inorganic nitrate. In particular large amounts may be released when grassland is ploughed to arable use, particularly where leguminous leys are ploughed. In general, loss of nitrogen will reflect the nitrogen content of the soil, the rate of uptake from the soil by plants and the rate of water drainage through the land. The highest losses will be in late autumn, winter and early spring where plant growth is slow, and precipitation (rainfall) exceeds evaporation. Spring application of nitrogen is the most beneficial. Its use in autumn should be combined with incorporation of organic residues so that the nitrogen can be bound into organic matter. However, loss due to leaching may still occur, depending on soil, drainage, etc. The main point is that it is not correct to believe that increased application of inorganic nitrogen fertiliser will, of necessity, increase environmental pollution which could be avoided by sticking to organic type farming. Due to the solubility of nitrate and the fact that microbial activity will degrade most nitrogen containing compounds to this level of oxidation, the degree of environmental (water) pollution will reflect the total amount from all sources, not the nature of the form in which is was applied to the field. In conclusion, there does not appear to be an environmental reason for avoiding the use of nitrogen fertiliser.

Other problems relate to the balance of ions in the soil. The crop itself is not capable of telling whether a particular molecule of ammonia or phosphate came from an organic or an inorganic source. However, for economic reasons high levels of inorganic fertiliser may be placed on the soil in a form governed by cost and ease of application rather than concern for the soil.

A reason for using agrobiological products is to ensure that inorganic fertiliser is supplied in a form that does not cause deleterious effects on the soil. Depending on the nature of the soil, harm may be caused as a result of both the form in which the material is applied, and the nature of the counter ion used (this may not be stated under present labelling requirements where, for instance, $K_2O$ will in general be KCl). In addition, impurities in the product such as sodium ($Na^+$) ions or ($Cl^-$) ions may not be known.

Effects caused by the use of unsuitable products are long term but may be redressed by use of lime and initiation of procedures which will increase the organic content of the soil and stabilise pH.

Since the basis of Green Growing is the production of a biologically active soil with a high humus (organic matter) content it is assumed that a significant proportion of the crop residues will be incorporated, directly, or indirectly into the soil. High levels of organic matter can only be incorporated into the soil if it is well aerated and contains a high population of aerobic bacteria and fungi, as well as being well supplied with earthworms. High organic matter levels also encourage the growth of beneficial microorganisms such as Azotobacter, which is capable of nitrogen fixation and produces chemical compounds which both stimulate plant growth and discourage some pathogenic soil microorganisms. Hence, analysis of the organic matter of the soil (and of the C:N ratio) is of importance since it can give an indication of the activity of such bacteria or indicate problems if it does not increase in a given situation. In addition increased organic matter will improve water holding capacity, decrease erosion and run-off and ease both working of the soil and root penetration.

In many soils the increased organic matter and hence cation exchange capacity will also increase the extent to which residues of some pesticides are bound, as well as acting as a pH buffer. In this context the nature of fertiliser addition, levels and time of application are also of significance since high levels of ammonium salts can reduce pH, and high levels of inorganic N or P can reduce the activity of nitrogen fixing organisms and mycorrhiza. Attention to soil improvement will decrease the incidence of fungal and bacterial pests, possibly due in part to a reduction of water stress (which can make them more susceptible) and in part to antibiotic effects of chemicals produced by microorganisms, the growth of which is favoured by the high content of organic matter.

# 12 The Final Choice

The objective must be to use as few chemicals as possible. However, the Green Grower may have difficulty in accepting that some classes of compounds should be used and others not, especially when other sources of information suggest that these are safe.

---

### Mammalian Toxicity

This can be judged from the $LD_{50}$ test where the concentration of chemical in milligrams per kilogram of body weight which kills 50% of a population of small mammals such as rats is determined. A value of less than 50 indicates a highly toxic compound, 50 to 500 is moderately toxic, 500 to 5000 poses some threat, whereas values of 5000 or greater may be regarded as practically non-toxic, and higher values still as harmless.

---

There are two ways for an individual to determine how Green his Growing will be: the first is to determine the minimum requirements for a given crop; for example, pre-emergent, post-emergent broad leaf weedkiller; specific grass or wild oat killer; specific fungicides for smut and mildew; insecticide and so on. Secondly, select the least harmful product of those available. The alternative is to list a set of characteristics and avoid compounds with high mammalian toxicity. However this approach may present problems due to the fact that hundreds of different compounds are approved in most countries; they may be formulated in different ways and given different names by manufacturers. They may be sold in formulations where the level of active ingredient or even the nature of the active ingredient is not obvious.

Some compounds have been the subject of academic studies or trials and results are reported in the literature. However, for many compounds information has to come from manufacturers.

Many agrochemicals which are now sold have a very specific use and mode of action if used as directed. This might give the impression that they are safe because they do not affect other organisms. However, specificity may be conferred through a variety of mechanisms, including variation in timing, separation in space, difference in ability to penetrate the surface of various organisms, sensitivity to dose rate, or specificity based on behavioural patterns. Such specificity does not of necessity relate to their effects on soil organisms, or the extent of residues in the crops.

In the first instance the use of MCPA, MCPB and CMPP may be acceptable. If asulam and glyphosate are also accepted then there would also appear to be similar grounds for acceptance of a grass and wild oat killer from the urea/triazine family. With fungicides it would appear that some formulations might be preferable to the use of copper and sulphur. With insecticides it would appear that some pyrethroids may be acceptable. The best attitude for the Green Grower would be to approve some compounds for general use (e.g. the broad leaf herbicides) and have a second category the use of which would be restricted, i.e. a given level of loss of crop would have to be predicted to justify the use.

# 13 Green Laws

Green laws do not exist as such. There are no standards of any sort that yet have any force in law. This includes an absence of standards in respect of either methods or products that may be used for green growing; no mandatory standards in respect of labelling the food products of green growing as 'green', organic, conservation, or anything else. There is a complete absence of any controls over what manufacturers of products used in growing plants may say on their labels.

Food products boast on their labels that they are 'natural', or have 'no added sugar', or 'no artificial ingredients' or whatever the boundless imagination of marketing people can invent. Crop growth and protection products are described as 'based on organic materials' or 'including organic materials' or 'biofriendly'; again, only imagination sets any limits to the implication that these products are not only not bad for you and the environment, they're even good for it.

This situation is changing at this time. Over the past decades, a variety of informal standards have been developed to which growers could elect to adhere voluntarily. The main standard was that of the Soil Association, a member of The International Federation of Organic Agricultural Movements (IFOAM), an international group of organic growers. If the standards, enforced by inspectors, were followed, the produce could display the symbol of the Soil Association, now virtually synonymous with 'organic'. The standards are now fairly sophisticated. They put products into four broad classes: recommended, permitted, restricted, and forbidden. Ideally, only recommended products should be used. Permitted products should only be used if the grower believes there is no practical alternative, but the decision to use them remains with the grower. Restricted products may be used in 'extreme' circumstances but only with the specific permission of the Soil Association. Forbidden products are totally proscribed.

In the 1970s, some growers recognised that the transition from conventional, chemical farming to full organic farming was not easy and farmers could lose their livelihood in the attempt. Consequently, a transitional standard was developed, called 'Conservation Grade', that allowed growers to wean themselves away from chemicals but not all at once, and without extreme jeopardy to their incomes. Later, the conservation grade developed into almost an alternative to 'organic', with a different but equally rigorous set of requirements. Each allows some products the other prohibits and good arguments can be made for both positions.

# United Kingdom Register of Organic Food Standards (UKROFS)

By the 1980s, it was clear that some codification was needed and the Ministry of Agriculture, Fisheries and Foods (MAFF) asked the Food From Britain organisation to establish the United Kingdom Register of Organic Food Standards (UKROFS). UKROFS is an independent body which sets production standards for organic food in the UK. Those meeting the standards can register as an approved producer of organic foods and will be able to use a symbol showing that they are approved. The organisation is governed by a Board appointed by the Council of Food From Britain 'such that no one interest predominates'.

The Board:

1    sets standards;

2    considers applications from other organisations for their standards to be recognised as valid;

3    appoints such organisations to act on behalf of UKROFS to police the regulations by farm inspections;

4    considers applications from individual producers to become recognised producers;

5    maintains the register of organic producers with a right to use the symbol.

The UKROFS Standards Manual for Organic Food Production contains the details of the standards which producers must follow if they wish to make an application for entry as an Approved Producer on the United Kingdom Register of Organic Food Standards. Once the EEC Regulation on organic production is passed, UKROFS standards will become the same as those in the EEC regulation, the only organic standard permitted will be the

UKROFS standards and all organisations operating to UKROFS standards will be legally obliged to conform. Some organisations may need to delete products not permitted by the EEC from their standards and to add hitherto forbidden products permitted by the EEC.

The UKROFS Manual, available for £15 from Food For Britain, reviews the principles of organic farming and the steps which have to be taken for a chemical-based farmer to convert to an acceptable organic production system. The manual details permitted methods for all aspects of organic food production from the on farm production of plants and animals to the method by which the end product is cooked and packaged. Layout of the standards has a rather confusing numbering system and many points are vague. Producers would be well advised to get details of organic standards through one of the approved organisations such as The Soil Association or Organic Farmers and Growers whose standards clarify the points more clearly and precisely and are easier to follow.

Most products listed in the UK Green Growers Guide are specifically permitted to organic farmers with the possible exception of the microbially-based products usually called biopesticides. The UKROFS Manual permits 'controlled use of biological methods using naturally occurring organisms against specific pest and disease targets'. However, elsewhere in the Manual there is a list of 'Methods and Substances for Pest and Disease Control' with 14 types of products including many listed in the UK Green Growers Guide, but the list does not specifically include biopesticides. It is worth noting that the list includes Sulphur and Bordeaux and Burgundy Mixtures which are in the UK Green Growers Guide section on chemical products accepted by some groups. They are clearly chemicals, albeit very old ones, and in some instance, clearly deleterious (like copper-based fungicides).

As with biopesticides, the Manual is unclear on several other important issues. It forbids silage additives, presumably meaning acids and chemical preservatives but also presumably not forbidding the addition of sugars as in molasses, or microbes or enzymes as contained in inoculants as these are wholly natural in origin and function. The use of such products under other current UK organic standards are only permitted after approval from a standards Committee. Similarly the Manual forbids 'non-feed' additives in animal feed that are designed to modify the intestinal microflora for the purpose of stimulating growth or production; presumably, the probiotics listed in the UK Green Growers Guide, being natural in origin and having some feed value (admittedly small), would be permitted to organic producers. As with biological silage, additives the use of probiotics under other UK organic standards is only permitted after approval by the standards committee.

Although this first attempt at standardising and validating organic production is not yet perfect, it is an important step in the direction of making organic production less of a 'muck and magic', kook-fringe activity. It should also begin to give all of us more confidence that the products we are buying at sometimes outrageous premiums are what they claim.

## European Community Regulation

The European Community will, in due course, adopt a regulation on organic production and labelling. Once adopted, this will have the force of law in the UK and the other states of the EC and will supersede all other types of regulation.

The EC believes that a regulation is required because demand from consumers for organically produced agricultural products and foodstuffs is increasing and a new market for higher-priced products is being created in the total absence of any control over claims about products or foods. The Commission favours the development of this new market because organic production involves less intensive use of land; it thinks that a better balance of supply and demand for agricultural products will ensue and it will become easier to protect the environment and conserve the countryside.

A legally enforceable regulation is needed to ensure fair competition within the EC between producers and to improve the credibility of such products in consumers' eyes. It will apply to unprocessed agricultural crops, animals and unprocessed animal products, and to virtually all products intended for human consumption. The regulation will restrict the use of the word 'organic' on labels. In future, it must refer only to the method by which the food was produced. This method may not include the use of synthetic chemicals or ingredients, irradiation or treatment with synthetic chemicals. Organic producers will be subject to inspection according to clearly set out procedures to verify this.

The regulation says clearly, *"products composed of or incorporating one or more synthetic chemicals may not be used as plant protection products, detergents, fertilizers, soil conditioner or animal feeding stuffs. "* There are some carefully controlled exceptions, similar in concept to the Soil Association's approach of allowing certain products under exceptional circumstances, while not encouraging their regular use. Imports from outside the EC must also comply or they cannot be called organic. Many of the details are given in the proposed regulation although there will be an advisory committee to make policy in the future.

## Regulation in the United States

Although not directly relevant to our situation in the UK, it is worth mentioning some important developments in the US as it is both one of the world's major food producers and the consumer of over 20% of the world's agrochemicals. In 1990 a bill was proposed in the US Senate to establish organic standards in the US. Although this specific bill was not voted on, and died at the end of the session, there is every likelihood that it, or a similar bill will eventually be re-introduced and become law. The bill as proposed would have had a profound effect on producers of agricultural products in that it strongly encouraged them in the direction of low-input, sustainable, or organic agriculture and in the use of the sort of products in the UK Green Growers Guide. It was intended to give consumers confidence in product labels, hitherto a welter of pleasant-sounding but meaningless phrases. It would also provide much stronger incentives to the chemical industry to move away from agrochemicals.

The introduction to the bill said that *"Congress finds that: consumers are demanding fresh and processed foods using organic methods; organic farming methods promote more sustainable agricultural practices than traditional farming methods using high levels of chemicals; ...there is a need for a national program designed to standardize and promote the production of food through organic and sustainable farming methods. "* The bill would have established honest and informative national standards governing the labelling of agricultural products as organically produced and would have given an enormous boost to the non-chemical grower.

These statements and objectives are very radical, especially in the USA where they are directly contrary to the beliefs and agricultural practices of the last 40 - 50 years. With the substantial economic power of the agrochemical and fertilizer industries in the US, it is not surprising this bill has not yet become law.

In summary, the bill would have allowed plants and animals grown to fully organic specification to be labelled 'organically produced' with the seal of the United States Department of Agriculture (USDA). Produce of farms in a new programme of low input sustainable agriculture (LISA) would be labelled as 'transition to organic' or 'produced on a LISA farm' and have the USDA seal. No one could use a label that implied, directly or indirectly, that a product was organically, naturally, or ecologically produced, grown, processed, or marketed unless it had been approved. Violations would have been punishable by up to five years imprisonment and or a fine of $100,000.

It would have forbidden the use of synthetic pesticides or fungicides, soil fumigants, 'natural poisons' such as arsenic or lead salts, synthetic growth regulators, nutrients at toxic levels, plastic, fertilizers containing synthetic ingredients including a number of named sources of nitrogen and phosphorus, or sub-therapeutic antibiotics in animals. Products such as those listed in the UK Green Growers Guide would virtually all have been acceptable.

# Chemical Regulation

# Pesticides

In the UK, pesticides are controlled by law. All chemical products used as pesticides require clearance from the Pesticides Safety Division of the Ministry of Agriculture, Fisheries and Food (MAFF). It is technically illegal even to use washing-up liquid to kill insects in your garden, although prosecution for this may be unlikely. Most biological products also require clearance, including all the products based on microorganisms described in the next chapter. However, pest control using larger organisms such as insects or nematodes to control insects, is allowed without regulation at present.

It usually takes many years for a new chemical to be approved. A wide variety of tests are carried out looking for toxicity to humans, animals and other living creatures, as well as environmental effects of many types. Passing these tests and receiving approval means that the product is *considered* safe if used as intended. Clearly, if the product is mis-used, deliberately or accidently, it may cause harm. This is not unique to agrochemicals but is true of most things.

However, it must be remembered that tests are designed to show those effects we know how to look for and measure. Unexpected results are, of course, always investigated further. But taking the example of DDT, no one thought to measure its longer term effect on the strength of bird's eggs. While it is reasonable for industry to say that science rather than emotion should be used to judge the safety of pesticides, it is also true to say that science is not always perfect; in fact, perfection is rare. The green grower might think therefore, that even if a product is approved, and is safe for use as intended, it might be best left unused. Economic necessity and the need for food might cause us to use chemicals anyway, but the principle of avoidance remains sound.

## Fertilisers

Fertilisers do not require registration of any sort, nor are any materials specifically permitted or forbidden. All the products in the UK Green Growers Guide used as fertilisers or added to seeds to promote growth are legally permitted without regulation.

## Animal feed

Animal feed is regulated by law. There is a list of specific substances that are permitted. The products in the UK Green Growers Guide are allowed to be added to animal feed as aids in promoting good general growth and health. However, there are severe restrictions on the claims that may be made for such products. Claims to increase growth rates or to cure specific ailments would lead these products to be treated as veterinary pharmaceuticals. Under this classification they would be unlikely to receive approval due to the somewhat unpredictable and unquantifiable results they produce.

## Residues

Most of our food, even organic food, contains some residues. In the UK and the EEC, residue levels have been set for each pesticide by assessing the daily intake at which effects are seen in tests on sensitive species of animals. The safe level for humans is then set at 1/100th of this level on an assumption that the average person is 10X as sensitive as the animals and that the most sensitive person is 10X more sensitive than the average.

Chemical companies worry that acceptable levels are being lowered as advances in analytical chemistry make it possible to detect lower levels of residues in food rather than because of any scientific evidence that shows the higher levels are detrimental. Companies believe some residue is inevitable if food production is to be maintained. They claim that residue levels rarely rise even to permitted levels and they argue that environmentalists are taking a political stance rather than basing their arguments about health on sound scientific data. They point to the fact that virtually all documented research comparing the nutritional value of food grown by conventional and organic methods fails to demonstrate any difference in available nutrients or in food quality.

Generally, groups concerned about the effects of pesticide residues on human and animal health have had relatively unsympathetic responses to their allegations from both companies and governments. The World Commission on Environment and Development states that, *"The use of agricultural chemicals is not in itself harmful... (but) overuse threatens the health of humans and the lives of other species. Long term exposure to pesticides and chemical residues in food and water is hazardous particularly to children. "* Others assert that pesticide accumulation may be reducing the effectiveness of our immune systems making us more prone to infections and diseases or even having effects on our mental state. Friends of the Earth have detected 16 different types of pesticides in water sources which could react with the chlorine used to disinfect the water. They worry about possible interactions between pesticides or with chemical residues from other sources and about the effects of gradual accumulation.

# 14  Biopesticides - Microbes for Crop Protection

Biopesticides are products used to kill insects (insecticides), weeds (herbicides) or prevent or stop many plant diseases (fungicides) in which the active ingredient is based on or derived from a microorganism. Microorganisms include bacteria, fungi, viruses, and protozoa. All groups of microorganisms, like people, include some good ones and some bad ones.

Until relatively recently biopesticides were not a realistic alternative to chemicals. Biopesticides were expensive and worse still, unreliable. Sometimes they worked well, and sometimes not at all. It was impossible to predict with certainty that a gardener or a grower would produce the same quantity and apparent quality of produce with biopesticides as that obtained by using chemicals.Recently, the prospects for new and better biopesticides have improved. They are now on their way to becoming a real and technically sound alternative to chemicals in crop protection.

Recent developments include:

1.  An increasing number of small market niches where biopesticides are likely to be useful. A major one of these is the demand by consumers for more food grown without chemicals. Other markets have been created by the activity of governments such as the banning of chemical insecticides in certain forests in Canada, or by international bodies such as the World Health Organisation's use of biopesticides in trying to control diseases carried by insects. A few markets have even been generated by the use of chemicals; some insects are so resistant to most chemicals that biological products have been developed to control them instead.

2.  An increasing interest in biopesticides by companies. These include some already well established in biopesticides, such as Abbott Laboratories (US) and Sandoz (Switzerland); some well-known and economically powerful companies taking a new interest in the field such as ICI (UK) and Shell (The Netherlands); some less well known

companies with great technical proficiency in other fields applying this skill to improving biopesticides. These include Novo (Denmark), better known for making insulin and the enzymes in our laundry detergents, and Christian Hansen, better known for making bacterial starter cultures for cheese and other dairy products. In addition, new companies have been started whose main business is to develop and sell biopesticides. Investment in most of these new companies is still very speculative and risky; in the UK, the only such company of any note is the Agricultural Genetics Company (AGC). In the US there are many more with high-tech names as like Ecogen and Mycogen.

3.    An increasing body of new technology. Important new research has produced new processing and formulation methods for biopesticides and techniques for genetic engineering to make microorganisms take on different properties to enhance their potency as biopesticides. Other work is attempting to genetically manipulate plants to make them resistant to insects and diseases, perhaps one day eliminating the need for any other crop protection products.

## What do Biopesticides do?

Unlike chemicals, the way many biopesticides work is not fully understood. There are relatively few actually on the market, despite many more that might yet be sold. In this section we consider the ones that are sold now and which could be the first of other, similar products in the future.

> ## BACTERIA
>
> Bacteria are used to make cheese and yoghurt and silage for animals; they live in our intestines and help digest food and they have many beneficial effects when grown together with plants, Other bacteria cause a wide range of human and animal diseases. Fortunately, most bacterial diseases are no longer a serious threat. This is due to the development of antibiotics, whose sole function is to stop the growth of bacteria.

## A bacterium - *Bacillus thuringiensis*

A variety of products including Bactospeine™, Thuricide™, Dipel™ and Biobit™ are all made from a bacterium, called *Bacillus thuringiensis* (*Bt*). *Bt* is used to kill insects that eat it. It was first discovered around 1901 killing silkworms and was a threat to that industry in Japan. The name *'thuringiensis'* was given to a strain from Thuringia in Germany found in 1911 and is now used for the whole species. The first product based on *Bt* was introduced in 1935 for use against caterpillars. All *Bt* products were used against caterpillars until 1978 when a new type of *Bt* was discovered to be effective against mosquitoes and related insects like blackfly, the carrier of river blindness (onchocerciasis) in West Africa. The new strain was brought to market very quickly and started to be used against blackfly, nuisance mosquitoes and carriers of malaria and yellow fever. In Britain, this strain is effective against Blandford fly, a serious pest in the West Country. Permission to use the product against Blandford fly was given recently but the market is so small as to be of little interest to most companies.

The realisation that *Bt* could be effective against insects other than caterpillars led to a vast increase in collection and screening of new types against economically important insect targets. Within a few years, many new strains of *Bt* had been discovered that were effective against the Colorado beetle of potatoes and other related beetles. Products for beetle control should be coming onto the market over the next few years. Also, still newer types of *Bt* are being discovered at present that may result in more new products.

## Making *Bt*

*Bt* is made by a process similar to that for making beer, called 'fermentation'. Large vats of from 10,000 to 200,000 litres are filled with water to which selected nutrients are added. One nutrient supplies energy in some form, usually as a type of sugar; other nutrients supply nitrogen and all the ingredients required for the microorganism to grow. Growth begins when a small number of microorganisms are added to the vat and begin dividing. Throughout the fermentation the broth is stirred with air bubbling through it and is kept at a constant temperature and constant pH (acidity). After 1-3 days, the nutrients are exhausted and the *Bt* cells begin to make small crystals and spores (seeds) inside their cell wells. At the end of the fermentation the crystals and spores are concentrated, dried and formulated into various products.

## Selling *Bt*

Worldwide sales of chemicals are over $20b of which about 25% is for insect control. Of the $5b, just $20m - $40m (approximately 0.4 - 0.8%), is accounted for by biopesticides of which *Bt* products account for 90 - 95%. Sales of *Bt* have grown in volume over the past 20 years as more products are used, particularly in forestry and in the control of insect-borne diseases. The Bt market is presently dominated by Abbott Laboratories (US) and Sandoz (Switzerland). However, Novo Nordisk (Denmark) and possibly CRC (Italy) may become serious competitors in the future. Many others, including Monsanto, Shell, DuPont, Bayer, BASF, Hoechst, etc have been in the past or are currently working on biopesticides or related technologies.

However, although volumes have increased, prices have fallen due to competition; the total sales value appears to have changed relatively little. One obvious use of *Bt* which should have grown, as 'green' issues came to the fore, was in domestic gardens. However, sales into this sector have remained small, perhaps due to poor marketing. In Britain there have been a number of attempts to sell *Bt* to gardeners, usually by selling sealed packs with a relatively small amount in each. Sometimes the product is diluted from the agricultural strength in order to allow the use of more manageable quantities, like a teaspoon, in the average domestic sprayer. What the consumer may not realize is that the cost of the packaging and selling products in this way is actually much higher than the cost of making them. Consequently, the cost per dose seems high by the time it's bought by the domestic gardener. The shelf-life of *Bt* is quite long, at least 2 years so it can be kept for later use in the same way as a chemical.

## How does *Bt* work?

In order to be effective, *Bt* needs to be eaten by insects which subsequently die. Looked at more closely, *Bt* kills insects with the crystal produced at the end of its fermentation. This crystal contains a variety of proteins called 'the δ-endotoxins', all of which are harmless to man and animals. The crystals dissolve in the gut of the target insect and disrupt its ability to feed, killing it either quickly or after a few days. Examined in more detail, the crystals are composed of a number of large proteins which are precursors of the actual toxins; when the crystal is dissolved in the gut of the insect, which is alkaline (high pH, i.e. low acidity, the opposite of human stomachs), its proteins are rapidly broken down yielding the actual toxins. These compounds attach themselves at specific points (i.e. to specific 'receptors') to the cells lining the gut. The attachment causes holes to occur in the cell walls; the cells fill with water and burst, losing their contents. The reason different strains of *Bt* kill different insects is because the broken down proteins attach to different types of receptors in each group of insects.

In the longer term, insects may become resistant to the *Bt* toxin. For at least two types of insect, resistance has recently been reported in laboratory experiments. As yet, there have been no reports of resistant insects occurring in the wild.

In summary, *Bt*, although the most successful and one of the oldest biopesticides, is actually rather similar to a chemical from a natural source. A precise understanding of how *Bt* works is growing rapidly due to vigorous experimentation in a number of laboratories. The genes that make *Bt* toxins are a favourite subject for genetic engineering; they have been put into plants and into a variety of other microorganisms. Therefore there is a great likelihood that more and better *Bt* products will become available for both domestic and agricultural use. Some of these products are likely to be the result of genetic manipulation and may pose a dilemma for those who favour natural pest control but oppose genetic engineering.

---

## FUNGI

Fungi make most of the antibiotics we use in medicine. Mushrooms, from supermarkets and from fields and woods are all fungi, including all the great culinary fungi like truffles, morels, chanterelles and many others. Yeasts, a group of small fungi, make bread rise and contribute to almost every other kind of baking. Yeasts turn grape juice into wine, stewed grains of barley into beer and lager, apple juice into cider and pear juice into perry. Other fungi, not many, are very poisonous such as death cap mushrooms. Some cause human ailments like athlete's foot or thrush; some of these ailments, although not common, can be very serious and hard to cure.

---

## A fungus - *Verticillium lecanii*

Some species of fungi are adapted to live on insects. They kill insects by attacking from the outside, boring through the insect's defenses, and then consuming the insect, often leaving an empty ghost. Most fungi then produce spores (seeds) which are usually sticky and attach to other insects and repeat the process. In this way, insect numbers may be kept in check, well below the thresholds of economic damage, and large insect populations decimated.

Fungi were the first identified as insect killers in 1836 although little was done until 1873 when the 'green muscardine fungus' was tried for control of sugar beet pests; other attempts were made with the 'white muscardine fungus'. Before chemicals, fungi were used against insects with some success.

*Verticillium lecanii*, a fungus that naturally infects aphids and scale insects in the tropics and subtropics, was the subject of considerable research over many years at what was known as the Glasshouse Crops Research Institute (GCRI) in Littlehampton. (Once part of the Agriculture and Food Research Council (AFRC), after a number of changes of name, GCRI will soon vanish.) In our climate, *V. lecanii* will work in a similar way in the controlled environment of glasshouses. It works exactly as described above. Due to its ability to grow and spread, the use of *V. lecanii* can control whitefly for from several weeks to several months after 1-2 applications. Products based on *V. lecanii* are formulated to allow growth to begin after application whether it hits an insect or not, resulting in production of more spores and increasing efficacy. However, to be effective, *V. lecanii* needs the temperature to be between 15-25°C and the relative humidity to be over 85% for 10-12 hours per day. This means that in our climate, *V. lecanii* can never be used outdoors and its effectiveness even in glasshouses may not be absolutely predictable.

## Selling *V. lecanii*

*V. lecanii* was the first such product ever to be sold in Europe. It was registered in the UK in 1981 by Tate & Lyle as Vertalec to control aphids in glasshouses. Another strain was later registered as Mycotal for the control of glasshouse whitefly. The products based on *V. lecanii* were ultimately sold to Koppert, based in Holland but with a UK branch, in 1988. Mycotal alone is now available on the UK market. Very similar products are made and sold in Denmark and also in Czechoslovakia and the USSR for use against thrips.

Other fungi are widely used for crop protection in developing countries, Central European countries and the USSR and one might wonder why they are not yet available in Britain. Until very recently it has been impossible to determine how successful these fungi actually were in practice. Assessing success is subjective and depends on the results the assessor needs to have. For commercial growers, the quality and reliability of crop protection is critical, as is its cost. Production and labour costs are likely to be much higher here, so using, for example, very generous amounts applied frequently would not be practical here. Similarly, product registration requirements for such products can be much more demanding, making impractical the introduction of a product with a relatively small market.

# Making *V. lecanii*

The products can be made in a manner similar to *Bt*, described above, by fermentation. The fungus is grown in large vats until it produces spores which are concentrated and formulated into saleable products. Alternatively, *V. lecanii* can be grown on trays, using ordinary cereal grains as its nutrient.

# The future for fungi

Unfortunately, the shelf-life of all fungal products is relatively short, around 6 months, and their use requires considerable skill. At present they are probably only suitable for commercial glasshouse growers, although they could certainly successfully control whitefly in smaller glasshouses that were sufficiently warm and humid. Unlike the future for *Bt*, the future for fungi is still uncertain. The key technical limitations are not about to be overcome although some slight progress is evident. Fungi have not yet been developed with greater tolerance to adverse environmental conditions, nor have any been found with more rapid or more effective infection cycles. Despite research, genetic engineering of better strains is still unlikely. Some really effective fungi that are difficult to grow, remain difficult.

Bayer appear to be the only major company working on a new fungal product. They report good results against black vine weevil, a common pest of pot plants, with the green muscardine fungus first tested in 1876 but grown by a new, special patented fermentation method. Quite high doses are needed for success so this product, currently code-named BIO 1020, is likely only to be useful in high-value horticultural crops or in domestic glasshouses. Bayer will market BIO 1020 on a small scale in Germany in 1991 and, if successful, may introduce it to the UK later. ICI was also interested in this fungus but for use against a more economically important pest of rice.

## VIRUSES

Viruses are the smallest of all microorganisms and perhaps the most difficult about which to find positive things to say. Viruses cause many common human and animal ailments ranging from the minor ones, like colds, through influenza and AIDS. Viruses are however, very specific in their targets, and there is one group, called the baculoviruses, that attack insects. One product in this guide is based on viruses and there may be more in the future.

## A virus - *Neodiprion sertifer* Nuclear Polyhedrosis Virus

Like bacteria, viruses have to be eaten in order to infect and kill insects. This infection usually happens during the larval insect stages (caterpillars) as most of the insects' eating is done at this stage. Once eaten, the virus, packaged in a protective envelope of protein, is released and enters its host by penetrating the cells in the wall of the gut. After penetration, the virus reproduces itself in large numbers inside each cell; the crowding eventually causes the cells to break open and release many more viruses. The insect dies shortly thereafter and the virus is released to attack and kill other insects. The effectiveness of viral applications depends on getting sufficient virus to the target insect and on the social behaviour of the insects concerned helping to spread the virus further through the population.

Viruses can only be made in the insects which they kill. Although the technology exists to grow them artificially, by fermentation, they must be grown on cells of the target insect rather than the cheaper nutrients used to grow bacteria and fungi. This process is so expensive as to be impractical at present.

Many viruses are known to attack and kill insects. However, very few have been used on any scale and most of those have been developed using public money in the US, Canada and Britain. Only one product is available commercially in the UK and that controls pine sawflies in forests. It is possible that other virus products may appear in the future or that genetically improved viruses may find more general use. At present, the most likely prospect, as with fungi, is that some of the products developed and used in Central European countries and the USSR will be useful enough to find a new market here.

## Biopesticide Markets

As described above, the main market for biopesticides is for products based on *Bt* against caterpillars in a variety of food crops. Although products used against disease-carrying and nuisance insects have little relevance in the UK, the new strains effective against Colorado beetles and other beetles may lead to new UK products.

New markets are being created by legislation and consumer demands which will no doubt lead to a significant increase in demand for Bt products in the near future. Although not a large market at present, one area where biopesticides are widely accepted is in the production of organic food. In spite of the fact that organic vegetables and fruit, as well as other organically-labelled produce, are often more expensive than similar products grown using chemicals, this sector continues to attract new consumers. The supply of organic products in countries such as West Germany, Holland, the UK, France and the west coast of the US, has moved away from a fringe sector typified by small street corner, health food, shops into the supermarkets. Safeways, Sainsbury's, Tesco's and Waitrose all now stock organically grown foods. One major chain reported *"we now sell a considerable amount of organically grown produce, far more than could be purchased by a few health food fanatics"*. In the UK it has been variously estimated that by the year 2000 between 10 and 15 percent of the market value of food bought will have been grown using organic or conservation (low chemical input) techniques. At present, it is estimated that less than 1% of UK food is organic, representing total sales of around $110m per year. Although this seems a relatively large sum, the majority of the sales are for organic or conservation grade grain (oats) for processing. Other products which command a significant market are fresh vegetables and fruit, with smaller amounts of milk and milk products, and still smaller quantities of organic meat. As the demand grows for food produced without chemicals, it is likely that the demand for biopesticides for use in this sector will show a similar rate of increase.

# Conclusion

Although the difficulties inherent in identifying, manufacturing and selling biopesticides are fairly obvious, many companies have tried the biopesticide business and been disappointed in the results. This may be because most of the literature on biopesticides is written by enthusiasts most of whom have little practical commercial experience, or it may be that the companies 'put a toe in the water', which usually costs more and achieves a great deal less than planned. We believe nevertheless, that current commercial, technical and legislative trends indicate that the future for biopesticides will be more profitable than their past.

# 15 Insects to Control Other Insects

The use of insects to control other insects has a long history; parasitic and predatory behaviour has been observed for centuries and exploited since at least 1200 AD; amongst other examples, the Chinese employed Pharaoh's ant, *Monomorium pharaonis*, to combat stored product pests in barns. However, the majority of these uses have been in situations where an insect not native to a particular area is introduced and establishes itself while reducing the population of the 'pest' insect. This is generally called 'classical' biological control. To be considered successful these one-off introductions must be permanent. In some crops such as citrus, these classical types of introduction are the principal means of pest reduction. A permanent solution to a pest problem is not very desirable if a company is hoping to sell more of its product every year in order to survive. Consequently, virtually all the developments and successes in classical biological control have come from work sponsored with public funds.

In contrast, some insects need to be re-introduced to every crop, where they seek out and destroy pests either as predators or parasites. The production and sale of insects in this way, in effect, as 'pesticides', began with the discovery in 1926 of *Encarsia formosa*, a wasp parasitizing the scale stage in the development of whitefly. By 1935, 1.5m wasps were being produced annually and were being distributed to seven countries. World War Two intervened and subsequently the discovery and widespread use of new chemical insecticides, such as DDT, impeded the progress of biological control. Chemicals were thought to be completely safe and effective alternatives to the sometimes uncertain biological methods. Eventually however, knowledge of and concern for the long term effects of these chemicals on the environment as well as the evolution of strains of resistant insect pests, particularly in intensively grown crops, led to a resurgence of interest in the use of insects for control purposes.

One key pest that rapidly evolved resistance both to DDT and to the organophosphorus compounds that followed was *Tetranychus urticae*, the red spider mite. In 1960 the red spider mite predator, *Phytoseiulus persimilis*, was discovered and within ten years was being produced commercially by a number of firms.

At present, the following commercial products are available somewhere in the world, many of them in Britain: *Crypoleamus montrouzieri*, a mealybug predator; six strains of *Amblyseius* used against thrips; *Aphidus aphidimyza* against aphids; *Aphytis melinus*, a scale parasite; *Bracon hebetor* versus caterpillars in stored grain; three strains of *Chrysoperla* (lacewings) for use against a broad spectrum of garden pests; *Cotesia melanoscela*, *Meteorus pulchricornis* and *Glyptapanteles*, parasites of gypsy moth; *Dacnusa sibirica* and *Diglyphus isaea* versus leaf miners; *Encarsia formosa* against whitefly; *Spalangia corona* and *Muscadifurax raptor* used against flies; *Hippodamia convergens* (ladybirds or ladybugs) against many pests; at least two strains of *Trichogramma*, a parasite of 600 types of moth eggs; *Tenodera aridifolia* (praying mantis); *Leptomastidea abnormis* and *Anagyrus pseudococci*, also mealybug predators; *Metaphycus helvolus*, a scale parasite; two strains of *Phytoseiulus* against mites; and *Xylocaris flavipes*, the warehouse pirate bug that attacks eggs and larvae of beetles and moths infesting stored grains.

The use of one beneficial insect predator to control a second insect pest meant that conventional insecticides could not be used to control other insects present in the same environment; in some cases fungicides could not be used either as they too would reduce the effectiveness of the predator. For these reasons a system of integrated control was developed, using a number of different insects, biopesticides and management practices, which allowed good yields of high quality produce without the use of chemical pesticides.

Insects as products for biocontrol must either be produced in insectaries or collected from the wild. Insectaries are intensive farms for insects which are sometimes raised on artificial diets and sometimes on their target host insect. The management of insectaries is a combination of art and science. The principal problem is that insects must be delivered to the customer at exactly the right stage and in good condition. The demand for insects is seasonal and insectary production must be able to reach quite high peaks at certain times yet not be too expensive to leave idle at times of low demand. Another key problem is that insects are mobile and can be said to have minds of their own. Therefore the 'formulation' of the insect product, how they are packaged, transported and applied to the crop, are of critical importance. Some companies provide insects on leaves, others provide them lightly stuck to cards or in carriers like sawdust. There are also a number of ways in which the gardener or grower can encourage naturally occurring insects to help control pests in various crops. These methods are described in a number of other books.

The last two decades have seen the development of a very strong interest in the use of insects to control other insects and the products and suppliers included in this Guide are evidence of the growing commercial success of these enterprises. A selection of insects in use and their mode of action are illustrated in greater detail below.

# PEST CONTROL INSECTS

## Parasitic wasps of whitefly

One key pest in everyone's glasshouse is the glasshouse whitefly (*Trialeurodes vaporariorum*). The adults are small, winged, white to creamy yellow insects. Their egg laying habits depend on which plant they are on and how many there are. Each female may lay up to 400 eggs in circles under leaves. The eggs hatch to produce crawling larvae, which soon settle down. The larvae moult (shed their outer layer) four times and become pupae. In all these stages, the insects resemble white waxy scales. The rate of growth from egg to adult will also depend on the host plant and the temperature, taking from 18-123 days. Relative humidity of from 75-80% suits the pest best. Low numbers of whitefly do not cause much visible damage to plants but at high densities there may be distortion of the young, rapidly growing, shoots. The principal damage is caused by the secretion of honeydew (sugary liquid) by the scales which falls onto the leaves below and onto fruit and encourages the growth of sooty mould and other plant diseases. Another whitefly that can infest UK crops is the sweet potato whitefly (*Bemisia tabaci*) which has scales that are more yellow than the normal glasshouse variety. The adult holds its wings more erect than the glasshouse whitefly should you have both types handy for comparison.

The first and one of the most successful insects used for pest control is the tiny parasitic wasp (*Encarsia formosa*). The wasps are introduced on cards (60 per card) which should be hung near the whitefly as soon as the first adult is seen. Use at a rate of 10,000 wasps per acre each fortnight at the first sign of whitefly or 5,000 per fortnight well before any whitefly are seen. This rate corresponds to one or two cards for a small domestic glasshouse. The adult female wasps are black with yellow abdomens and lay their eggs into the larva and pupae of glasshouse whitefly. Adults live up to 27 days and will lay 50-100 eggs each. Wasps prefer 50-80% relative humidity and light at around half the strength of diffuse sunlight (4500 lux or 30 watts per square meter). The wasp has three larval stages and a pupal stage. Whitefly scales that have had wasp eggs laid in them will change colour from white to black, after which the wasp larvae with hatch. The length of the wasp's life cycle depends on the temperature and ranges from 13 days at 27°C to 39 days at 18°C. Unfortunately, effective though *Encarsia* is against glasshouse whitefly, it will not parasitise the tobacco or sweet potato whitefly sufficiently to provide control.

# Predatory mites

One of the most intractable problems in both glasshouses and on house plants is the Two Spotted or Red Spider Mite (*Tetranychus urticae*). This pest was one of the first to develop resistance to most insecticides which it treats as a form of insect salad cream. Mites will appear on the plants near to where the they have over-wintered, in your house or glasshouse. When they eat your plants they produce minute, yellowish speckled marks and the leaves may shrivel and die. At high densities, the mites migrate to leaves at the growing points of the plant and spin silken webs. They can travel to neighbouring plants by producing silk threads. Severe damage may resemble the yellowing of magnesium deficiency.

The red spider mites have two dark spots on the back of their bodies. They lay their eggs laid under leaves and hatch out as white six-legged larvae. Subsequent stages, called protonymph and deutonymph, can either eat your plants or go into a resting phase called diapause. Maturing females can lay eggs at a rate of 4-8 eggs/day beginning 36 hours after they are born. The complete life cycle of from 3-30 days depends on how warm it is. The first adults to appear from diapause are bright red in colour and as the days shorten in Autumn the adults will again turn bright red in preparation for diapause.

Dramatic control fo the red spider mite is provided by a vigorous predator (*Phytoseiulus persimilis*). The predators should be concentrated near the first sign of infestation. Introducing more later will help build up the population of predators which can then keep red spider mite under control. The adult female red spider mite predator is orange to red and pear-shaped, and slightly longer than the red spotted mite. Eggs are laid individually, two to three every day for three weeks. As they develop, they turn from translucent to pinkish orange. A six-legged larva hatches, developing an eight-legged protonymph, which can eat four to five red spotted mite eggs before developing into the deutonymph. This stage can consume six eggs or young red spotted mites. Adults can eat seven mites per day. The life cycle is shortest and the population growth is greatest at higher temperatures which should not exceed 30°C. In the US, they recommend a humid environment of 60-90% relative humidity and temperatures between 21°c to 30°C for red spider mite predators. They also have available *Phytoseiulus longipes*, similar to *P. persimilis* but more tolerant to lower humidity (40% at 21°C). It will carry on working up to 38°C, although it requires more humidity as the temperature increases. Another predatory mite, *Metaseiulus occidentalis*, is also often combined with other species in the USA. It is somewhat more flexible in where it will live and is more catholic in its diet. It is well adapted for outdoor use and can perform in hot situations where humidity remains above 50%. It also tolerates to some pesticides including Guthion, closely related organophosphates, and Carbaryl (Sevin R).

## Parasitic wasps of leafminers - *Dacnusa sibrica* and *Diglyphus isaea*

Leafminers (*Liriomyza bryoniae* and *Phytomyza syngenesise*) form pale white tunnels or mines in leaves, ruining their appearance and depriving the plant of the nutrients it makes from sunlight. The mines usually meander around the leaf becoming larger, bigger and broader. The tomato leafminer (*Liriomyza bryoniae*) is a small black fly with yellow spots between the wings. The chrysanthemum leafminer (*Phytomyza syngenesise*) is larger and dark grey. The females puncture leaves, looking for egg laying sites. The punctures show as pale white spots and not all punctures will contain eggs. About 60 eggs can be laid over three weeks. Eggs hatch after one week and the larvae will tunnel for ten days, moulting three times causing the mines they are creating to enlarge. Leafminer larvae will emerge from their tunnels to pupate after which *Liriomyza bryoniae* pupae will fall to the ground. Adults will appear 25-30 days after egg laying.

Leafminers can be controlled with *Dacnusa*, black wasps with long flexible antenna. Adult females live for about two weeks and can lay up to 900 eggs inside leafminer larvae. The eggs hatch in four days after which the larvae will take up to 16 days to mature, killing the leaf miner when it pupates. *Dacnusa* are often used with *Diglyphus*, small and black to metallic green with shorter antenna than *Dacnusa*. Adult females lay up to 60 eggs beside leafminer larvae and then begin to parasitise the leaf miner. The larva hatches in two days and moults three times over the next six days while eating leafminers. To use these parasites, you should introduce 700 per acre at the first sign of leafminer egg laying in tomatoes, or at the rate of 500 per acre in chrysanthemums. Introductions may need to be repeated if more than one generation of leafminer is present in the crop.

## Thrips predators *Amblyseius cucumeris* and *Amblyseius barkeri*

Thrips (*Thrips tabaci* and *Franklinella occidentalis*) feed on sap after piercing plants. The tissue around the punctures dries out with a speckled or window-like appearance. The greatest damage is done to flowers - as the buds break, the petals can be severely distorted. Thrips can also carry Tomato Spotted Wilt Virus (TSWV). Adults are barely visible, long, slender and grey to yellow brown in colour. They have two pairs of narrow wings fringed with fine hairs. The female can lay 60 whitish eggs, each into a slit cut in a leaf or flower. The larvae is even smaller with bright red eyes. It takes 10-14 days to pass through two larval stages, to form a pre-pupa which will drop to the ground to form a full pupae in two days. A large proportion of Western flower thrip will pupate in the leaf and not drop to the ground. Adults will appear four to seven days later.

The thrip predator (*Amblyseius*) must be is well established in the crop before the thrip is present, particularly to control Western Flower Thrip. Predators will go into a resting stage (diapause) if the day length is less than 13.5 hours and the temperature is below 20°C. Therefore the first introductions in March should wait until the days are long enough and the temperature high enough. Higher temperatures at this stage can help the predators multiply and control more thrips; clearly, introducing larger numbers of predators will also help keep thrips under control. Rates of half a million per half acre per fourteen days to three quarters of a million per half acre per week may be required according to the time of year and thrip pressures. Predator adults are pear shaped and pale whitish brown and are smaller and flatter than *Phytoseiulus*. The eggs are small and white and are laid on plant hairs (at the axil of midrib and lateral (side) ribs) on the underside of leaves. There are five development stages: egg, larva, protonymph, deutonymph and adult. The predator's life cycle takes from 11 days at 21°C to 20 days at 15°C. *Amblyseius* will control the hatching eggs and first larval stages. Adults and deutonymphs are the most effective at thrip control and each can consume two to five thrips per day. In general *Amblyseius cucumeris* is a more voracious consumer of thrips than *Amblyseius barkeri*. *Amblyseius* is also effective against red spider mite and at least six strains are available commercially for this purpose in North America but not in Britain. One in particular, *Amblyseius californicus*, currently sold only in the USA and Canada, consumes spider mites quite slowly but will survive longer under starvation condition when the pests disappear. Consequently, it will usually be present if the pests re-infest the plants. It needs a minimum of 60% humidity and will tolerate temperatures up to 90°F.

## Aphid midges (*Aphidoletes aphidimyza*)

Aphids are a chronic problem for everyone; there are many species that cause serious economic damage. Aphids are small soft bodied insects which live on plants in dense colonies. They feed on plant sap by inserting their mouthparts into plant tissue. This weakens the plant and causes distortion. Secretion of honeydew (sugary liquid) also encourages the growth of sooty mould and other plant diseases. If that were not sufficient, aphids are also a common carrier of diseases caused by plant viruses. They are pear shaped and lack segmentation. The legs and antennae are very slender and two tubes project from the hind end. Adults can have wings in order to spread themselves out or may be without wings when they are congregated in colonies. In the Summer, young aphids are born fully formed and after moulting four times can reach maturity in a week. A female can produce three to six young per day. At high densities winged adults appear which can fly off and establish new colonies or remain to complete their reproductive cycle after the transition from Winter to Summer (or the reverse) host plants.

Aphid midges (*Aphidoletes aphidimyza*) are small and slender. Adults live for two weeks and are active mainly at night laying up to 100 orange oval eggs on aphid infected plants. In two to three days an orange to red larva emerges and grows to 2-3mm. The larvae feed on many aphids species, taking 7-14 days to develop, during which time each larva eats a minimum of two adults or 15 juvenile aphids. Once developed, the larva falls to the ground, burrows and pupates. Insufficient light and low temperatures induce a resting phase (diapause) (although the short day blackouts used in commercial chrysanthemum growing do not affect this midge). The adult emerges 10-11 days after pupation and begins the cycle over again.

## Mealybug predator (*Cryptolamus montrouzieri*)

Mealybugs (*Planoccoccus citri*) sap the strength from plants and cause both yellowing and distortion of the leaves, often followed by leaves dropping off. They also produce copious amounts of honeydew (sugary liquid), encouraging sooty mould and other plant diseases, which, together with waxy threads, make the plants unsightly. The bugs are small soft bodied insects with sucking mouthparts and a white waxy body covering. Only the adult male has wings. The oval females lay eggs in groups under a layer of waxy threads. Egg laying takes five to ten days during which time 100-400 eggs are produced. On hatching a crawling stage is formed. Males settle and metamorphose under a waxy cocoon but females remain mobile, moulting three times. Development takes from 30 days at 30°C to 90 days at 18°C.

The mealybug predator (*Cryptolamus montrouzieri*) adult is a brown beetle with an orange head, wing tips and abdomen. One predator should be introduced for every three mealybugs. To be successful it is very iimportant that they be introduced when the mealybug population is low. Predator females lay eggs singly into mealybug masses at ten per day up to a total of 500. Adult beetles and young larvae feed on mealybug larvae, eggs and nymphs, while large larvae feed on all stages. The larvae will grow up to half an inch, consuming over 250 mealybugs during their development. The life cycle can take from 25 days at 30°C but 72 days at 18°C. The temperature should be between 16°C and 33°C or the predators will die.

# Lacewings (*Chrysoperla carnea*)

The common green lacewing is widely used to control many different pests. Actually, most species of the adult lacewing do not kill other insects but live on pollen, sweet nectar etc. It is the offspring that do the job. The adult lacewing lays her eggs on foliage, each on the top of hair-like filaments. After a few days the eggs hatch and tiny larvae emerge which are also known as the "aphid lion" because of their voracious appetite. The aphid lion is similar in appearance to an alligator with pincers like tiny ice tongs. It vigorously attacks its prey, injecting a paralysing venom and drawing the body fluids out of its helpless victim. Besides aphids they feed on just about any soft bodied pest they can find, including citrus mealybugs, cottony cushion scale, spider mites, thrips, caterpillars and insect eggs etc. Lacewings will even eat each other if no other food is available. During the two to three weeks the insects spends in this stage it will devour up to 200 victims a week. After this, it will pupate by spinning a cocoon with silken thread and approximately five days later the adult lacewing emerges to repeat the life cycle.

# Ladybirds

Ladybirds are probably the best known beneficial insect. Both the adult beetle and larvae will feed on insects that are not hard shelled, too fast moving or too large. The adults tend to be near the tops of plants, the larvae lower down. The only ladybirds sold in Britain are an Australian variety for use against mealybugs. The common British ladybird is famous for its voracious consumption of aphids. Unfortunately, ladybirds are very difficult to produce artificially in insectaries and all the products available in the USA and Canada are collected from the wild.

The next two insects, trichogramma and fly predators are not available in the UK but are widely available in North America. They are included primarily for interest.

# Trichogramma

*Trichogramma* adults are amongst the smallest insects. Despite its size, it is an efficient destroyer of the eggs of more than 200 species of moths and butterflies which are leaf eaters in the larval stage. The *Trichogramma* seeks out eggs, but does not feed or harm vegetation. It is particularly effective because it kills its host before the plant can be damaged. Some moth eggs attacked by *Trichogramma* are: armyworm, bagworm, European corn borer, peach borer, squash borer, cankerworm, alfalfa caterpillar, cutworm, corn earworm, wax moth, tomato hornworm, cabbage looper and codling moth. Release should begin when the moths are first present and continue periodically thereafter. Timing is the key to getting a good kill of pest eggs. The use of traps to monitor pest presence can be a very helpful tool in determining when to start releases.

## Fly Predators

Fly predators are wasps. Currently marketed species include: *Splangia enduis*, *Muscidifurax zaraptor*, *Sphegigaster* species, and *Tachineaphagus zealandicus*. The first three are pupal parasites as they attack the pest fly's pupa stage, while the fourth is a larval parasite which attacks the pest fly's larval stage. Fly predators are what biologists call parasitoids, that is, they are classified somewhere between predators and parasites. Like parasites, fly predators are much smaller than their pest fly host and usually only consume food in their larval stage. However, the effect that they have on the pest fly's population is exactly like a predator in the sense that they kill the immature pest flies and as they develop they consume the pest fly's body as a source of nourishment.

Fly predators are specific to and attack common manure and filth breeding pest flies including: the common house fly (*Musca domestica*), the biting stable fly (*Stomoxys calcitrans*), the horn fly (*Musca autumnalis*), and the lesser house fly (*Fannia canicularis*). In addition, they also attack other problem causing, filth breeding pest flies, such as the garbage fly and the blow fly. Fly predators are sometimes called minute wasps, but unlike other such insects like bees, wasps, and ants, they are completely biteless and stingless. Fly predators cannot become a pest themselves. In fact, since fly predators live their entire life cycle on or near the surface of the manure and other decaying organic matter and because they are so small in size, they go virtually un-noticed.

When predators are released from their containers on or near pest breeding sites, the females search through the host area seeking out the pest fly's pupa (the cocoon-like structure that houses the pest fly during its metamorphosis from larva to full-sized adult). After locating the pest fly pupa, the female drills a hole in the pupa case, inserts her ovipositor, and then deposits from one to seven eggs inside. After her eggs are deposited, she removes her ovipositor and obtains nourishment by ingesting the blood of the developing pest fly. She then moves on and repeats the process until all her eggs have been deposited.

The eggs that were deposited inside the pest fly pupa will develop into mature adults within 30 days. The developing pest fly larva is completely consumed as a source of food by the developing predators, thus interrupting the reproductive cycle of the pest fly. Immediately upon emergence from the pest fly pupa, the predators are ready to mate and start the process again.

The life span of the female fly predator ranges from as little as two weeks to as long as six months. She will live long enough to deposit all of her 200 to 300 eggs. When the pest fly's population is under control and there are no hosts available, the female fly predator is able to live up to a month or so while waiting for the pest flies to appear and redevelop so that she may continue the process of depositing her remaining eggs. As there is no method of fly control that offers 100% eradication, fly predators do not eliminate the fly problem, but they do minimize it.

# 16 Nematodes to Control Insects

Nematodes are small worms that live in the soil and feed on organic matter; they are called free living nematodes. Others (plant parasitic nematodes) live on plants, especially their roots. Some of these are serious agricultural pests; the potato cyst nematode is an example. In addition, many species attack insects. Nematodes that attack insects are called entomophilic (insect-loving). They are slender, cylindrical in shape, about half of a millimeter long and practically invisible to the naked eye. The nematodes used against pest insect are not harmful to crops, humans, animals, birds, earthworms, the environment or beneficial insects. There are two main groups of insect-killing nematodes. One group kills insects by infecting them with lethal bacteria; the nematodes then feed on the dead remains. They are called entomopathogenic (causing disease to insects). The other group is called entomophagous (insect eating) because they are parasites of the insects themselves. Where the target insects are crop pests, entomophilic nematodes can be used effectively in crop protection.

One of the earliest observations of entomophilic nematodes was recorded by Aldrovandi in 1623, who found dead grasshoppers covered with worms which he considered to be responsible for the death of the insects. Eight nematode families have now been identified containing entomophilic species. Nematodes seek out and reach insects underground or in protected plant parts. They enter the insect and release pathogenic bacteria into the host insect's blood stream. Typically the target insect is killed within 48 hours. The nematodes breed inside the insect and deposit eggs that hatch and begin a second generation. This generation leaves the host and enters the environment to seek other insects and continue the life cycle. Depending on soil moisture and temperature, entomophagous nematodes can live in soil and continue killing insects for months. They are also highly resistant to some chemical insecticides.

Each species is capable of killing many different kinds of insect pests. Extensive research has been carried out to determine which nematode species are most effective in a given situation. There is no evidence that any insect has ever developed an immunity to these nematodes while many insect pests are becoming resistant to increasingly powerful chemical pesticides. Nematodes can be used against pests including: borers, root weevils, caterpillars, wireworms, beetle grubs, fungus gnats, mole crickets, corn rootworms, navel orange worms, artichoke plume moths, japanese beetles, Colorado potato beetles.

It is unusual for enough nematodes to be present in soil to suppress or control insect infestations to a level that provides adequate crop protection. Adding extra nematodes has been shown to control insects in tests in laboratories, in glasshouse trials and even in field conditions. Nematodes may be added as a precaution before any insects are seen or they may be used to eliminate insect infestations after they occur. 100% control of some insect pests (those which have a soil habitat or soil stage in their life cycle) is possible after several weeks; an impressive level compared with many other biocontrol methods.

## Producing nematodes

A number of laboratories and companies have taken an interest in producing nematodes in artificial conditions to be sold to replace or supplement the naturally-occurring population. Methods were investigated for years before production became practical in controlled conditions. Although it was possible to grow nematodes artificially, yields were often poor and were certainly unpredictable. The other key problem was encountered with the bacteria that grow in culture with the nematodes. The bacteria were capable of adopting either of two forms, a primary one in which they were effective at killing insects, and another, secondary form in which they were apparently impotent against insects; production of the secondary type was pointless. Recent research shows that nematodes can be produced on a variety of odd substrates: dog food agar, chicken offal and microorganisms. Commercially they are produced by a variety of methods including in the target insects themselves, in bags on various materials such as sponges, and in fermenters, usually largish high-tech steel vessels in which all environmental conditions for growth can be controlled. Producing them in target insects can be quite expensive although it has the advantage in respect of the potency of the final product; the weaker secondary form of the bacteria doesn't occur. Producing in fermenters is considerably cheaper although it can be more difficult to obtain effective product.

Once produced, nematodes have to be stabilised. A number of systems are in use including drying and formulating into a powder, using sponges as carriers, or suspending them in a gel made with some, usually natural, gum. Different methods preserve the nematodes for varying lengths of time. However, existing commercial claims cover a very wide range: one product claims a refrigerated shelf-life of nine months on sponges whereas another, apparently similar, product claims only two days; one powder product claims one month's life while a gel-based product claims effectiveness even after six months cold storage.

A number of companies make nematodes and several different brands are available in Britain. Application is generally in water, either sprays or through a trickle system. They can be applied in furrows as the seed is planted, sprayed on trees or on the ground and even sprayed from the air. Typical commercial sprayers are suitable for applying nematodes. Other application methods are being investigated.

Like insects, nematodes are exempt from regulation as pesticides. This gives them an economic advantage over chemicals, insect growth regulators and biopesticides such as fungi and bacteria, as the price of nematodes does not have to include the high cost of regulatory testing and registration.

One pest controlled by nematodes is vine weevil *Otiorhynchus sulcatus*. Occurring both outdoors and under glass, vine weevil larvae attack roots, corms and tubers of many plants and are especially troublesome on pot plants and container grown nursery plants. Damage to the roots causes wilting and collapse of shoots and leaves. Adult weevils eat notches in the leaves and kill young shoots. Vine weevil adults are large with a pointed snout. Females lay more than 1500 eggs and have a wide range of hosts. Outdoors, adults emerge in May and lay eggs in August and September. Under glass the majority of weevils emerge in Autumn and lay through the Spring and Summer. Vine weevil larvae are white and up to 8mm long.

Another pest against which nematodes are effective is sciarid flies (*Lycoriella auripila* and others). In mushrooms the larvae attack the tiny mushrooms turning them brown and leathery. Dense populations can prevent the development of young pinheads and buttons can be killed by larvae tunnelling into the stalks and caps and by cutting the mycelium. In pot plants the larvae feed on root hairs, killing young plants, whilst mature plants are weakened and large numbers can even kill mature plants. Sciarids are small black flies that run rapidly over the surface of mushroom compost with their long thin antenna held erect. They lay up to 170 eggs into the compost. The larvae are white, almost transparent, legless and with shiny black heads. The life cycle is completed in about five weeks, three and one-half of which are as larvae.

Nematodes are delivered in a variety of ways. One, available in the UK is sponges impregnated with nematodes, which are immersed in water and then diluted and drenched onto the target crops. Each sponge contains approximately 10 million nematodes. Nematodes are applied to mushroom compost at a rate of 1 million per square meter or 20,000- 30,000 per pot for potted plants. They can also be fed in via an irrigation system. They should not be applied in hot sunny conditions. Different products containing nematodes will keep for different lengths of time. One common one must be refrigerated at 2-5°C and will keep for only 48 hours before they must be used. The nematodes search out and parasitise pests by entering through natural body openings. On entry, bacteria (carried within the infected nematode) are released and multiply in the host. The nematode feeds on these bacteria and multiplies after which it goes looking for another host.

# 17 Pheromones for Insect Control

Pheromones are one of a group of chemicals, called semiochemicals, produced by insects to inform and attract other insects. They are produced in very small quantities and are highly volatile, that is, they are designed to evaporate into the air and be sensed at very low concentrations by the intended recipient of the information. These chemicals can be collected or synthesized and formulated into products for gradual release. They can be used to change the behaviour of various insects and hence are called generically, Behaviour Modifying Chemicals (BMC).

The United States Environmental Protection Agency (EPA) defines semiochemicals as: *"Chemicals emitted by plants or animals that modify the behaviour of receptor organisms of like or different kinds are termed semiochemicals. They include pheromones, allomones, and kairomones, Pheromones are substances emitted by members of one species that modify the behaviour of others within the same species. Allomones are chemicals emitted by one species which modify the behaviour of a different species to the benefit of the emitting species. Kairomones are chemicals emitted by one species which modify the behaviour of a different species to the benefit of the receptor species."*

These chemicals have three main uses for crop protection: pest monitoring on an ongoing basis usually using traps to determine the most suitable time to use pesticides; disruption of mating by confusing the insects with conflicting messages about the whereabouts of potential mates by releasing sexual attractant pheromones; and luring insects to a place where they are killed by other chemicals (mass trapping). Pheromones can also be combined with insecticides. The best aspects of the use of pheromones is that they replace or reduce pesticide use and since only targeted insects are attracted to them, beneficial insects are rarely affected.

Although scientists have been aware of pheromones for many years, it is only in the last decade that a variety of useful products and the companies that make and sell them have evolved. The technology of commercial pheromone use is fairly specialized although there is no reason why traps with pheromones could not be used by domestic gardeners.

# 18 Nitrogen-fixing Seed Treatments

All plants (and animals) need nitrogen to grow. It is an essential component of the proteins and nucleic acids (DNA and RNA) required for all life processes. The air contains 80% nitrogen but in an inert and unavailable form, as the stable molecule $N_2$. No plant or animal can use the nitrogen in the air directly. Only certain microorganisms, mainly bacteria and blue-green algae, can 'fix' nitrogen from the air. These organisms may be free-living or may live 'symbiotically' with a host, trading fixed nitrogen to the host in exchange for the high-energy compounds (sugars) they need in order to fix the nitrogen and to grow. The most important group of nitrogen fixing organisms, known as *Rhizobia*, form such a symbiotic relationship with a large group of commercially important plants called legumes which include both grain varieties (peas, beans, peanuts, etc) and forage species (clover, alfalfa) as well as floral varieties (notably lupins). In addition there are other organisms (*Azospirillium* and in some instances *Azotobacter*) which form a loose association with the roots of tropical grasses of agronomic importance. A third type of organism, *Frankia*, forms a symbiotic relationship with some species of trees and bushes.

The only organisms which have been used commercially to any extent are *Rhizobium*. Seeds are treated in order to provide plants with an improved ability to obtain nitrogen from the air, reducing the need for chemical fertilisers. Cultures are supplied in various forms. The bacteria colonises the roots where it forms small nodules in which it grows, fixing nitrogen from the air and producing ammonia which it gives to the host plant.

The presence of the *Rhizobium* enables crops to obtain sufficient nitrogen to meet much of their needs. The result is:

a      reduced fertiliser costs;

b      a source of nitrogen that cannot be lost due to leaching;

c      significant amounts of useful nitrogen left in the soil for the following crop;

d    improved growth in relatively harsh environments e.g. white clover with *Rhizobium* may be grown on poor upland pastures where previously no clover could grow;

e    supplementing the nitrogen nutrition of an associated crop e.g. where clover is grown with grass and provides nitrogen without artificial fertilisers.

For more than 50 years farmers in many countries have treated their legume seed with *Rhizobium* bacteria to help with nodulation for nitrogen fixtion. However, in some countries, such as Britain, growers think that native strains of *Rhizobium* are adequate for most crops. Only crops introduced relatively recently, such as alfalfa, are inoculated as the soil is thought not to have built up sufficient of them to ensure colonization of all plants.

The development of commercial products required first that strains of *Rhizobium* could be cultured in quantity and second, that formulations delivered a live and active preparation to the seed. To be of benefit, the commercial strain must be able to compete with the native strains already in the soil and to give a higher rate of active nodulation. Typical commercial formulations deliver *Rhizobium* in a peat or clay base. The key performance criteria required of commercial products are that they must be convenient to use; alive at the time of application; highly competitive with native strains in the soil; and they must produce high nodule formulation and also high nitrogen fixation.

## Markets

The worldwide market potential of improved *Rhizobium* products has been variously estimated from £40 to £150 million. Soyabean is thought to be the largest single market for *Rhizobium*. Other legumes that have good market potential include alfalfa, peanuts, and dried beans. The current market is only about £4 million, largely because many existing products do not produce much of an improvement in yield. Most people who buy and use *Rhizobium* do so as an insurance prolicy; it assures that some nodulation will occur even if native bacteria are not present. Prices for *Rhizobium* products are low, typically on the order of £0.55 to £1.10 per hectare for a *Rhizobium* product for soybean. Low soybean prices between

102

1985 and 1987 and consequent reductions in acreage, pressed inoculant producers in the US as the market shrank.

To sell at all, any product must meet the basic performance criteria above. Many companies are seeking, or indeed claiming, to have a better product. To really succeed in the market, any improved product should not only be effective, it must be made by a low cost production and formulation process, it should be cost-effective enough to overcome resistance from buyers used to low 'insurance product' pricing, and it must develop a brand image to differentiate itself and its improved performance from currently available 'insurance' products.

Several products are available in the UK and as better, cheaper and higher performance products are developed, it is likely that more will come onto the market.

# 19 Green Products for Animal Feed

The green products for animal feed are called probiotics, the opposite of antibiotics. They are preparations of living organisms fed to animals as feed ingredients or dietary supplements in order to promote good general health, decrease stress and increase feed intake and improve conversion rates (give more meat per pound of feed) in a range of domestic animals, including pigs, cattle and chickens and other fowl.

Considerable research has been carried out in attempts to show that probiotics really do have an effect and to figure out how they work (if they do). The problem in assessing probiotics is in finding experimental methods which prove that using them is cost-effective. Much of the 'data' showing efficacy is anecdotal are rather than statistical. Effects tend to be rather small and need to be shown statistically rather than by visible and direct observation of the treated group. At present, virtually all of the many products on the market have yet to be proven and have not had a dramatic effect on either the health of animals or the feed markets. Many problems have been solved, such as formulation, delivery and shelflife; the difficulty that remains is demonstrating they work. It may, of course be that, dispite the logic, the theory is wrong. The jury is out.

Suggestions as to the way probiotics work to promote good general health vary from competition with 'bad' organisms in the gut, to a lowering of gut acidity, to production by the probiotic of anti-microbial substances that prevent 'bad' bugs from growing. It has even been suggested that probiotics have some direct effect on the immune system although proof is scarce. Similarly, whether, and if so how, probiotics cure diseases is debatable. They are used against scours in pigs and many users have reported good results with starter pigs. Positive effects on growth rate and feed efficiency have also been found.

The use of unidentified cultures from the chicken gut can effectively prevent *Salmonella* infection, common in chickens and recently a high-profile food scare costing Edwina Curry her job. If other measures to control *Salmonella* prove ineffective and $\gamma$-irradiation is not eventually allowed, then the use of probiotic treatments should increase.

The main reason for the great interest in probiotics is concern about the use of chemicals in intensive animal husbandry. This ranges from consumer anxiety about antibiotic and hormone residues to concern that the overuse of therapeutically valuable antibiotics will reduce their effectiveness and create other problems through the generation diseases resistant to antibiotics.

Intensive rearing causes physical and emotional stress and provides far too much chance for diseases to be spread. Animals in this situation are thought to have less resilient immune systems and to be more susceptible to infection. The use of incubators for hatching fowl and the early separation of young from their parents reduces the passing of any beneficial bacteria from parent to offspring. Probiotics, by promoting the acquisition of the normal microorganisms that live in animals' guts are suppossed to aid disease resistance, reducing the need for use of therapeutic drugs.

The organisms in probiotics are usually strains of *Lactobacillus*, the same bacteria used to make cheese and yoghurt, although other, similar organisms including *Bacillus subtilis* are also used. Some positive results have also been obtained using yeasts as probiotics. Which miroorganism is chosen is often based on how easy it is to make rather than on how well it works.

Over the last few years there has been a proliferation of products of which a number are listed in this Guide. However, this commercial activity and the type of commercial data used to support claims of efficacy or cost-effectiveness has to be weighed against the independent research reports which frequently indicate that no effect on feed conversion efficiency, average daily weight gain or health was observed in spite of ensuring that the animals received live cultures of carefully selected strains. Some apparently positive results were reported by Chr. Hansen using 2.5 million chicks given *Lactobacillus acidophilus* in their drinking water. However, the product and labour costs of this method made the practice uneconomic.

At present this makes the decision about using probiotics a little difficult. They are very unlikely to cause any harm and they may be a low cost insurance policy to promote animal health. A proven cost-effective product would undoubtedly sell well. The potential market may yet be increased by direct legislation and/or consumer pressures against the use of 'drugs' in meat production.

In summary, it appears that the probiotic concept has merit, although exploiting its potential will require a better understanding of the microbiology and immunology of animal growth than we presently possess. Production will be of a carefully chosen organism, requirin good process control both qualitatively and quantitatively. In view of the difficulties it is unlikely that the market will grow extensively in the immediate future. What is more likely is a more gradual move away from intensive animal production to more open methods where stress and risk of cross infection is reduced.

# 20 Silage Additives and Inoculants

Approximately 25 million tonnes of silage are made in the UK every year. Widely used for animal feed, silage is made by the bacterial fermentation of green plants. During the fermentation, organic acids are formed by strains of the bacteria *Lactobacillus* (typically *plantarum*) and *Pediococcus* (typically *acidilactici*) which stabilise the material, prevent further decay and allow long-term storage. Although silage can be made from any plant, and in the United States is frequently made from corn (maize), in the UK it is generally made from grass (often rye grass) and so provides an alternative to hay. Silage grass may be cut earlier than grass for hay; consequently the plant is more nutritious for the animal, containing more protein and sugar. Several cuts of grass may be taken to provide a series of silage 'crops' although these decrease in quantity and nutritional value over the season.

Silage making requires that the conditions for the fermentation are correct or the plant tissue may decay due to the action of unwanted microorganisms, primarily *Clostridia*, producing a foul smell and making it of useless as animal feed. The correct conditions include the presence of sugar for the *Lactobacillus* to grow and produce organic acids to stabilise the silage.

Farmers sometimes add sugar, in the form of molasses, to supplement the natural sugars present, or enzymes to help produce extra sugar from the other plant tissues. Alternatively, farmers may add acid to lower the pH to a level where only the desired bacteria will grow, or use chemical preservatives to kill unwanted bacteria. A third alternative is for farmers to add additional *Lactobacilli* to ensure that the fermentation occurs quickly and efficiently; these are 'inoculants' and are added to around 5% of UK silage. Inoculants may also be combined with sugars from molasses and enzymes.

A recent development originated by Microbial Developments Limited (UK) has been to add a Clostridial bacteriophage or 'Clostridiaphage' to their *Lactobacillus* - based inoculants. This additional organism, a type of virus, attacks and destroys the *Clostridia* which can ruin the fermentation.

Other producers now include some of the biggest agricultural companies such as ICI and Shell as well as a number of smaller ones such as Biocon.

# Making good silage

Making good silage needs careful management for a successful outcome since the material to be ensiled can vary widely in age, composition and percentage of dry matter. Ensiling technique is the single most important aspect of silage making. Reports show that there are relatively few of the correct bacteria on grass growing in the field. Even when the grass is put into a silo, the bacterial numbers are often quite low, as few as 0.01% the number provided by an inoculant. However, regardless of the number of bacteria, if the right conditions are not established within the silo as quickly as possible the desirable bacteria will not grow and the silage will spoil. Other key features of silage making besides inoculants are:

The stage of maturity of grass - The ideal cutting time is 6-7 weeks after the last cut (assuming normal vigorous growth) or at 50% ear emergence of the grass heads. The ideal is not always attainable because of weather conditions, contractor unavailability etc.

Dry matter - The principle component of grass is water. The amount can vary widely, but is normally 75-85% on a fresh weight basis at harvesting. High moisture tends to encourage the wrong bacterial types leading to less silage being eaten by the animals. It also causes effluent problems and makes the grass more expensive to harvest and more difficult to handle. Wilting will overcome these problems.

Nitrogen fertilisation - Nitrogen is extensively used to increase growth of grass for silage and the levels used can be very high. While this increases yields of dry matter, the level of grass sugars can become depressed in the initial weeks after heavy fertilisation so grass must not be harvested for silage for at least four to five weeks after fertilisation.

With attention to these points plus a good inoculant, quality silage should be assured.

# PART II

## The Products
### and
### Where to Get Them

# AMBLYPACK

Amblypack is for use against thrips and western flower thrips in protected crops and flowers.
Amblypack contains predatory mites *Amblyseius barkeri* and *Amblyseius cucumeris*. Both the mites actively search out and eat the thrips.

**How to use** Apply 2 - 5 weeks after planting or release the predatory mites as soon as the thrips are seen in the crop. Open the flask and sprinkle the contents among the infested plants.

**How much** Use 1 - 2 flasks per 1000 m² depending on level of infestation. Apply at weekly or fortnightly intervals in cucumbers, aubergines and beans.

**Other** Amblypack is supplied as 50000 adult mites mixed with bran and some prey as a food source in a litre flask. It is also available in a puffer pack for use on ornamental plants.

**Supplier** Bunting Biological Control Ltd Tel 0206 271300 and from Brinkman UK Tel 0243 531666 (South) or 0482 42123
Price on application to supplier.

**Accepted** All

**Use**

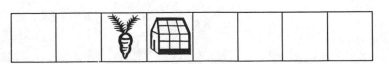

# AMBLYPACK CRS

Amblypack CRS is for use against thrips and western flower thrips in protected crops and flowers. It allow a controlled release of the mites during treatment.
Amblypack CRS contains predatory mites *Amblyseius barkeri* and *Amblyseius cucumeris*. Both the mites actively search out and eat the thrips.

**How to use** The Amblypack CRS allow a gradual and continuous release of predatory mites into the crop over a long period.

**How much** For cucumbers place 1 bag every third plant and replace after 4 - 6 weeks. For early and summer planting place 1 bag every third plant and replace every 2 - 3 weeks. For pepper crops place 1 bag every sixth plant and apply twice during the season.

**Other** Amblypack CRS is supplied as bags of mites in bran with a supply of feed prey.

**Supplier** Bunting Biological Control Ltd Tel 0206 271300 and from Brinkman UK Tel 0243 531666 (South) or 0482 42123 (North) Price on application to supplier.

**Accepted** All

**Use**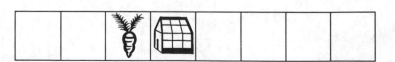

# AMBLYSEIUS CUCUMERIS

> *Amblyseius cucumeris* is for use against Thrips (*Thrips tabaci*) and western flower thrip (*Franklinella occidentalis*) and is suitable for use in all infested plants.
>
> Amblyseius cucumeris contains the mites *Amblyseius cucumeris* and *Amblyseius barkeri*. The mites actively search out and eat the thrips.

**How to use**  Establish mite population before thrips appear.

**How much**  For cucumbers apply 200,000 per acre and repeat every 2 weeks. For interior displays apply 100 per m2 and repeat the application every week. For chrysanthemums apply 1 per 10 cuttings 12 hours before planting out and 1 per 5 cuttings 2-3 weeks after planting. Repeat twice fortnightly.

**Other**  Amblyseius cucumeris is supplied as adult mites in vermiculite in packs of 5,000, 10,000 and 25,000. Use immediately on receipt.

**Supplier**  Technoverde Ltd Tel 0734 661243 or 0860 327831
Price on application to supplier.

**Accepted**  All

**Use**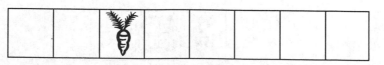

# APHEX

Aphex is for use against aphids in greenhouses particularly the cotton aphid *Aphis gossypi* and the peach (potato) aphid *Myzus persicae*. Aphex is produced by Koppert, one of the leading suppliers of biological control agents.

Aphex contains the gall midge *Aphidoletes aphidimyza*. The adult midges lay their eggs near aphid colonies and the larvae that emerge feed on the aphids. The aphids are paralysed by the injection of a poison and then the orange midge larvae suck the aphids dry leaving the dead aphid attached to the plant.

**How to use** Sprinkle the midge cocoons evenly throughout the crop. The midges will emerge over a period of about 10 days. The midges will automatically search out the aphid colonies. Adult midges are very sensitive to chemical pesticides although the larvae are less so and it is advisable to control other pests in the crop with biological controls.

**How much** To prevent any buildup of aphids low numbers of midges can be released into the crop. As soon as the first aphids are seen large numbers of aphids must be released.

**Other** Aphex is supplied as a plastic bottle of gall midge pupae in cocoons. It should be used immediately upon receipt.

**Supplier** Koppert (UK) Ltd Tel 0892 884411
Price available on request from supplier.

**Accepted** All

**Use**

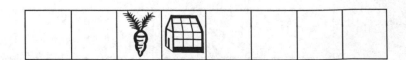

# APHIDIUS MATRICARIAE

> *Aphidius matricariae* is for use against aphids and is particularly good when used against peach potato aphid *Myzus persicae*.
> *Aphidius matricariae* is a parasitic wasp. The adult wasps lay their eggs in the aphid which then become mummified as the wasp larvae eats the insides of the aphid. After a few days the new generation of wasps emerge and fly off to locate more aphids to parasitise.

**How to use**   Place open tube on its side beneath infested plants. Adults emerge over 2-3 days. For small patches of aphid use 100 wasps. For larger areas use 1,200 wasps per 1000m².

**How much**   1 domestic pack per outbreak should suffice. 1 large commercial pack will treat approximately 850m².

**Other**   Aphidius matricariae is supplied as wasp pupae in a tube. It is available in a three packs one suitable for use by gardeners and two for commercial growers and contain 100, 100 and 1000 pupae respectively. Use immediately upon receipt.

**Supplier**   English Woodlands Ltd Tel 07986 574
Price for 125 (domestic pack) - £6.00 (inc VAT)
Price for 100 (commercial pack) - £3.50 (+ VAT)
Price for 1000 (commercial pack) - £30.00 (+ VAT)

**Accepted**   All

**Use**

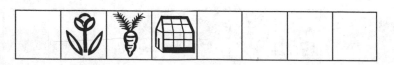

# APHIDIUS MATRICARIAE

*Aphidius matricariae* is for use against aphids and is particularly good when used against peach potato aphid *Myzus persicae*.
  *Aphidius matricariae* is a parasitic wasp. The adult wasps lay their eggs in the aphid which then become mummified as the wasp larvae eats the insides of the aphid. After a few days the new generation of wasps emerge and fly off to locate more aphids to parasitise.

**How to use** Introduce wasps before or immediately when aphids appear on crops. Place open tube on its side beneath infested plants. Adults emerge over 2-3 days.

**How much** For general use apply 1000 per acre every 2 weeks throughout the season. Requirements are 4 packs per acre.

**Other** Aphidius matricariae is supplied as 250 adult wasps in bottles. Use immediately upon receipt.

**Supplier** Technoverde Ltd Tel 0734 661243 or 0860 327831
Price on application to supplier.

**Accepted** All

Use

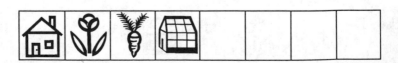

116

# APHIDOLETES APHIDIMYZA

*Aphidoletes aphidimyza* is used against aphids in cucumbers, nursery stock, pot plants, and tomatoes and chrysanthemums. It is particularly useful when used against *Myzus persicae* (peach potato aphid),*Aphis gossypii* and *Macrosiphomiella sanborni.*
  *Aphidoletes aphidimyza* is a predatory midge and actively searches out the aphid and lay their eggs near them. The resultant midge larvae eat the aphids.

**How to use**   Introduce as soon as aphids are seen. Place the given material in a shaded spot below the infested plants and cover with an inverted flower pot. Keep the peat or matting damp, allowing a fortnight for the midges to emerge from it. N.B. These midges do not bite humans.

**How much**   Use 1 domestic pack per outbreak. For commercial growing use 1 large commercial pack will treat approx 850m² (690sq yd).

**Other**   Aphidoletes aphidimyza is supplied as pupae in a tube of damp peat or in capillary matting. It is available in a three packs one suitable for use by gardeners and two for commercial growers and contain 100, 100 and 1000 pupae respectively. Use immediately upon receipt.

**Supplier**   English Woodlands Ltd Tel   07986 574
Price for 125 (domestic pack) - £6.00 (inc VAT)
Price for 100 (commercial pack) - £3.50 (+ VAT)
Price for 1000 (commercial pack) - £ 30.00 (+ VAT)

**Accepted**   All

**Use**  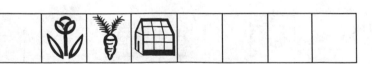

# APHIDOLETES APHIDIMYZA

> *Aphidoletes aphidimyza* is used against aphids in cucumbers, nursery stock, pot plants, and tomatoes and chrysanthemums. It is particularly useful when used against *Myzus persicae* (peach potato aphid), *Aphis gossypii* and *Macrosiphoniella sanborni*.
>
> *Aphidoletes aphidimyza* is a predatory midge and actively searches out the aphid and lays its eggs near them. The resultant midge larvae eat the aphids.

**How to use**   Introduce at first signs of aphid colonization. For heavy infestation repeat application twice at fortnightly intervals. Cut corner off pack and place where adults can fly away. Avoid getting pack wet.

**How much**   For cucumbers, nursery stock and pot plants use 1 pack per 1250m² or 2 packs per acre. If infestation is small use 1 pack. For chrysanthemums use 1 pack per 35,000 cuttings.

**Other**   Aphidoletes aphidimyza is supplied as midge pupae in peat in a tetrapack of either 250 or 1000 pupae. Use immediately upon receipt.

**Supplier**   Technoverde Ltd Tel 0734 661243 or 0860 327831
Price on application to supplier.

**Accepted**   All

**Use**  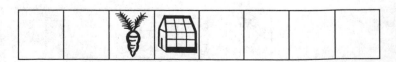

118

# APHIDPACK AA

> Aphidpack Aa is for use against aphids in protected crops. It contains the predatory midge *Aphidoletes aphidimyza*. Both the adult and larvae stages of the midge eat the aphids. Adult midge are particularly good at clearing pocket infestations as they can actively search out the aphid populations.

**How to use** Apply as soon as the aphids are seen in the crop. Open the boxes by removing the lid and place among the crop in shade. Avoid areas where the boxes might get watered. The midge will automatically search out the aphids.

**How much** Apply 2 - 4 units per 1000 m² every two weeks during the growing season.

**Other** Aphipack Aa is supplied as 250 midge pupae in vermiculite packed in boxes. It will keep for 1 week if kept at 12°C.

**Supplier** Brinkman UK Tel 0243 531666 (South) or 0482 42123 (North) Price on application to supplier.

**Accepted** All

**Use**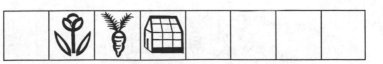

# APHIDPACK AM

> Aphidpack Am is for use against aphids in protected crops. It contains the parasitic wasp *Aphidius matricariae*. The adult wasp lays its eggs in the aphid larvae. The aphid host then becomes mummified.

**How to use** Apply as soon as the aphids are detected in the crop. Open the boxes by removing the lid and place among the crop in shade. Avoid areas where the boxes might get watered. The wasps will automatically search out the aphids.

**ow much** Apply 1 unit per 1000 m² every week during the growing season.

**Other** Aphipack Am is supplied as 250 wasp pupae in vermiculite packed in boxes.

**Supplier** Brinkman UK Tel 0243 531666 (South) or 0482 42123 (North) Price on application to supplier.

**Accepted** All

**Use**

# APHID PARASITES

---

Aphid parasite as its name implies is for use against aphids. It contains the aphid parasitic wasp *Aphidius matricariae*. The adult wasp lays eggs in the aphid. The aphid host then becomes mummified.

---

**How to use**   This product can be used at any time of the year. In the summer the wasp is prone to attack other wasps and may be less effective at this time of year. The wasps should be introduced as soon as aphids are seen in the crop.

**How much**   For a localised or pocket infestation use 1 pack of wasps. For a heavy infestation use 1 pack per 80 m$^2$ or 6 packs per 500 m$^2$.

**Other**   Aphid parasite is supplied as 100 wasps in a tube. The wasps should be used immediately upon receipt.

**Supplier**   Organic Farmers and Growers Ltd Tel 0449 720838
Price for a pack of 100 - £3.50 delivery included

**Accepted**   Organic Farmers and Growers Ltd and all others

**Use**

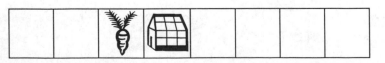

# APHID PREDATOR

> Aphid predator as its name implies is for use against aphids. It contains the predatory midge *Aphidoletes apidimyza* the larvae and adults of which eat aphids. The adults are particularly good at clearing pockets of aphids that may have infested a crop.

**How to use** The midges should be introduced as soon as aphids are seen in the crop.

**How much** For a localised or pocket infestation use 1 pack of midges. For a heavy infestation use 1 pack per 80 m² or 6 packs per 500 m².

**Other** Aphid predator is supplied as midges on damp peat or capillary matting in tubes. The midges should be used immediately upon receipt.

**Supplier** Organic Farmers and Growers Ltd Tel 0449 720838
Price for a pack of 100 - £3.50 delivery included

**Accepted** Organic Farmers and Growers Ltd and all others

**Use**

122

# APHID PREDATOR

Aphid predator as its name implies is for use against aphids. It contains the predatory midge *Aphidoletes* the larvae and adults of which eat aphids. The adults are particularly good at clearing pockets of aphids that may have infested a crop.

**How to use** The midges should be introduced as soon as aphids are seen in the crop.

**How much** For a localised or pocket infestation use 100 midges. For a heavy infestation use 100 midges per 80 m² or 600 midges per 500 m².

**Other** Aphid predator is supplied in packs of 100 and 1000 midges. The midges should be used immediately upon receipt.

**Supplier** Natural Pest Control Tel 0243 553250
Price for a pack of 100 - £3.00 + VAT, P&P included. (1990 price)
Price for a pack of 1000 - £25.00 + VAT, P&P included. (1990 price)

**Accepted** All

**Use**

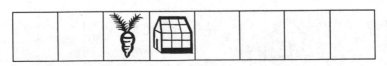

# AXEL

Axel is a trap for specific use against wasps and is suitable for use in gardens, on patios and anywhere that wasps are found to be a nuisance. Axel is a two part trap the base of which is coloured with yellow and black stripes as these colours specifically attract wasps. The top of the trap is clear plastic. A liquid attractant is placed in the base of the trap and the wasps fly into the trap from beneath. The clear plastic top prevents the wasps from flying out of the bottom of the trap and they finally drown in the liquid.

**How to use**  Fill the base of the trap with the liquid bait and fix the top in position. Attach the hanging wire to the trap and position the trap where wasps are being a pest.

**How much**  Empty the trap when there is no longer sufficient liquid to drown the wasps. Clean the trap with water and refill with bait.

**Other**  Axel is supplied as a complete unit.

**Supplier**  Urbio UK Tel 0734 661243
Price on application to supplier.

**Accepted**  All

**Use**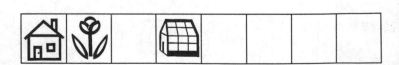

# BACILLUS SPRAY

---

Bacillus spray is suitable for use against all leaf eating caterpillar pests. This product will however kill virtually all caterpillars, pest insects and non-target species. However, it is effective for only a few days outdoors so the likelihood of harming non-target caterpillars is small. It should still be used with care on crops grown outdoors.

Bacillus spray contains the bacteria *Bacillus thuringiensis*. When the caterpillars ingest leaves with spores of the bacteria release toxins which cause paralysis. The caterpillars therefore stop feeding and die within 1 - 5 days.

---

**How to use**  The powder should be mixed with water and sprayed onto the crop leaves. Use of a wetting agent will help the product to stick to the leaves and increase intake by the caterpillars.

**How much**  For rates of application please contact the supplier.

**Other**  Bacillus spray is supplied in packs of 500g of wettable powder. The product should be stored in a dry place and extremes of temperature should be avoided.

**Supplier**  Organic Farmers and Growers Ltd Tel 0449 720838
Price for a pack of 500g - £10.00 delivery extra

**Accepted**  Organic Farmers and Growers Ltd and most others although some guidelines are unclear

**Use**

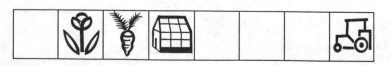

# BACTOSPEINE

Bactospeine is suitable for use against pest caterpillars of butterflies and moths and can be used in conjunction with other biological control systems. Although the product is harmless to other animals and insects such as bees care must be taken is used outdoor as it can also kill non target species of butterfly.

Bactospeine contains the bacteria *Bacillus thuringiensis* which becomes activated when it reaches the gut of the caterpillar. The bacteria releases toxic protein which causes paralysis of the caterpillar within a few hours of spraying. The caterpillar ceases feeding and dies after a few days.

**How to use** Mix 50 - 100 grams with 100 litres of water and apply through standard spraying equipment. Apply as soon as the pest appears as small caterpillars are easier to treat.

**How much** Requirements will depend on the pest species and the size of the caterpillars when treated. Consult the supplier for details.

**Other** Bactospeine is supplied as a powder in sachets for liquid application. Store in cool dry conditions.

**Supplier** Koppert (UK) Ltd Tel 0892 884411 and from
Suffolk Herbs Tel 0787 227247
Price on application to Koppert. One 5 gram sachet costs 35 pence and a pack of 10 sachets costs £2.99 from Suffolk Herbs (including postage).

**Accepted** All in principle although some guidelines are unclear

**Use**

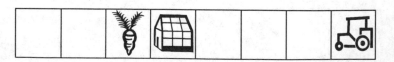

# BIOBIT

Biobit WP is for use against all leaf eating pest caterpillars and is suitable for use on all crops. This product will however kill non target caterpillars and should be used with great care on crops grown outdoors.

Biobit WP contains the bacteria, *Bacillus thuringiensis*. When the caterpillars ingest the leaf covered with bacteria, toxins are released which cause paralysis. The caterpillars therefore stop feeding and die within 1 - 5 days. It is harmless to humans and wildlife.

Although now made in Denmark by Novo and sold in the UK by a Dutch company, Biobit was originally a British product.

**How to use**  Mix with water and spray onto the infested crop. It is best to apply when the caterpillars are young as the bacteria are more effective.

**How much**  For general use apply at a dilution of 0.1%. For mix 100 grams of powder in 100 litres of water.

**Other**  Biobit is supplied as a wettable powder in packs of 500 grams.

**Supplier**  Brinkman UK Tel 0243 531666 (South) or 0482 42123 (North) Price on application to supplier.

**Accepted**  All in principle, although acceptability is not always made clear in guidelines

Use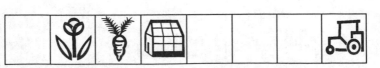

Insect Control

# BIO FRIENDLY GREENHOUSE FLY CATCHER A

Bio Friendly Greenhouse Fly Catcher is a product by Pan Britannica Industries Ltd which is made with nontoxic glue. The fly catcher has an Aureolin yellow surface that reflects light at a wavelength which attracts the pests to the panel where they stick to the strong adhesive Bio Friendly Greenhouse Fly Catcher can be used for trapping whitefly, greenfly, blackfly, thrips, midges and other flying insects without routine spraying and without pesticides.

**How to use** Hang just above the plant canopy,using twist ties,string or hooks. Quickly pull off the outer (single sided) panel and place to one side. Pull off as you need and hang them up. Replace the outer panels over unused traps. When the 5 double-sided panels have been used, put up both outer panels to make another working trap. Move the panels upwards as plants grow. To dispose of used traps, wrap in newspaper and put in the bin.

**How much** Application will depend on the level of infestation.

**Other** Bio Friendly Greenhouse Fly Catcher is supplied in packs of 7 panel which is sufficient for a medium sized house.

**Supplier** Pan Britannica Industries Limited  Tel 0992 23691

Price for a pack of 7 panels in a poly bag -  £2.75 (1990 Price)

**Accepted** All

**Use**

Insect Control

# CERTAN

Certan is for use against wax moth *Galleria mellonella* which is a pest in apiculture (bee keeping). It is nontoxic to bees and humans and will not cause a taint to the honey.

Certan is made by Sandoz Inc in the USA. It contains a special strain of the bacteria *Bacillus thuringiensis*. The bacteria when eaten by the moth larvae release a toxic protein that causes paralysis and the caterpillar stops feeding and dies within a few days.

**How to use** Mix with water as directed on the packet and spray into shallow combs.

**How much** Apply 1 ml per comb diluted in water. 1 litre will treat 1000 combs.

**Other** Certan is supplied in 120 ml and 1 litre plastic containers.

**Supplier** Steel & Brodie Ltd Tel 0794 388698
Price for 120 ml bottle - £4.70 (1990 price)
Price for 1 litre bottle - £23.60 (1990 price)

**Accepted** All in principle although some guidelines are unclear

**Use**

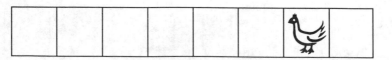

# CHRYSOPA

Chrysopa is for use against aphids but will also attack other soft bodied insects or larvae such as mealybug and caterpillars.

Chrysopa contains the lacewing species *Chrysopa carnea* and it is the larvae rather than the adults that attack the aphids. The larvae, which eat the aphids, are also called aphid lions as they have a very ferocious appetite.

**How to use** Place the cards among the crop avoiding areas where the cards may get wet.

**How much** Information about numbers of lacewings to apply is not supplied. Consult the supplier.

**Other** Chrysopa is supplied as 1000 lacewing larvae on a card. Use immediately on receipt.

**Supplier** Technoverde Ltd Tel 0734 661243 of 0860 327831
Price on application to supplier

**Accepted** All

Use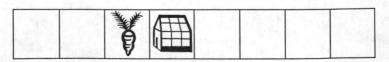

# CRYPTOLAEMUS MONTROUZIERI

> *Cryptolaemus montrouzieri* is for use against mealybugs, usually citrus mealybug *Planococcus citri* and is suitable for use on all plants including ornamentals.
> *Cryptolaemus montrouzieri* is a black and brown ladybird beetle that originates from Australia. Both the adult and larvae stages of the beetle eat the mealybugs and reductions of mealybug populations is rapid.

**How to use**  Carefully transfer the beetles to infested plants at a minimum rate of one per plant, allowing more for larger plants. Will be most effective at temperatures of 20-30°C.

**How much**  For general use apply 1 ladybird per plant. For domestic use release 1 pack per 15 plants. For commercial use apply 1 large pack per 50 - 100 plants.

**Other**  *Crytolaemus montrouzieri* is supplied as adult beetles or large larvae. Three pack sizes are available one for domestic use and two for commercial use containing 15, 10 and 100 ladybirds respectively.

**Supplier**  English Woodlands Ltd Tel 07986 574
Price for 15 (domestic pack) - £6.00 (inc VAT)
Price for 10 (Commercial pack) - £3.00 (+ VAT)
Price for 100 (commercial pack) - £25.00 (+ VAT)

**Accepted**  All

**Use**

# DELTA TRAP

> The Delta Trap is a proven method of catching moths and other winged insects. It is suitable for use in most situations but not where airborne dust is a problem as this will render the trap ineffective by covering the sticky surface.
> The Delta Trap is made of plastic, cut and creased to shape for on site assembly. Pheromone lures can be placed on the stick surface at the base of the trap.

**How to use** Assemble the trap as directed and hang up in a well aired site. If pheromone attractants are to be used simply position the capsule on the sticky base. Inspect the trap regularly and remove dead insects to retain maximum efficiency.

**How much** Replace the base of the trap after approximately 5 weeks depending on level of infestation present. The base can be removed and replaced with out having to move the trap.

**Other** The trap is 280 mm x 200 mm x 120 mm when assembled and is supplied either as a single trap shrink wrapped in plastic or as a box of 3 traps. Standard colour is white but other colours can be supplied on request.

**Supplier** Agrisense - Biological Control Systems Ltd Tel 0443 841155 and from Agralan Tel 0285 860015
Price on application to supplier.

**Accepted** All

**Use**

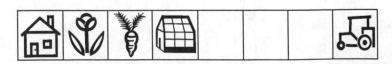

132

# DIGLYPHUS AND DACNUSA

*Diglyphus* and *Dacnusa* are for use against tomato leaf miner (*Liriomyza bryoniae* and leaf miner (*Phytomyza syngenesige*) and is suitable for use in all plants.

*Diglyphus* and *Dacnusa* contains two species of parasitic wasp namely *Dacnusa sibirica* and *Diglyphus isaia*. The leafminer larvae are attacked internally and externally by the parasitic wasps.

**How to use**  Apply at the first signs of egg laying by the pest. For tomatoes introduce 700 parasites per acre. For chrysanthemums introduce 500 per acre.

**How much**  For tomatoes apply 3 packs per acre. For chrysanthemums apply 2 pack per acre or [1 pack for 90,000 cuttings]. Repeat fortnightly if more than one pest generation present.

**Other**  *Diglyphus* and *Dacnusa* are supplied as 250 parasitic wasp pupae in a Tetrapack. Use immediately upon receipt.

**Supplier**  Technoverde Ltd Tel 0734 661243 or 0860 327831
Price available on request to supplier.

**Accepted**  All

Use

# DiPel WP

---

DiPel WP is for use against all leaf caterpillars and is suitable for use on all crops. Care should be used if appying to outdoor crops as DiPel will will kill non target caterpillar species.

DiPel WP contains the bacteria *Bacillus thuringiensis var kurstaki*. The bacteria, once ingested by the caterpillar, releases a toxic protein causing the pest to stop eating and die in a few days. DiPel is made by Abbott Laboratories in the USA.

---

**How to use**  Spray affected crops as soon as caterpillars are seen. For domestic use  mix 1 pack in 4 litres waterand spray onto the infected area. Half fill spray tank, sprinkle in the required amount of DiPel and add a spreader-sticker to improve coverage. Agitate whilst adding the rest of the water. Stir during spraying to prevent settling.

**How much**  For young caterpillars use 1/2 commercial pack (in 1125 litres water). Repeat every 3 weeks indoors and more frequently outdoors.

**Other**  DiPel is supplied as a wettable powder in a 10 gram domestic user pack and 500 gram commercial user pack. Keep dry, shelflife greater than 2 years.

**Supplier**  English Woodlands Ltd Tel 07986 574
Price for 10 gram (domestic pack) - £0.40 (inc VAT)
Price for 500 grams (commercial pack) - £10.00 (+ VAT)

**Accepted**  In principle by everyone although some of the guidelines are unclear.

**Use**

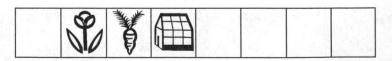

# ENCARSIA FORMOSA

*Encarsia formosa* is for use against Glasshouse whitefly (*Trialeurodes vaporariorum*) and is suitable for ue in all protected crops.
*Encarsia formosa* is a parasitic wasp that attacks whitefly scales. The adult wasp lays its eggs into the whitefly scale which turns black after a few days as the wasp larvae develops. The whitefly larva is killed and an adult wasp emerges from a small hole in the scale.

**How to use** Cut leaf into 10-20 pieces. Place each piece scales upward across a leaf stem about half way down the plant, shaded from direct sunlight.

**How much** For tomatoes introduce 3,000 Encarsia per acre per week if no whitefly have been seen.If some whitefly are seen introduce 6,000 wasps per acre per week. If more than 1 fly per 50 plants is observed introduce 10,000 per acre per week. For cucumber propogation apply 1 wasp per 2 plants and follow up with 1 wasp per plant per week. For ornamental plants apply 1 wasp per plant per week.

**Other** *Encarsia formosa* is supplied as infected scales on fresh tobacco leaf. It is available in a pack of 500 wasps for domestic use and 1000 wasps for commercial growers. Use immediately upon receipt.

**Supplier** English Woodland Ltd Tel 07986 574
Price for 500 wasp domestic pack - £6.00 (inc VAT)
Price for 1000 wasps commercial pack - £3.85/£5.50 (+ VAT)

**Accepted** All

**Use**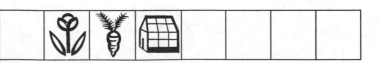

135

# ENCARSIA FORMOSA

> Encarsia formosa is for use against Glasshouse whitefly (*Trialeurodes vaporariorum*) and is suitable for ue in all protected crops.
> *Encarsia formosa* is a parasitic wasp that attacks whitefly scales. The adult wasp lays its eggs into the whitefly scale which turns black after a few days as the wasp larvae develops. The whitefly larva is killed and an adult wasp emerges from a small hole in the scale.

**How to use** Hang cards in areas of whitefly incidence as soon as adults are seen. Place evenly throughout the crop and where the cards are unlikely to get wet.

**How much** For nursery stock use 10 packs per acre each fortnight at first signs of whitefly. Repeat 4 times. For tomatoes & Pot plants apply 5 packs per acre each fortnight before any signs of whitefly. Repeat until August. For cucumbers use 6 packs per acre each week for 6 weeks.

**Other** Encarsia formosa is supplied as 60 Parasitized scales on a card. Use within two days of receipt.

**Supplier** Technoverde Ltd Tel 0734 661243 or 0860 327831
Price on application to supplier.

**Accepted** All

**Use**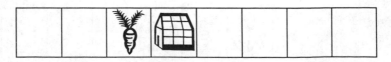

# ENPACK

Enpack is for use against glasshouse whitefly *Trialeurodes vaporarium*. The adult whitefly resemble small moths and are approximately 1.5 mm long and will be found mainly on the underside of the leaves. Shaking of the plant will cause the whitefly to rise off the leaves in a white cloud only to resume their underleaf position. Larvae will be found further down the plant.

Enpack contains the parasitic wasp *Encarsia formosa*. The wasp is approximately 0.6 mm long and has a black thorax (upper body) and yellow abdomen (lower body). The adult wasp lays its eggs into the whitefly larvae which turn black in about ten days, and from which an adult wasp will emerge after about 25 days.

**How to use** Introduce the Enpack as soon as white fly are first observed in the crop. Hang the cards of parasitised pupae in the crop and the adult wasps will emerge. Try to avoid areas where the cards will get wet. The wasp is susceptible to chemical products and it is advised to treat other pests with biological controls if possible.

**How much** One pack will treat an area of 400 square feet (approximately 350 m².)

**Other** Enpack is supplied as a pack of 25 cards each with 60 parasitised whitefly pupae on, giving a total of 1500 wasps. Use immediately upon receipt.

**Supplier** Bunting Biological Control Ltd Tel and also from
HDRA Sales Ltd Tel 0203 303517
Price per pack from HDRA - £6.90

**Accepted** All

**Use**

# En-Strip

> En-Strip is for use against the glasshouse whitefly *Trialeurodes vaporarium*. The adult whitefly resemble small moths and are approximately 1.5 mm long and will be found mainly on the underside of the leaves. Shaking of the plant will cause the whitefly to rise off the leaves in a white cloud only to resume their underleaf position. Larvae will be found further down the plant.
> En-Strip contains the parasitic wasp *Encarsia formosa*. The wasp is approximately 0.6 mm long and has a black thorax (upper body) and yellow abdomen (lower body). The adult wasp lays its eggs into the whitefly larvae which turn black in about ten days, and from which an adult wasp will emerge after about 25 days.

**How to use** Introduce the En-Strip as soon as white fly are first observed in the crop. Hang the cards of parasitised pupae in the crop and the adult wasps will emerge. Try to avoid areas where the cards will get wet. The wasp is susceptible to chemical products and it is advised to treat other pests with biological controls if possible.

**How much** The amount of En-Strip to use will depend on the severity of the problem. Treatment should be repeated throughout the growing season and each crop should be treated individually to ensure successful control. Contact the supplier for advice.

**Other info** En-Strip is supplied as black parasitised pupae of the whitefly attached to cards. Use the product as soon as possible upon receipt.

**Supplier** Koppert (UK) Ltd Tel 0892 884411
Price on application to supplier.

**Accepted** All

**Use**

# FIGHTAFLY

Encarsia formosa is for use against Glasshouse whitefly (*Trialeurodes vaporariorum*) and is suitable for ue in all protected crops.
*Encarsia formosa* is a parasitic wasp that attacks whitefly scales. The adult wasp lays its eggs into the whitefly scale which turns black after a few days as the wasp larvae develops. The whitefly larva is killed and an adult wasp emerges from a small hole in the scale.

**How to use** Hang cards in areas of whitefly incidence as soon as adults are seen. Place evenly throughout the crop and where the cards are unlikely to get wet.

**How much** For nursery stock use 10 packs per acre each fortnight at first signs of whitefly. Repeat 4 times. For tomatoes & Pot plants apply 5 packs per acre each fortnight before any signs of whitefly. Repeat until August. For cucumbers use 6 packs per acre each week for 6 weeks.

**Other** Encarsia formosa is supplied as a pack of 1000 wasps containing 3 strips of 6 cards. Each card has 60 wasp pupae on it. Use within two days of receipt.

**Supplier** Applied Horticulture (a division of Fargro Ltd) Tele 0903 721591
Price for 1 pack (1000 wasps) - £4.90

**Accepted** All

**Use**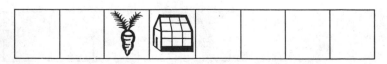

139

# FIGHTAGRUB

> Fightagrub is used against vine weevil and sciarid and is suitable for use in all infected crops.
> Fightagrub contains nematodes of the *Heterorhabditis* spp. The nematodes search out and parasitize the pest. When in the host they release bacteria that kill the pest insect after approximately 2 days.

**How to use**   Immerse each sponge in 1 litre of water at 20-25*o*C,squeeze after 20 minutes. Dilute to total volume required. Do not use in hot sunny conditions.

**How much**   For use as a compost admix 2 sponges per m³. For use as a drench 1 sponge per m³.

**Other**   Fightagrub is supplied as an impregnated sponge containing 1 million nematodes. Best used on receipt. Can be stored for up to 48 hours if refrigerated at 2-5°C.

**Supplier**   Applied Horticulture (a division of Fargro Ltd) Tel 0903 721591 Price for 1 sponge - £9.00

**Accepted**   All

**Use**

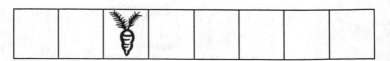

# FIGHTAMEAL

Cryptolaemus montrouzieri is for use against mealybugs, usually citrus mealybug *Planococcus citri* and is suitable for use on all plants including ornamentals.

*Cryptolaemus montrouzieri* is a black and brown ladybird beetle that originates from Australia. Both the adult and larvae stages of the beetle eat the mealybugs and reductions of mealybug populations is rapid.

**How to use** Introduce while mealybug populations are low. Carefully transfer the beetles to infested plants at a minimum rate of one per plant, allowing more for larger plants. Will be most effective at temperatures of 16-33°C.

**How much** For general use apply 1 ladybird per 3 mealybugs. 1 pack will treat 30 plants.

**Other** Crytolaemus montrouzieri is supplied as adult beetles in packs of 10 or 25. Use immediately upon receipt.

**Supplier** Applied Horticulture (a division of Fargro Ltd) Tel 0903 721591
Price for 10 beetles - £5.00
Price for 25 beetles - £12.50

**Accepted** All

**Use**

 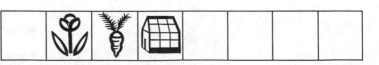

# FIGHTAMINE

---

Diglyphus and Dacnusa is for use against tomato leaf miner (*Liriomyza bryoniae* and leaf miner (*Phytomyza syngenesige*) and is suitable for use in all plants.
Diglyphus and Dacnusa contains two species of parasitic wasp namely *Dacnusa sibirica* and *Diglyphus isaia*. The leafminer larvae are attacked internally and externally by the parasitic wasps.

---

**How to use**   Apply at the first signs of egg laying by the pest. For tomatoes introduce 700 parasites per acre. For chrysanthemums introduce 500 per acre.

**How much**   For tomatoes apply 3 packs per acre. For chrysanthemums apply 2 pack per acre or [1 pack for 90,000 cuttings]. Repeat fortnightly if more than one pest generation present.

**Other**   Diglyphus and Dacnusa are supplied as 250 parasitic wasp pupae in a Tetrapack. Use immediately upon receipt.

**Supplier**   Applied Horticulture (a division of Fargro Ltd) Tel 0903 721591 Price for 250 parasites - £12.00

**Accepted**   All

**Use**

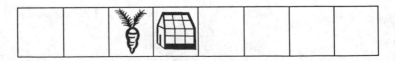

# FIGHTAMITE

---

Fightamite is for use against red spider mite (two spotted mite), a common pest of on house plants and in glasshouses. Infestation with red sider mites causes the leaves, especially the upper ones, to curl, become mottled and yellow, and then wither and die. Small wbs are visible on the leaf but the red spider is too small to see with the naked eye.
Fightamite contains another mite *Phytoseiulus persimilis*. All stages of the mite predate the red spider mite.

---

**How to use** Concentrate application on areas where red spider mite are first seen in the crop as these will be near the hibernation sites. For chrysanthemums apply 2-3 weeks after planting.

**How much** For pot plants use 1 pack per 200m². For strawberries use 1 pack per 2000 plants. For tomatoes/nursery stock use 1 pack per 400 plants. Chrysanthemums 1 pack per 20,000 cuttings.

**Other** Fightamite is supplied as 2000 adult mites in vermiculite in a shaker bottle. Use immediately on receipt.

**Supplier** Applied Horticulture (a division of Fargro Ltd) Tel 0903 721591
Price for 1 bottle (1000 mites) -£15.20
Alternatively the supply of mites can be leased for - £17.00

**Accepted** All

**Use**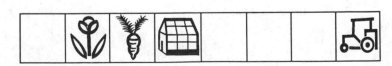

# FIGHTAPHID

Fightaphid is for use against aphids and is suitable for use in cucumbers, nursery stock, pot plants, tomatoes and chrysanthemums. It is particularly useful when used against *Myzus persicae* (peach potato aphid), *Aphis gossypii* and *Macrosiphoniella sanborni*.
Fightaphid contains the predatory midge *Aphidoletes aphidimyza* which actively searches out the aphid and lays its eggs near them. The resultant larvae eat the aphids.

**How to use** Introduce at first signs of aphid colonization. For heavy infestation repeat application twice at fortnightly intervals. Cut corner off pack and place where adults can fly away. Avoid getting pack wet.

**How much** In cucumbers, nursery stock and pot plants use 1 pack per 1250m² or 2 packs per acre. 1 pack for total infestation if small. For use in chrysanthemums use 1 pack per 35,000 cuttings.

**Other** Fightaphid is supplied as mdge pupae in peat in a tetrapack of either 250 or 1000 pupae. Use immediately upon receipt.

**Supplier** Applied Horticulture (a division of Fargro Ltd) Tel 0903 721591
Price for a pack of 250 pupae - £4.25
Price for a pack of 1000 pupae - £17.00

**Accepted** All

**Use**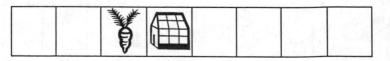

# FIGHTAPHIDIUS

Fightaphidius is for use against aphids, particularly peach-potato aphid (*Myzus pericae*).
Fightaphidius contains the parasitic wasp *Aphidius matricariae*. The adult wasps lay their eggs in the aphid which then become mummified as the wasp larvae eats the insides of the aphid. After a few days the new generation of wasps emerge and fly off to locate more aphids to parasitise.

**How to use**  Introduce wasps before or immediately when they appear on crops. For general use apply 1000 per acre every 2 weeks throughout the season.

**How much**  For general use apply 4 packs per acre every 2 weeks.

**Other**  Fightaphidius is supplied as 250 adult wasps in bottles. Use immediately upon receipt.

**Supplier**  Applied horticulture (a division of Fargro Ltd) Tel 0903 721591 Price for 250 wasps - £4.25

**Accepted**  All

**Use**

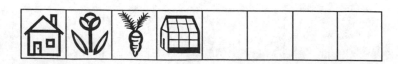

# FIGHTASCALE

---

Fightascale is for use against soft scale and is suitable for use in all plants. Fightascale contains the parasitic wasp *Metaphyous helvolus*. The wasp is tiny and black and yellow in colour. The adult wasp lays its eggs into the soft scale. The resultant larvae eat the insideds of the scales.

---

**How to use** Release onto infected plants in morning or evening to prevent excessive dispersal. Most effective April to September as requires temperatures above 22°C and bright sunlight.

**How much** Apply 5 wasps per m². Repeat 3 times at weekly intervals through the growing season. (1 pack per 5m² per treatment. 4 packs per 5m² per season.)

**Other** Fightascale is supplied as packs of 25 adult wasps. Use immediately on receipt.

**Supplier** Applied Horticulture (a division of Fargro Ltd) Tel 0903 721591 Price for 25 wasps - £12.50

**Accepted** All

**Use**

# FIGHTATHRIP

> Fightathrip is for use against thrips (*Thrips tabaci*) and western flower thrip (*Franklinella occidentalis*) and is suitable for use in all infested crops especially cucumbers and chrysanthemums.
> Fightathrip contains two species of mite *Amblyseius cucumeris* and *Amblyseius barkeri*. The mites actively search out and eat the thrips.

**How to use**  Establish mite population before thrips appear.

**How much**  In cucumbers apply 200,000 per acre. Repeat every 2 weeks. For interior displays apply 100 per m2 and repeat application weekly. For chrysanthemums use 1 mite per 10 cuttings 12 hours before planting out. Follow up with 1 mite per 5 cuttings 2-3 weeks after planting and repeat twice fortnightly.

**Other**  Fightathrip is supplied as adult mites in vermiculite in a shaker bottle. Three pack sizes available are 5000, 10000 and 25000 mites per pack. Use immediately on receipt.

**Supplier**  Applied Horticulture (a division of Fargro Ltd) Tel 0903 721591
Price for 5000 mites - £1.80
Price for 10000 mites - £3.60
Price for 25000 mites - £8.25

**Accepted**  All

**Use**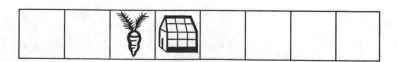

# FIGHTAWING

---

Fightawing is for use against aphids but will also attack soft bodied insects or larvae such as mealybug and caterpillars.
Fightawing contains the lacewing larvae *Chrysopa carnea* and it is the larvae rather than the adults that attack the aphids. The larvae, which eat the aphids, are also called aphid lions as they have a very ferocious appetite.

---

**How to use** Place the cards among the crop avoiding areas where the cards will get wet.

**How much** Information about numbers of lacewings to apply is not supplied. Consult supplier.

**Other** Fightawing is supplied as 1000 lacewing larvae on a card. Use immediately upon receipt.

**Supplier** Applied Horticulture (a division of Fargro Ltd) Tel 0903 721591
Price for 1000 larvae pack - £9.00

**Accepted** All

**Use**
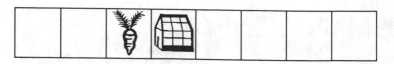

# FLY AND WASP TRAP

Fly and Wasp Trap is a chemical free trap for use against flies, wasps and mosquitos where ever these insects make themselves a nuisance.
The Fly and Wasp Trap is made of plastic with a funnel shaped base (like an upturned ring mould) and a clear plastic lid. The insects are attracted to the liquid bait in the base and enter the trap from beneath and the clear top ensures they do not fly downwards and back out of the trap. The insects then drown in the liquid bait.

**How to use** Pour the liquid bait into the base of the trap place on the lid and hang the trap up at about head height in a tree or from another suitable support where the insects are being a pest. Place in a shaded spot if possible as this will attract more insects. Inspect the trap every 2 - 3 days top up with water if the liquid level is low. Do not remove the insects until the trap is full as this adds to the effectiveness of the bait to attract the insects.

**How much** Remove the insects when the trap is full and there is no longer sufficient liquid to drown the insects. Wash the trap well with fresh water and replace the liquid bait.

**Other** The trap is of two part construction and comes supplied with a bottle of liquid bait which is sufficient for two refills of the trap. Refill bottles of bait are available separately.

**Supplier** AgriSense Biological Control Systems Ltd Tel 0443 841155 and from Agralan Tel 0285 860015
Price for 1 trap with refill from Agralan - £10.95 inc VAT (1990 price)
Price for liquid bait refill from Agralan - £4.45 inc VAT (1990 price)

**Accepted** All

**Use**

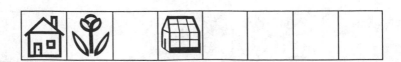

# FLYING INSECT TRAPS

Flying Insect Traps are for use against insects such as whiteflies, leafminer flies, midges, aphids, thrips and fungus gnats but will not trap house flies. They are useful to detect the first arrival of a pest so that biological controls can be introduced at the optimum time.

Flying Insect Traps are bright yellow to attract the insects which then become trapped on the plastic panels by a nontoxic odourless glue.

**How to use** Hang the traps within the crop or nearby the plants to be protected. Hang traps up before insects are seen so that regular checking of the traps will allow early detection of a pest. Avoid areas where the panels may become wet during watering, etc.

**How much** Replace the traps when approximately 75% of the surface is covered.

**Other** Flying insect traps are available in two sizes, standard suitable for all use and mini which is more suited to use in a house. A holder is available for the mini size trap.

**Supplier** HDRA Sales Ltd Tel 0203 303517
Price for standard size trap - £3.30
Price for mini trap - £1.10
Price for mini trap stand - 85p

**Accepted** All

Use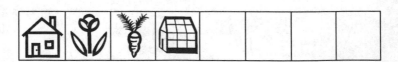

150

# FUNNEL TRAP

The Funnel Trap is a preferred trap for use in warehouses and stored products where airborne dust would quickly contaminate sticky traps. It is suitable for use against moths and other flying insect pests.

The Funnel Trap is made from plastic and has an attachment in the lid to facilitate the use of pheromone attractants. The base of the trap where the insects collect houses the killing agent.

**How to use** Place the desired killing agent in the base of the trap and the pheromone attractant in the lid receptacle. Various killing agents are available including a desiccant for use where chemical control is unacceptable. Hang the trap as required in the area to be protected.

**How much** Check the trap regularly and replace the contents as necessary. Rate of renewal will depend on the protected product and the pest species.

**Other** The trap is 230 mm x 170 mm diameter and is available in standard yellow or green lid with white base but other colours can be supplied on request.

**Supplier** Agrisense - Biological Control Systems Ltd Tel 0443 841155
Price on application to supplier.

**Accepted** All

**Use**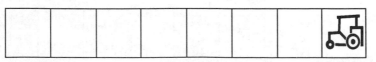

# GRAIN PROBE TRAP

Grain Probe Trap is for use against pests of stored grain such as grain weevil, confused flour beetle, saw-toothed grain beetle, rust red grain beetle and lesser grain borer. The trap is very effective at detecting the presence of pests so that remedial measures can be taken before extensive damage is caused.

The Grain Probe Trap is made from 25 mm diameter acrylic tubing in the upper part of which there are numerous and accurately sized and positioned drill holes which are angled towards the base of the tube. A small specimen tube is inserted in the base of the trap and this the top of this is coated with PTFE a very smooth surfaced plastic. Insect pests moving in the grain pass into the trap via the drill holes and fall into the base of the trap as they cannot grip on the PTFE surface.

**How to use** Attach a label with a length of string to the top of the trap and bury the trap vertically in the grain. Inspect the traps once a week, remove and identify any pests present.

**How much** In small grain stores at least 3 traps should br used in each parcel of grain up to 250 tonnes. In larger stores use 4 traps per 1000 tonnes of grain.

**Other** The trap is 25 mm in diameter and 37 cms long and is supplied with labels in a pack of 4 or ten traps.

**Supplier** AgriSense - Biological Control Systems Ltd Tel 0443 841155 and from Agralan Tel 0285 860015

Price for pack of 4 traps from Agralan - £49.00 + VAT (1990 prices)

**Accepted** All

**Use**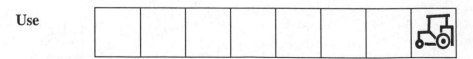

Insect control

# IGLU

Iglu is for use as a trap for flies and mosquitos and is suitable for use in stables, dairy parlours, near manure heaps and refuse tips, etc. Iglu is constructed from plastic and has two fit together sections. The base is shaped like a ring mould and the top is clear plastic. A liquid bait is placed in the base of the trap and this attracts the flies into the trap. The clear top to the trap ensures that the flies do not fly back out of the base of the trap and the flies eventually drown in the bait.

| | |
|---|---|
| **How to use** | Fill the base of the trap with liquid bait and twist the top into place. Attach the hanging wire and position the trap in a shady place as this will attract more flies. |
| **How much** | Replace the liquid bait when there is no longer enough surface liquid to drown the flies. Clean the trap with water and refill. |
| **Other** | Iglu is available as a complete unit. |
| **Supplier** | Urbio UK Tel 0734 661243 |
| | Price on application to supplier. |
| **Accepted** | All |

**Use**

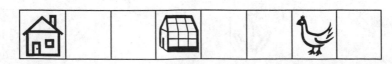

153

# KILL BOX

---

Kill Box is for use against flies in stables, dairy parlours, near manure heaps and on refuse sites.

Kill Box contains fly parasites the adults of which actively search out the flies. They lay their eggs into the fly larvae. When the larvae pupates it dies and the new generation of parasites emerges.

---

**How to use** Place the box near the slurry, rubbish pit or dung heap preferably in a dry position next to a wall if possible. The parasites will emerge over a period of 7 days at temperatures of 18 - 25°C.

**How much** Allow 1 Killbox per 25 m² of dung heap or refuse. In house stock allow 1 box per 500 chickens, or 15 cows, or 30 calves, or 1 horse, or 5 sheep, or 5 pigs. Replace the box every 10 - 15 days.

**Other** Kill Box contains 500 fly parasites. Use immediately upon receipt or store at 4 - 6°C in a fridge which will keep the parasites viable for up to 3 weeks.

**Supplier** Urbio UK Tel 0734 661243
Price on application to supplier.

**Accepted** All

**Use**

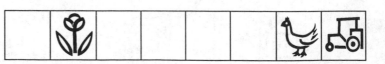

# LASIOTRAP

Lasiotrap is for use against the cigarette beetle (*Lasioderma serricorne*) which as its name gives away is a pest of tobacco during storage. It can be used to detect pests and will control low levels of infestation.
   Lasiotrap consists of a card with a sticky coating with a hole in the middle in which a pheromone vial can be placed. The beetles are attracted by the pheromone and get stuck to the card.

**How to use**   The traps are packed flat during transportation and are easily erected by twisting the base into position and folding out the flaps which act as a stand. The film covering the sticky surface can then be removed and the pheromone capsule inserted in the hole in the card. Alternatively hang the cards from roof trusses or pallet racking.

**How much**   The pheromone lure will last 6 weeks and can be replaced if the traps are not yet fully covered with dust or beetles. If the trap is covered it should be replaced.

**Other**   The traps are 150 mm x 150 mm x 300 mm and are supplied in a pack of 50 traps.

**Supplier**   AgriSense Biological Control Systems Ltd Tel 0443 841155 Price available on request.

**Accepted**   All

**Use**

# LIQUIBAITOR

Liquibator is for use with a liquid attractant against wasps and flies. It is suitable for use in any situation where flies and wasps are a nuisance for example near manure heaps, in dairy parlours, stables, and in the garden.
Liquibaitor is a plastic trap in two fit together sections. The base is shaped like a ring mould and the liquid attractant is placed in this section. The top is clear so that flies and wasps entering the base of the trap are attracted to the light and do not fly back out of the trap. The flies drown in the liquid bait.

**How to use** Place the box near the slurry, rubbish pit or dung heap preferably in a dry position next to a wall if possible. The parasites will emerge over a period of 7 days at temperatures of 18 - 25°C.

**How much** Allow 1 Killbox per 25 m² of dung heap or refuse. In house stock allow 1 box per 500 chickens, or 15 cows, or 30 calves, or 1 horse, or 5 sheep, or 5 pigs. Replace the box every 10 - 15 days.

**Other** Kill Box contains 500 fly parasites. Use immediately upon receipt or store at 4 - 6°C in a fridge which will keep the parasites viable for up to 3 weeks.

**Supplier** Technoverde Tel 0734 661243
Price on application to supplier.

**Accepted** All

**Use**

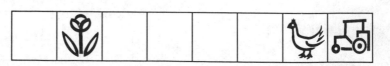

# MEALYBUG PREDATOR

Mealybug predator is as its name implies is for use against mealybugs. It contains the Australian ladybird **Cryptolaemus montrouzieri**. This particular ladybird is a black and brown beetle and rapidly reduces mealybug populations. Both larvae and adult stages of the beetle eat the mealybugs.

**How to use** The ladybird should be introduced as soon as the mealybug population is observed. The ladybirds will be very effective at reducing the mealybug population. However once the food source becomes depleted the effectiveness of the ladybirds will be reduced. Therefore effectiveness against a re-infestation of mealybugs cannot be guaranteed and a reintroduction of the product is advised.

**How much** Introduce the ladybirds at a rate of one per plant. 1 pack will treat 10 plants.

**Other** Mealybug predator is supplied as 10 ladybird beetles in a special tube. The ladybirds should be used immediately upon receipt.

**Supplier** Organic Farmers and Growers Ltd Tel 0449 720838
Price for a pack of 10 - £3.00 delivery included

**Accepted** Organic Farmers and Growers Ltd and all others

**Use**

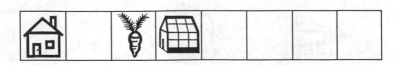

# MEALYBUG PREDATOR

> Mealybug predator is as its name implies is for use against mealybugs. It contains the Australian ladybird *Cryptolaemus montrouzieri*. This particular ladybird is a black and brown beetle and rapidly reduces mealybug populations. Both larvae and adult stages of the beetle eat the mealybugs.

**How to use** The ladybird should be introduced as soon as the mealybug population is observed. The ladybirds will be very effective at reducing the mealybug population. However once the food source becomes depleted the effectiveness of the ladybirds will be reduced. Therefore effectiveness against a re-infestation of mealybugs cannot be guaranteed and a reintroduction of the product is advised.

**How much** Introduce the ladybirds at a rate of one per plant.

**Other** Mealybug predator is supplied in packs of 10 and 100 beetles. The ladybirds should be used immediately upon receipt.

**Supplier** Natural Pest Control Tel 0243 553250
Price for a pack of 10 - £3.00 + VAT< P&P included (1990 price)
Price for a pack of 100 - £25.00 + VAT, P&P included (1990 price)

**Accepted** All

**Use**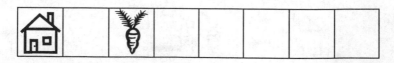

# MINERPACK

Minerpack is for use against leafminer insects and is suitable for use on all crops, for example, tomatoes that get attacked by leaf miners.
Minerpack contains the parasitic wasps *Diglyphus isea* and / or *Dacnusa sibirica*. The adult wasps feed on the larvae and lay the eggs are laid in the leafminer larvae. The eggs hatch and parasitise the leaf miner larvae.

**How to use** Release the parasitic wasps as soon as leafminers are observed in the crop. Open the pack and sprinkle the contents among the infested crop.

**ow much** Apply 1 to 40 flasks per ha depending on the levels of infestation.

**Other** Minerpack is supplied as 250 adult wasps in a flask with feeding strips.

**Supplier** Bunting Biological Control Ltd Tel 0206 271300 and from Brinkman UK Tel 0243 531666 (South) or 0482 42123 (North) Price on application to supplier.

**Accepted** All

**Use**

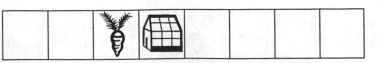

Insect Control

# MINEX

Minex is for use against the leafminer **Liriomyza bryoniae** which is a pest in tomatoes, capisicums, aubergines, beans and flower crops and also against **Liriomyza trifolii**. The two leafminers can only be told apart in the larval stage. Damage by the 2 mm long yellow-black larvae is easily identified as the leafminer eats a tunnel into the leaf of the crop.

Minex contains two parasitic wasps **Dacnusa sibirica** and **Diglyphus isaea**. The 3 mm long black wasps parasitise the leafminer by laying their eggs inside the larvae. The larvae appears to develop and pupate as normal but when it hatches a wasp emerges.

**How to use** The parasitic wasps should be released evenly into the crop.

**How much** Either or both species of wasp may be present naturally in the crop however it is difficult to assess the activity of the wasps in the greenhouse. Contact Koppert for an analysis of the crop and for further advice. Leaf samples will be taken and examined in the laboratory so that the situation can be assessed. If there are sufficient numbers of parasites then no action need be taken. If there are too few leafminer larvae that have been parasitised then application of one or both of the two parasitic wasp species should be applied.

**Other** Minex is supplied as adult wasps in a plastic bottle. Use immediately upon receipt.

**Supplier** Koppert (UK) Ltd Tel 0892 884411
Price on application to supplier.

**Accepted** All

**Use**

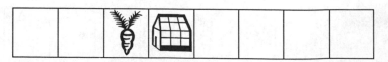

# MUSCALURE

Muscalure is used as a fly attractant in baits, electrical fly traps and other fly traps used against house flies.

Muscalure is a sex and aggregation pheromone of the house fly **Musca domestica** and works by natural attraction of the flies. Muscalure is 98% pure pheromone and is non-toxic.

**How to use**    Can be used in baits and traps of various kinds. It can be dissolved in most organic solvents.

**How much**    Amount to use will vary depending on the type of trap used.

**Other**    Muscalure is a pale amber coloured liquid. Store in a cool place and protect from frost and direct sunlight.

**Supplier**    AgriSense Biological Control Systems Ltd Tel 0443 841155

Price available on request from supplier.

**Accepted**    All

**Use**

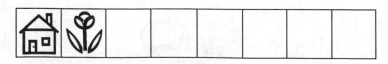

# MYCOTAL

Mycotal is for use against thrips, greenhouse whitefly *Trialeurodes vaporariorum* and the cotton whitefly *Bemisia tabaci*. The two species are very similar but the former attacks protected crops while the latter also attacks field crops.

Mycotal contains a strain of a fungus called *Verticillium lecanii*. As with all fungi it is most effective in high humidity conditions, and will kill larvae, pupae and adults of whitefly and larvae and adults of thrips. In low humidity conditions it is only effective against whitefly larvae.

This product was developed in the UK and is now made and marketed by Koppert BV, one of the companies that has pioneered the use of insects and other safe products in growing crops, particularly in glasshouses.

**How to use** Mix at a ratio of 1 kg of powder to 1,000 litres of water and apply as a spray early in the crop cycle when insect numbers are low. The high volume application is required to provide water for the fungus spores to germinate and grow and raises local humidity. For best results keep humidity above 85% and temperature between 18 and 30°C. It is best to avoid the use of fungicides.

**How much** Apply 3 kg of powder in 3,000 litres of water per ha. This is equivalent to 1.2 kg of powder in 1,200 litre of water per acre. For good control of whitefly apply three times with a 7 day interval. Control of thrips will require more applications.

**Other** Mycotal wettable powder in 500 gram containers. Stored at 4 - 6°C the product will keep for 6 months.

**Supplier** Koppert (UK) Ltd Tel 0892 884411 Price on application

**Accepted** Acceptable in principle under all guidelines but the specific details of some guidelines is unclear

**Use**

# NEMASYS

Nemasys is a new product for use against black vine weevil (*Otiorhynchus sulcatus*) and fungus gnats (sciarid flies). Years of research at the former Glasshouse Crops Research Institute and also in Australia and the USA led this to becoming the very first new product of the Agricultural Genetics Company, Britain's entry in the world's agricultural biotechnology race.

Nemasys contains the nematode (threadworm) *Steinernema bibionis* as its active ingredient. The nematodes seek out and infect pests into which they release bacteria that kill the pests within 48 hours.

**How to use** For use against black vine weevil, mix the pack contents with water and apply as a drench to the compost surface. This product can be tank mixed with some other products; follow label instructions. For use against sciarids, mix the pack contents with 100 litres of water and apply at a rate of 2 litres/m² or 50ml per plant. Best results are obtained at compost temperatures greater than 15°C.

**How much** Against black vine weevil use 1 pack per 1000 pots in the size range 0.5-3 litre. Against black vine weevil in cyclamen apply 1 treatment (at 3-9 weeks after potting) per 16 week season. For specific details of rates against black vine weevil on other plants consult supplier. For use against sciarid flies use 1 pack per 50m².

**Other** Nemasys is supplied in polythene packs containing a moist, sterile powder carrier with 50 million nematodes. Keep refrigerated until used. The product will keep for 28 days at 3-10°C.

**Supplier** MicroBio Division - Agricultural Genetics Company Ltd Tel 0763 208198 and from
Monro Horticulture Ltd
Price on application and will depend on quantity.

**Accepted** Formal approvals as a suitable green product will probably be forthcoming in due course. This is new product.

**Use**

# NEMASYS H

> Nemasys H is for use against black vine weevil in nursery stock and strawberries.
> Nemasys H contains nematodes of the *Heterohabditis spp*. The nematodes actively seek out and infect pest. When in the host they release bacteria which kill the host in 48 hours.

**How to use** Use as soon as possible otherwise refrigerate at 3-10°C. Apply as soon as larvae of the weevil are found. Mix the nematodes with water and spray onto the crop. If crops are known to be at risk treat from mid August to early September.

**How much** For nursery stock mix 1 pack in 50 litres of water and spray at a rate of 1 litre/m² to damp compost. For strawberries mix 1 pack in 200 litres of water and drench the crown of each plant with 100 ml.

**Other** Nemasys H is supplied as 4 small bags of nematodes in one outer pack that contains a total of 50 million nematodes.

**Supplier** MicroBio Division - Agricultural Genetics Company Ltd Tel 0763 208198
Price on application to supplier.

**Accepted** None yet gained.

**Use**

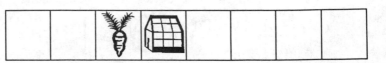

# PHYTOPACK

Phytopack is for use against red spider mites, a very common pest on house plants and in glasshouses. Infestation with red spiders causes the leaves, especially the upper ones, to curl, become mottled and yellow, and then whither and die. Small webs are visible on the leaf but the red spider is too small to be seen with the naked eye. Many chemical insecticides are no longer effective against red spider mite. The active ingredient in this product is another mite *Phytoseiulus persimilis*. Although they are smaller than their prey, once released, these mites seek out and eat the red spider mites, eliminating them.

| | |
|---|---|
| **How to use** | Introduce the predatory mites as soon as the red spider mites are seen in the crop. Distribute the mites evenly among the crop plants. The predatory mites will search out the red spider mites. |
| **How much** | 1 pack will treat an area of 400 square feet (approximately 250 m².) Apply 2 - 4 times per year. |
| **Other** | Phytopack is supplied as 2000 mites in bran in a 0.5 litre bottle. It will keep for 1 week if stored at 12°C. |
| **Supplier** | Bunting Biological Control Ltd Tel 0206 271300 and from Brinkman UK Tel 0243 531666 (South) or 0424 2123 (North) and from HDRA Sales Ltd Tel 0203 303517 Price for 1 bottle from HDRA - £6.90 |
| **Accepted** | All |

**Use**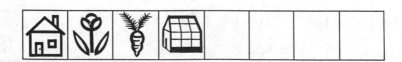

# PHYTOSEIULUS PERSIMILIS

Phytoseiulus persimilis is for use against red spider mite (two spotted mite), a common pest of on house plants and in glasshouses. Infestation with red sider mites causes the leaves, especially the upper ones, to curl, become mottled and yellow, and then wither and die. Small webs are visible on the leaf but the red spider is too small to see with the naked eye.

*Phytoseiulus persimilis* is species of mite thet is smaller than its prey. All stages of the mite predate the red spider mite.

**How to use** Concentrate application on areas where red spider mite are first seen in the crop as these will be near the hibernation sites. For chrysanthemums apply 2-3 weeks after planting.

**How much** For pot plants use 1 pack per 200m². For strawberries use 1 pack per 2000 plants. For tomatoes/nursery stock use 1 pack per 400 plants. Chrysanthemums 1 pack per 20,000 cuttings.

**Other** Fightamite is supplied as 2000 adult mites in vermiculite in a shaker bottle. Use immediately on receipt.

**Supplier** Technoverde Ltd Tel 0734 661243 or 0860 327831
Price on application to supplier.

**Accepted** All

**Use**

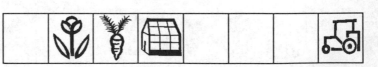

# PHYTOSEIULUS PERSIMILIS

**A**

Phytoseiulus persimilis is for use against red spider mite (two spotted mite), a common pest of on house plants and in glasshouses. Infestation with red sider mites causes the leaves, especially the upper ones, to curl, become mottled and yellow, and then wither and die. Small webs are visible on the leaf but the red spider is too small to see with the naked eye.

*Phytoseiulus persimilis* is species of mite thet is smaller than its prey. All stages of the mite predate the red spider mite.

**How to use**  Place the leaves or leaf sections right way up on the infested crop leaves paying particular attention to the upper plant. The predatory mites do not hibernate so will need to be reapplied each year.

**How much**  Depending on level of infestation allowing 1 predatory mite per plant should generally suffice. Therefore 1 domestic pack will treat 500 plants and 1 commercial pack will treat 1000 plants. Please consult supplier for specific details.

**Other**  Phytoseilius persimilis is supplied as all stages of development on bean leaves. PAck size available for domestic use contains 500 mites. Pack for commercial use contains 1000 mites. Use immediately upon receipt.

**Supplier**  English Woodlands Ltd Tel 07986 574
Price for 500 (domestic pack) - £6.00 (inc VAT)
Price for 1000 (commercial pack) - £8.50 (+ VAT)

**Accepted**  All

**Use**

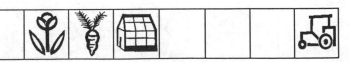

# PIANBIOT

> Pianbiot is for use against insect larvae that live on the parts of the plant that are above ground such as butterfly and moth caterpillars.
> Pianbiot contains *Steinernema* spp which are nematodes parasitic on the pest insects. The nematodes search out and parasitise the pest where they release bacteria that kill the host after approximately 2 days.

**How to use** Immerse the sponge in 5 litres of water at 20 - 30°C. After 15 minutes remove the sponge and squeeze it to ensure there are no longer and nematodes in the sponge. This will give a dilution of 2 million nematodes per litre of water. Use immediately after preparation.

**How much** For fruit trees up to 2 metres tall apply 1 million nematodes per tree by diluting 500 ml of stock solution in 10 litres of water. For trees over 2 metres tall apply 2 million nematodes by diluting 1 litre of stock solution in 20 litres of water. For herbaceous plants use 5 ml of stock solution per plant.

**Other** Pianbiot is supplied as 10 million nematodes in a sponge. Best used immediately upon receipt but can be stored for up to 48 hours if refrigerated at 4 - 5°C.

**Supplier** Technoverde Ltd Tel 0734 661243 or 0860 327831
Price on application to supplier.

**Accepted** Formal approvals as a suitable green product will probably be forthcoming in due course. This is new product.

**Use**

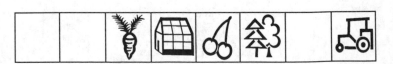

Insect Control

# SEBON

Sebon is for use against whitefly, aphids, thrips, mealybugs, etc on all crops.
Sebon contains salts of fatty acids obtained from natural sources and works as a contact insecticide. It is 100% biodegradable and does not harm wildlife, beneficial insects or bees.

**How to use** Dilute Sebon with water and spray onto the affected crops. Use soft water if possible and mix thoroughly but gently to avoid foaming. Mix new solution for each application.

**How much** For use against whitefly in vegetables, fruit trees and shrubs make a dilution of 1% Sebon by mixing 1 litre of Sebon in 100 litres of water. (1 ml per 100 ml). For use against aphids, thrips and scale in vegetables, fruit trees and shrubs make a dilution of 2% Sebon by mixing 2 litres of Sebon in 100 litres of water (2 ml per 100 ml).

**Other** Sebon is available in 1 litre and 5 litre plastic containers.

**Supplier** AgriSense Biological Control Systems Ltd Tel 0443 841155
Price on application to supplier.

**Accepted** All except GCFP

Use

169

# SPIDEX

Spidex is for use against red spider mites (*Tetranychus urticae*), a very common pest on house plants and in greenhouses. Infestation with red spider mites causes the leaves, especially the upper ones, to curl, become mottled and yellow, and then wither and die. Small webs are visible on the leaf but the red spider is too small to be seen with the naked eye. Many chemical insecticides are no longer effective against red spider mites. Spidex contains a predatory mite *Phytoseiulus persimilis* which although smaller than their prey, once these mites are released they will seek out and eat the red spider mites.

**How to use**    Sprinkle the predatory mites rapidly but evenly throughout the crop direct from the bottle. Relative humidity should not be too low and temperatures should regularly rise above 20°C to ensure rapid results.

**How much**    One application per season will keep the red spider mites under control.

**Other**    Spidex is supplied as adult mites in plastic shaker bottles. Use immediately upon receipt.

**Supplier**    Koppert (UK) Ltd Tel 0892 884411
Price on application to supplier.

**Accepted**    All

**Use**

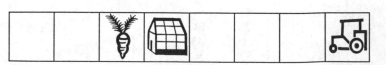

Insect Control

# STICK-A-PEST

Stick-a-pest is for use with a pheromone attractant against flying and crawling insects. Standard pheromones are for cockroaches, codling moth, tortrix moths and plum fruit moth but other pheromones are available.
Stick-a-pest traps for flying insects are made from plastic panels that slot together and the traps for crawling insects are made from card panels. Both trap types have sticky inserts to which a pheromone attractant can be attached and to which the insects become stuck on entry to the trap.

**How to use** Construct the trap and place the pheromone attractant in the centre of the sticky panel. For flying insects hang the traps at about head height in a shady spot as this will attract more insects. For crawling insects place in humid areas where the insects tend to congregate.

**How much** Number of traps to use will depend on the species of insect being trapped.

**Other** Stick-a-trap is supplied packed flat ready for construction.

**Supplier** Technoverde Ltd Tel 0734 661243 or 0860 327831
Price on application to supplier.

**Accepted** All

 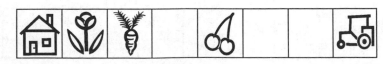

# SWARM LURE

Swarm Lure is used to lure swarming bees into a hive. Swarm Lure has been developed at the Rothampsted Experimental Station at Harpenden and has been tested in cage and field trials both in the UK and the USA. The trials show that the baited hives were made significantly more attractive to swarming bees.

Swarm Lure contains a pheromone that is naturally produced by the worker bees during 'fanning'. When the bees swarm they cluster together often in trees and scout bees fly off to find a suitable new home. When the scout bees find a baited hive they consider it to contain a proportion of the swarm and fly back to the cluster and relay the message that a new home has been found. The bees then move into the baited trap.

**How to use** Position the hive to be baited in shade 1 - 2 metres (4 -6 feet) off the ground. It should contain one or two combs that have previously been used for brood-rearing and the entrance should not be hidden. Remove the capsule of Swarm Lure from the sachet and place just inside the entrance to the hive. Do not open the capsule it is designed to release the pheromone slowly through the walls.

**How much** Replace the capsule after 4 - 6 weeks if the swarming continues and the hive has not attracted a swarm.

**Other** Swarm Lure is supplied as capsules in individual sachets and is available in packs of 5 and 10 lures.

**Supplier** AgriSense Biological Control Systems Ltd Tel 0443 841155 and from Steel & Brodie Ltd Tel 0794 388168
Price on application to supplier.

**Accepted** All

**Use**

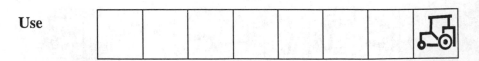

# TERBIOT

Terbiot is used against insect larvae that live in the soil such as vine weevil, wireworm, snout beetles and sciarid in strawberries, salad crops, ornamental and other plants.
Terbiot contains *Heterorhabditis spp* and which are nematode parasites of the pest insects. The nematodes search out and parasitize the pest where they release bacteria that kill the host after approximately 2 days.

**How to use** Immerse each sponge in 1 litre of water at 20-25$o$C,squeeze after 20 minutes. Dilute to total volume required. Do not use in hot sunny conditions.

**How much** For use as a compost admix use 2 sponges per m$^3$.
For use as a drench use 1 sponge per m$^3$.

**Other** Terbiot is supplied as 1 million nematodes impregnated into a sponge. Best used immediately upon receipt but can be stored for up to 48 hours if refrigerated at 2 - 5°C.

**Supplier** Technoverde Ltd Tel 0734 661243 or 0860 327831
Price on application to supplier.

**Accepted** Likely to be approved in the future

**Use**

# TERRIX

> Terrix is for use against larvae of broad nosed weevils, sugar beet beetles and curculionids in general.
>
> Terrix contains a mix of *Heterorhabditis* spp and *Steinernema* spp of nematodes in a peat carrier. The nematodes parasitise the larvae of the pests which die within a couple of days. The nematodes combined with the peat help to condition the soil.

**How to use**  Apply Terrix to the soil near the stem of the plant by using the measure provided in the pack. It should be slightly buried and watered to allow the nematodes to go down into the soil more easily and to maximise the activity of the nematodes humid conditions should be promoted.

**How much**  For plants in rows use 5 - 6 measures full of Terrix per metre. For individual treatment of plants use 2 - 3 measures full of Terrix per metre.

**Other**  Terrix is supplied as nematodes in a peat base in 1 litre, 5 litre and 25 litre sacks. Terrix can be kept for 6 months from the packing date. Once the pack is opened the peat should be kept wet and the sack carefully closed.

**Supplier**  Technoverde Ltd Tel 0734 661243 or 0860 327831
Price on application to supplier.

**Accepted**  Acceptable to all in principle but no formal approvals yet

**Use**

# 'TRAPPIT' CODLING MOTH TRAP

Trappit Codling Moth Trap is, as its name implies, for use against the codling moth (*Cydia pomonella*) which lays its eggs on apples and the larvae that hatches burrows into the fruit.

Trappit Codling Moth Trap releases female pheromones (female sex hormones) into the air and this attracts the male moths into the trap. The base of the trap is coated with a non-toxic glue and the male moths become stuck to this and unable to mate with the females so that less eggs are laid on the apples.

**How to use** Assemble the trap as directed on the packet, placing one pheromone capsule onto the sticky base. Hang the traps up by mid-May or full bloom which ever is earlier. Hang at head height in a well ventilated area of the chosen tree centrally to other trees to be protected by the trap. To maintain the efficiency of the trap remove dead moths with the spatula provided. When finished with the bases should be burnt.

**How much** 1 trap will be sufficient to protect 5 trees if within a 25 yard radius and the base should be replaced every 5 weeks.

**Other** Trappit Codling Moth Traps are supplied as a single trap with two sticky bases and two capsules of pheromone.

**Supplier** AgriSense Biological Control Systems Ltd Tel 0443 841155 and from Agralan Ltd Tel 0285 860015 and from
HDRA Sales Ltd Tel 0203 303517
Price for 1 trap kit from Agralan - £4.99 (1990 price)
Price for replacement bases and capsules - £3.95 (1990 price)
Price for 1 trap kit from HDRA - £5.75
Price for replacement bases and capsules from HDRA - £4.75

**Accepted** All

**Use**

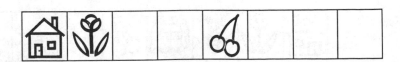

# 'TRAPPIT' GLUE TUBE

> 'Trappit' Glue Tube is for use as a barrier against crawling pest insects such as vine weevil, winter moth, ants and woodlice. It is suitable for protecting single pots and tubs or to protect whole benches in greenhouses or as a 'grease band' on trees.
> 'Trappit' Glue Tube contains a non-drying glue to which the insects stick and are trapped.

**How to use**  Apply a even coat of glue approximately 2 - 3 mm thick to the required surface to form an effective barrier to the pest. For best results do not apply to a dusty or porous. For banding on trees apply a continuous band 15 - 20 cms deep on the trunk of the tree.

**How much**  One tube will treat just over 1 metre of surface for barrier protection.

**Other**  'Trappit' Glue Tube is supplied as a standard mastic gun containing 280 grams of glue. (The not drying glue is also available from AgriSense in tubs or buckets.)

**Supplier**  AgriSense Biological Control Systems Ltd Tel 0443 841155 and from Agralan Tel 0285 860015 and also from
HDRA Sales Ltd Tel 0203 303517
Price for 1 tube from Agralan - £4.65 (1990 price)
Price for 1 tube from HDRA - £6.45

**Accepted**  All

**Use**

176

# 'TRAPPIT' ROACH TRAPS

Trappit Roach traps can be used against a range of crawling insects including all species of cockroach, ants, earwigs, flour beetles, grain weevils, larder beetles, silverfish, carpet beetles and crickets.

The Trappit Roach Trap consists of a trap constructed of cardboard with a sticky base and a lure of pheromones and chemical attractants that are generally considered as safe. The insects are attracted by the lure enter the trap and get stuck to the base.

**How to use** Fold out the trap and remove the protective cover from the base. Place the lure tablet on the centre of the sticky base and assemble the trap as directed on the pack. Place the assembled trap in a dark humid area where cockroaches and other crawling insects are likely to accumulate.

**How much** For monitoring of pest levels place traps at a density of 1 - 2 traps per 10m². For control of pests place at a density of 3 - 5 traps per 10m².

**Other** Trappit Roach Traps are available as three different types, original, lo-line and monitoring and are supplied as a box of 200, 200 and 1000 traps respectively.. The lures are available in three sizes 200 mg, 750 mg and 2.5 grams and are supplied foil wrapped in pairs in strips of ten.

**Supplier** AgriSense Biological Control Systems Ltd Tel 0443 841155 and from Agralan Tel 0285 860015

Price available on request to supplier.

**Accepted** All

**Use**

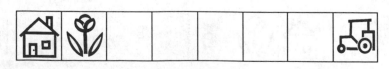

# TRAPPIT YELLOW STICKY TRAP

> Trappit Yellow Sticky Trap is for use primarily against whitefly but can also be used against winged aphids, thrips, gnats, leaf miners and some smaller flies. It is suitable for use both indoors and outdoors.
> The Trappit Yellow Sticky Trap is made of plastic that is coloured a specific yellow that attracts pests species. Beneficial insects such as bees and ladybirds are not attracted by the yellow colour so they are not normally caught.

**How to use**  Remove the outer protective covering to expose the sticky surface. Hang over the crop to be protected using the coated wire provided. Place the traps in the crop early in the season so that the first whitefly are caught and a build up of pests is avoided. As the trap rely on its colour not a pheromone to attract pests the traps can be left in place until harvest. Outdoors and in dusty situations the trap may need replacing if it becomes coated with dust.

**How much**  Number of traps to use varies with the crop. For very crops that are highly attractive to pests use 1 trap for every 4 m$^2$ of floor area. For less attractive plants less traps can be used.

**Other**

**Supplier**  The trap is 25 cm x 20 cm and is supplied in a pack of 5 traps. AgriSense Biological Control Systems Ltd Tel 0443 841155 and from Agralan Tel 0285 860015

Price for a pack of 5 traps from Agralan - £3.20

**Accepted**  All

**Use**

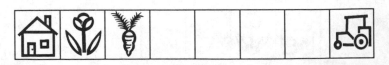

Insect Control

# TRIBOLIUM TRAP

Tribolium Trap is for use for monitoring levels of confused flour beetles *Tribolium confusum* and *Trifolium castaneum* in stored grain products. Tribolium Trap contains a pheromone attractant entrapped in a plastic polymer which gives a steady release of the pheromone. The trap is a simple disposable plastic box with a fluted sticky base. The beetles crawl into the trap and become stuck to the sticky base.

**How to use** Peal off the protective covering from the sticky base and place the capsule in place. Position the traps in a grid pattern preferably close to beams and machinery. Place the traps horizontally to prevent dust contamination. Number the traps and date them to facilitate assessment. Replace the traps when full.

**How much** Place 1 trap for every 5m².

**Other** Tribolium Trap is 70 mm x 90 mm x 5 mm and is supplied packed in individual sachets in boxes of 10. They are further packaged into cases of 200 traps.

**Supplier** AgriSense Biological Control Systems Ltd Tel 0443 841155 Price on application to supplier.

**Accepted** All

**Use**

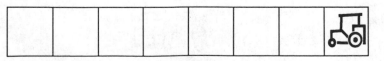

# TRIPEX B

Tripex-B is for use against thrips in cucumbers, namely Western Flower Thrips *Frankliniella occidentalis* and onion thrips *Thrips tabaci*. The adult thrips can be found on the leaves and flowers of infected plants. Eggs are laid on the leaves and develop into larvae within a few days. The larvae can destroy large areas of leaf and damage young fruit. The adult thrip emerges after a pupal stage that occurs on the ground.

Tripex-B contains predatory mites from the genus *Amblyseius*. The female mite lays 2 - 3 eggs on the underside of the leaf at the tip of the leaf hairs. The mites actively search for their prey in the crop. An adult mite will eat 2 - 3 thrips each day.

**How to use** Distribute the mites evenly throughout the crop. As the mites do not multiple as quickly as the thrips it is important to introduce them as soon as the thrips are observed in the crop.

**How much** Number of mites to use will depend on the level of infestation in the crop. If introduced early enough into the crop then the thrips will be kept at low levels and damage can be prevented with one application. Consult Koppert for advice on a specific problem or refer to the product label.

**Other** Tripex-B is supplied as adult mites in a convenient plastic shaker bottle. Use immediately upon receipt.

**Supplier** Koppert (UK) Ltd Tel 0892 884411
Price on application to supplier.

**Accepted** All

**Use**

Insect Control

# TRIPEX C

Tripex-C is for use against thrips in capsicum, namely Western Flower Thrips *Frankliniella occidentalis* and onion thrips *Thrips tabaci*. The adult thrips can be found on the leaves and flowers of infected plants. Eggs are laid on the leaves and develop into larvae within a few days. The larvae can destroy large areas of leaf and damage young fruit. The adult thrip emerges after a pupal stage that occurs on the ground.

Tripex-C contains predatory mites called *Amblyseius cucumeris*. The female mite lays 2 - 3 eggs on the underside of the leaf at the tip of the leaf hairs. The mites actively search for their prey in the crop. An adult mite will eat 2 - 3 thrips each day.

**How to use** Distribute the mites evenly throughout the crop. As the mites do not multiple as quickly as the thrips it is important to introduce them as soon as the thrips are observed in the crop.

**How much** Number of mites to use will depend on the level of infestation in the crop. If introduced early enough into the crop then the thrips will be kept at low levels and damage can be prevented with one application. Consult Koppert for advice on a specific problem or refer to the product label.

**Other** Tripex-C is supplied as adult mites in a convenient plastic shaker bottle. Use immediately upon receipt.

**Supplier** Koppert (UK) Ltd Tel 0892 884411
Price on application to supplier.

**Accepted** All

**Use**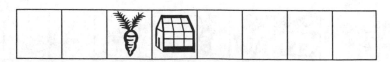

# UNITRAP

> Unitrap is for use with a pheromone attractant against flying insect pests. A range of pheromone attractants are available and include those for use against house flies, wasps and codling moth.
>
> Unitrap consists of a plastic funnel and pheromone dispenser fitted to the top of the trap. The insects attracted to the pheromone loose their grip on the sides of the funnel and fall down into the base of the trap from which they cannot escape. The base of the trap is made of clear plastic to prevent the insects flying back out of the trap and if desired a toxicant strip can be placed in the base to kill the pests.

**How to use**  Place the toxicant strip if used in the base of the trap, fix the pheromone in place in the lid and fix the trap together. Hang the trap where the insects are being a pest, preferably in a shady spot as this will attract more insects.

**How much**  Number of traps to use will depend on the insect pest being trapped.

**Other**  Unitrap is supplied as a complete unit. A variety of pheromones are available.

**Supplier**  Technoverde Ltd Tel 0734 661243 or 0860 327831
Price on application to supplier.

**Accepted**  All

**Use**

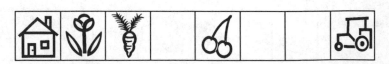

# VIROX

---

Virox is for use against pine sawfly larvae which attack young pine trees and can cause severe damage by eating the needles. In severe cases the tree may die due to complete defoliation.

Virox contains a virus *Neodiprion sertifer* NPV (nuclear polyhedrosis virus). When ingested by the sawfly larva Virox attacks the gut wall. The larva stops feeding and dies in 10 - 21 days.

Virox was developed in Britain by the Natural Environment Research Council's Institute of Microbiology and Virology in Oxford. It is made in the UK and sold by a new UK biotechnology company, OV Ltd.

---

**How to use** Virox can be applied by aerial application but written permission must be obtained from the manufacturer (OV Ltd). Application should coincide with the peak of egg hatching. Fill the sprayer tank to half the required volume with water add the Virox and fill the tank.

**How much** A 1 litre pack of Virox will treat 10 ha. For high volume air application mix 100 ml in 10 litres of water. Apply 10 litres of this mix per ha. For ULV mix 100 ml of Virox in 1 litre of water and apply 1 litre of this mix per ha.

**Other** Virox is supplied as a liquid in 1 litre containers. Store the product in a cool place away from direct sunlight. Do not leave in the spray tank for more than 12 hours.

**Supplier** O V Ltd Tel 071 222 9272
Price on application to supplier.

**Accepted** As a forestry product only, Virox would not enter into the thinking of most organic groups. It would be accepted in principle by most.

Use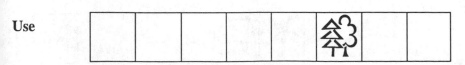

# WHITEFLY PARASITE

Whitefly parasite as its name implies is for use against whitefly. It contains the parasitic wasp *Encarsia formosa*. The adult wasp lays its eggs in the scales of the whitefly. The scales then turn black and when the developed wasp has emerged a small hole can be seen in the scale surface.

**How to use** The parasitic wasp pupae should be introduced into the crop as soon as the crop is planted. Larvae are supplied on leaves which should be cut up and pieces placed around the crop to give as even a distribution as possible.

**How much** In tomatoes introduce 2,000 - 6,000 (2 - 6 packs) per acre per week. Other crops need a lower rate of introduction and a rate of 1 pupae per plant per week. Therefore 1 pack will treat 1000 plants.

**Other** Whitefly parasite is supplied as packs of 1000 parasitic wasp larvae on fresh tobacco leaves. Use immediately upon receipt.

**Supplier** Organic Farmers and Growers Ltd Tel 0449 720838
Price for a pack of 1000 - £5.50 delivery included

**Accepted** Organic Farmers and Growers Ltd and all others

**Use**

# WHITEFLY PARASITE

Whitefly parasite as its name implies is for use against whitefly. It contains the parasitic wasp *Encarsia formosa*. The adult wasp lays its eggs in the scales of the whitefly. The scales then turn black and when the developed wasp has emerged a small hole can be seen in the scale surface.

**How to use** The parasitic wasp pupae should be introduced into the crop as soon as the crop is planted. Larvae are supplied on leaves which should be cut up and pieces placed around the crop to give as even a distribution as possible.

**How much** In tomatoes introduce 2,000 - 6,000 per acre per week. Other crops need a lower rate of introduction and a rate of 1 pupae per plant per week.

**Other** Whitefly parasite is supplied as packs of 1000 parasitic wasps. Use immediately upon receipt.

**Supplier** Natural Pest Control Tel 0243 553250
Price for orders of 1 -2 packs - £5.50 + VAT per 1000 wasps, P&P included. (1990 price)
Price for orders of 3 - 9 packs - £4.50 + VAT per 1000 wasps, P&P included. (1990 price)
Price for orders of 10 or more packs - £4.00 + VAT per 1000 wasps, P&P included. (1990 prices)

**Accepted** All

**Use**

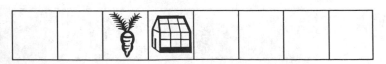

# BINAB T WETTABLE POWDER

B

Binab T wettable powder is for use against silver leaf fungus (*Chondostereum purpureum*) which can attack fruit trees including plum, apple, apricot and other rosaceous trees. It can be used to protect healthy trees from infection and to save infected trees.

Binab T contains the *Trichoderma* spp of fungus which is actively antagonistic to the silver leaf fungus.

Binab T wettable powder is currently approved by MAFF for use only by commercial growers. It also has to be sold by qualified personnel and because of these two factors it has been removed from sale by HDRA. The manufacturers have applied for full MAFF approval so the product should be available to domestic users in the near future. The product is also produced as a pellet but the manufacturers have declined to register this form for full MAFF approval.

**How to use**  Make a paste of Binab T by adding some water and paint onto pruning cuts and wounds. If preferred dilute further and apply as a spray to the required points.

**How much**  50 grams will be sufficient to treat 2 -3 standard apple trees.

**Other**  Binab T wettable powder id supplied in 50 gram and 500 gram sachets. Can be stored in a freezer for up to 3 years but is best used within 1 year of purchase.

**Suuplier**  Binab USA Inc (Swedish Branch) - Tel 01046 506 42005 Contact Jacques Rickard

Prices available on request from supplier. (It was previously available from HDRA at a price of £3.20 for 50 grams and £25.60 for 500 grams.)

**Accepted**  All

**Use**

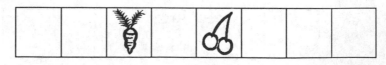

# TRITACK

Tritack is for uses against *Fusarium* crown and root rot in tomatoes. It can be used to protect plants from infection and to save infected plants. Tritack contains the spores of the fungus *Trichoderma harzianum* which is actively antagonistic to the *Fusarium* and root rot fungi.
Tritack comes from a Dutch company, Brinkman B.V. and is sold throughout the world. It is not currently listed as approved by MAFF for use in the UK although very similar products are approved for use here. It could probably be made available here fairly quickly if Brinkman apply for MAFF approval. If interest is shown in the product by the UK growers they may be prompted to do this.

**How to use** Spray onto the crop to be protected or treated.
**How much** A single application is sufficient to prevent *Fusarium* crown and root rot.
**Other** Tritack is supplied as a liquid in a 5 litre can.
**Supplier** Brinkman UK Tel 0243 531666 (South) or 0482 42123 (North).
**Accepted** All in principle, although acceptability is not always made clear in guidelines

Use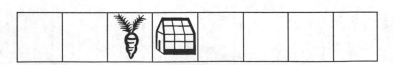

# MICRO N FIX

> Micro N Fix is used to provide an organic source of nitrogen for leguminous crop plants such as peas and beans. Legumes such as clover when planted in leys will also provide nitrogen for the grasses in the sward.
> Micro N Fix contains strains of *Rhizobium* bacteria. The Rhizobium bacteria form nodules in the plant roots where they trap gaseous nitrogen and convert it into an organic form that can be utilised by the plant.

**How to use** Micro N Fix should be applied to the soil before the crop is sown. Inoculants are available for white clover, lucerne, soya beans, peas, beans, lentils, etc. Ensure that you have the correct inoculant as the strain of rhizobium varies with the crop.

**How much** Rate of application will depend on the crop grown.

**Other info** Micro N Fix is supplied as bacteria in a peat base in 200 gram packs. Shelflife is 6 months.

**Supplier** Microbial Developments Ltd Tel 0684 568434
Price on application to supplier.

**Accepted** All

**Use**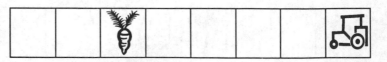

Nitrogen Fixing Seed Treatment

# NITROBAC

NitroBac is used to supply legumes with an organic source of nitrogen especially in poor soils. It is suitable for use with lucerne, clovers, beans and peas.

NitroBac contains *Rhizobium* bacteria which form nodules in the roots where they trap gaseous nitrogen and convert it to an organic form. This can then be utilised by the plant.

**How to use** For lucerne and clover scatter granules loosely by hand after sewing and initial watering. Rake in and re-water. For peas and beans sprinkle the granules along the bottom of the seed drill. Plant seeds as close as possible to the granules. Water the open drill. Cover the drill and re-water.

**How much** Use one pack for 60 square yards of lucerne or clover and 1 pack will treat a 10 yard row of peas and beans.

**Other** NitroBac is supplied as granules in 150 gram packets. Keep in a cool place, below 25°C and away from sunlight. Once opened use within 12 hours.

**Supplier** MicroBio - Agricultural Genetics Company Ltd Tel 0763 208198 and also from HDRA Sales Ltd Tel 0203 639229 Price on application to supplier.

**Accepted** All

**Use**

# NPPL GRANULAR

> NPPL Granular is used to supply legume plants (peas, beans, etc) with an organic source of nitrogen especially in poor soil.
> NPPL Granular contains *Rhizobium* spp of bacteria. The Rhizobium bacteria form nodules in the plant roots where they trap gaseous nitrogen and convert it into an organic form that can be utilised by the plant.

**How to use**  Apply at sowing through a standard pesticide granule applicator on the drill.

**How much**  Apply 1 bag per hectare.

**Other info**  NPPL Granular is supplied as free flowing granules in 10 kg bags. Store in a cool place at less than 25°C. Keep away from sunlight and keep the bags sealed.

**Supplier**  MicroBio Division - Agricultural Genetics Company Ltd Tel 0763 208198

Price on application to supplier.

**Accepted**  All

**Use**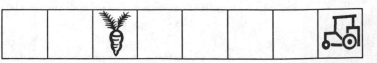

Nitrogen Fixing Seed Treatment

# NPPL HiStick

---

NPPL HiStick is used supply legume plants with an organic source of nitrogen especially in poor soil.
  NPPL HiStick contains *Rhizobium* bacteria. The bacteria coating the seed enter the roots of the plant and form nodules where they trap nitrogen which can be utilised by the plant.

---

**How to use** For use dry, pour inoculant onto layers of seed in the drill hopper & mix. For use damp, apply approx. 100 ml water to dampen seed then mix with inoculant. For use as a slurry, add inoculant to water (250 grams in 500 ml; 70 grams in 150 ml). Pour over seed and mix well.

**How much** 1 x 70 gram pack treats 5 kg of white clover seed or 10 kg lucerne seed. 1 x 250 gram pack 50 - 100 kg of seed depending on seed size.

**Other** NPPL HiStick is supplied in 70 gram and 250 grams of inoculant on a moist peat base in polythene bags. Store in a cool place between 2°C and 25°C, away from direct sunlight. Inoculant or treated seed will keep for 6 months.

**Supplier** MicroBio Division - Agricultural Genetics Company Ltd Tel 0763 208198
Prices on application to supplier.

**Accepted** All

**Use**

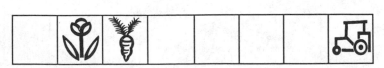

Nitrogen Fixing Seed Treatment

# NPPL RHIZOBIUM GRANULES

NPPL Rhizobium Granules are used to supply legume plants (peas, beans, etc) with an organic source of nitrogen especially in poor soil.
NPPL Granular contains *Rhizobium* spp of bacteria. The Rhizobium bacteria form nodules in the plant roots where they trap gaseous nitrogen and convert it into an organic form that can be utilised by the plant.

**How to use** Sprinkle the contacts of the packet along the trench or over the area os soil where the legumes will be planted.

**How much** 1 pack for beans and peas will treat a row 10 yards long. 1 pack for alfalfa (lucerne) will treat 60 square yards.

**Other info** NPPL Rhizobium granules are available in two packs one for broad and runner beans and peas and one for alfalfa.

**Supplier** HDRA Sales Ltd Tel 0203 303517
Price for 1 pack for beans/peas - £3.40
Price for 1 pack for alfalfa - £3.40

**Accepted** All

Use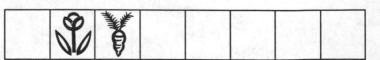

# ACID-PACK 4-WAY

Acid-Pack 4-Way is used to reducing incidence of scours and severity of stress in piglets and poultry.
Acid-Pack 4-Way contains the bacteria *Lactobacillus acidophilus*, *Streptococcus faecium*, as well as organic acids, enzymes and electrolytes. The bacteria reduce gut pH inhibiting pathogens which prefer more alkaline conditions while the enzymes and electrolytes alleviate stress.

**How to use** Mix with the solid feed or incorporate into the drinking water supply. Feed at times of stress.

**How much** Incorporate 3 - 4 kg per tonne finished feed or mix 1 gram per litre of drinking water.

**Other** Acid-Pack 4-Way is supplied as a water soluble powder in 4 kg home mixer packs or 40 kg compounder packs. Keep in dry conditions and avoid extreme temperatures. Shelflife is 2 years.

**Supplier** Alltech (UK) Tel 0978 660198
Price for 4 kg (home mixer pack) - £26.60
Price for 40 kg (compounder pack) on application to supplier.

**Accepted** Acceptable to most organisations with special permission, but not GCFP.

**Use**

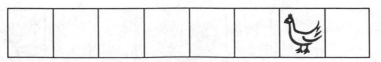

# ALL-LAC

> All-lac is used for calves, or other livestock at birth to initiate gut with beneficial microflora or for following stress or antibiotic treatment to re-establish balanced gut flora.
> All-lac contains the bacteria *Lactobacillus acidophilus* and *Streptococcus faecium*. The bacteria produce lactic acid from sugars present in the feed which discourages coliform growth and promotes beneficial microbes.

**How to use** Mix with the feed or water.

**How much** For calves feed 1 capsule at birth and 1 capsule 5 days later or dissolve 1 gram of powder in 10 ml water and administer as a drench at birth and again 5 days later. For other cattle: 1 capsule or 1 gram. in 10 ml water as required. For piglets dissolve 0.25 gram per 2 ml. of water per piglet. Administer as a drench at birth and times of stress or after antibiotics. For poultry mix 100 grams in 5 litres of water and spray over eggs. Use 5 litres for 10,000 eggs. Post hatching use 25 grams in sufficient water for 1000 chicks supply for the first 48 hours.

**Other** All-lac is supplied as a capsule or powder in packs of 50 capsules or 100 grams of powder. Keep in dry conditions and avoid extremes of temperature. Shelflife 2 years.

**Supplier** Alltech (UK) Tel 0978 660198
Price for 100 grams of powder - £30.00
Price for 50 capsules - £30.00

**Accepted** Acceptable to most organisations with special permission, but not GCFP.

**Use**

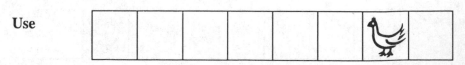

# ALL-LYTE

---

All-lyte is used to help prevent scours in bought in stock and following scours to help clear up an infection
All-lyte contains *Lactobacillus acidophilus, Streptococcus faecium,* dextrose, electrolytes, organic acids and enzymes. The bacteria produce lactic acid from sugars in the feed which help prevent the growth of pathogens which prefer more alkaline conditions. The organic acids, electrolytes and enzymes restore the electrolytes, replaces digestive enzymes and buffers gut acidity.

---

**How to use** Dissolve the powder in milk, colostrum or milk replacer.

**How much** Dissolve 25 grams per litre in warm water and feed in place of milk or milk replacer at 2 litres per feed twice a day for 2 days. For bought in calves use for first two feeds.

**Other** All-lyte is supplied as a powder in 100 gram sachets. Keep in dry conditions and avoid extreme temperatures. Shelflife is 2 years.

**Supplier** Alltech (UK) Tel 0978 660198
Price for 100 gram sachet - £0.90
Price for 4 kg pack - £28.00

**Accepted** Acceptable to most organisations with special permission, but not GCFP.

**Use**

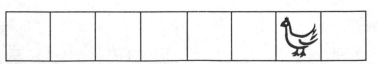

Products for Animals

# BIO-SACC

Bio-Sacc is used to increase feed intake and animal production by stabilizing gut pH and promoting beneficial bacteria in ruminant livestock. Bio-Sacc contains beneficial bacteria, cultured yeast, enzymes, B vitamins and biotin. The yeast cells reduce rumen acidity by utilising sugars produced during breakdown of the feed that would otherwise be converted to acids. The bacteria and enzymes aid and speed up the digestion of the feed allowing more feed to be eaten.

**How to use** Mix into feed or top dress (sprinkle) on to the ration after premixing with cereals.

**How much** For mixing include 1 pack per tonne of feed. For top dressing 1 pack will last 4 days for 100 animals.

**Other** Bio-Sacc is supplied as a powder in 1 kg bags.

**Supplier** Britmilk Tel 0387 75459
Price on application to supplier.

**Accepted** Acceptable to most organisations with special permission, but not GCFP.

**Use**

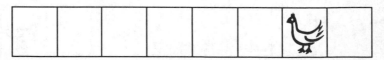

196

# BIO SAVOR

Bio Savor is used to promote health, growth and feed conversion efficiency in all livestock. It is made by Kemin Industries Incorporated in Iowa, USA.

Bio Savor contains the bacteria *Lactobacillus acidophilius casei* and *Lactobacillus plantarum*. The bacteria produce lactic acid from sugars present in the gut and the acid creates conditions that are unfavourable to pathogens.

**How to use** Bio Savor can either be mixed into the feed or the drinking water. For complete feed mixes it can be added directly into the feed mixer.

**How much** For mixing into the water supply allow 125 grams for 5000 litres of water. For mixing into the feed include 125 grams per tonne of feed.

**Other** Bio Savor is supplied as a powder.

**Supplier** Kemin (UK) Ltd Tel 0522 514148
Price on application to supplier.

**Accepted** Acceptable to most organisations with special permission, but not GCFP.

**Use**

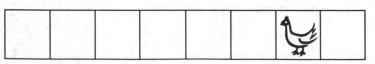

# BIO-START

> Bio-Start is used to establish and maintain a healthy balance of beneficial bacteria in the gut of calves.
> Bio-Start contains beneficial bacteria which dominate the gut producing lactic acid which lowers the gut pH and makes conditions less favourable to pathogens.

**How to use** Mix the powder in water or milk at blood temperature (39°C). Do not use boiling water as this will kill the bacteria.

**How much** Allow 2.5 grams per calf per dose during the milk feeding period. 1 tub contains 400 calf doses.

**Other** Bio-Start is supplied as a powder in 1 kg tubs and comes supplied with a 2.5 gram scoop.

**Supplier** Britmilk Tel 0387 75459
Price on application to supplier.

**Accepted** Acceptable to most organisations with special permission, but not GCFP.

**Use**

Products for Animals

# BIOSURE

Biosure is a new product from Alltech developed in conjunction with BP Nutrition (UK). It is used to increase performance in pigs of all ages. Biosure combines a yeast culture Lacto-Sacc, De-Odorase and a high intensity sweetener. For details of Lacto-Sacc adn De-Odorase please see the separate product entries. The combination of products increases the levels of beneficial microbes in the gut allowing more rapid digestion of the feed and increases palatability of the feed so that voluntary feed intake is increased. Production of ammonia and hydrogen sulphide is reduced, both these gases suppress growth.

How to use  Mix into the finished feed or concentrate ration.
How much  Amount to use is not stated in the literature.
Other  Biosure is supplied as a powder.
Supplier  Alltech (UK) Tel 0978 660198
Price on application to supplier.
Accepted  Accepted by most organisations with special approval, but not GCFP.

Use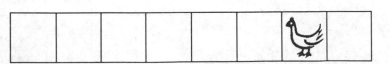

# BOVIFERM

---

Boviferm is a system of probiotic products for preventing scours and encouraging fast growth in calves, lambs and kids. Boviferm has four different mixes to match the development of the gut.
Boviferm contains lactic acid producing bacteria that reduce the gut pH making conditions unfavourable to pathogens such as *E. Coli*. The bacteria compete directly with pathogen for available nutrients and also coat the lining of the gut making it more difficult for the pathogens to attack the gut wall.

---

**How to use** Mix the Boviferm product with colostrum, milk or water and feed as you would normal milk from a bucket or machine. For promoting a health gut flora from birth feed Boviferm start twice in the first day. Follow up with Boviferm process fed daily until 9 days old. Following antibiotic treatment or during scours feed Boviferm start and Boviferm diät together twice in the first day. Follow up with Boviferm process fed daily for the next 8 days. For long term feeding to older stock feed Boviferm finale.

**How much** For each administration of Boviferm start, process and diät use one sachet. For Boviferm finale feed 5 grams per calf and 2 grams per lamb or kid.

**Other** Boviferm start, process and diät are sold together in a pack called Boviferm 2.8.2 as it contains 2, 8, and 2 packs of the respective Boviferm mixes. Boviferm finale is supplied in 100 gram sachets.

**Supplier** Agil Ltd Tel 0734 785531
Price on application to supplier.

**Accepted** Acceptable to most organisations with special permission, but not GCFP.

**Use**

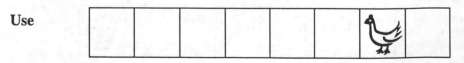

# CATTLE LAC PLUS

> Cattle Lac Plus is used for rapid establishment of beneficial gut microflora in newborn calves and after antibiotic treatment, worming or surgery. It can also be used to bring cows back to maximum appetite upto 14 days earlier than normal after calving. It can also be used to establish a healthy gut flora in sheep, pigs and horses.
> Cattle Lac Plus contains live, interacting micro-organisms which flood the gut and prevent the growth of pathogens by producing lactic acid which lowers gut pH.

**How to use** Mix into either the solid feed or into the milk and feed as normal.

**How much** For calves and foals feed 5 grams per head per day. For piglets feed 2.5 grams per head per day. For mares and working horses allow 10 grams per head per day. For cows, sheep and sows mix 5 lb (2 kg) per tonne into the feed. For bought in pigs either weaners or growers mix 2.5 lb (1 kg) per tonne of feed.

**Other** Cattle Lac Plus is supplied as a soluble powder.

**Supplier** Nutrimix Tel 0253 730888
Price on application to supplier.

**Accepted** Acceptable to most organisations with special permission, but not GCFP.

**Use**

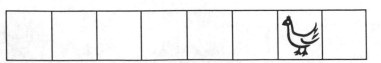

# CLP Pet Tabs

CLP Pet Tabs is a supplement for cats and dogs suitable for use with newborn pups and kittens to strengthen their resistance to disease or for all ages when stressed.
Colostart contains antibodies from colostrum collected from cows in at least their third lactation. Some of the fat and sugars are removed to concentrate the antibodies which fight against infection in the dog or cat. The addition of broad spectrum probiotics which maintain the gut at a pH which inhibits growth of pathogens help to eliminate any bacteria that may be present and the production of lactic acid by these beneficial bacteria helps to maintain appetite. Vitamins and minerals are also included to make this an all round supplement for good health and disease resistance.

**How to use** Feed the tablet with the food either whole or crushed and sprinkled on the meal. If administered by a veterinarian follow the directions given.

**How much** Feed one tablet per day. 1 pack will last 50 days for one cat or dog.

**Other** CLP Pet Tabs are supplied as 50 wafer tablets in a plastic bottle.

**Supplier** Alan Haythornthwaite Tel 0772 634782
Price available on request from supplier.

**Accepted** Acceptable to most organisations with special permission, but not GCFP.

**Use**

# COLORON

Coloron is for use as an orally administered combined iron, colostrum and probiotic to give the piglet protection against diseases and to establish a good gut flora. Coloron has been developed by Smarte International Inc in Canada and is one of their range of products based on dried cows' colostrum.

Coloron contains antibodies required by the piglet to fight infections. The inclusion of iron makes routine iron injections unnecessary and the presence of a probiotic adds beneficial bacterial that promote conditions in the gut that suppress any pathogens that may be present.

**How to use**   Coloron is administered orally and is very palatable so is not spit back up after dosing. It is supplied in an easy to use natural pump action dispenser (similar to those used for liquid soap). Depression of the pump releases a set amount of Coloron into the mouth of the piglet. The bottle should be thoroughly shaken each time before use.

**How much**   Administer two pumps (1.4 gram) per piglet at birth and repeat at three to five days of age. Extra treatment can be given if required for example a runt may require more than its litter mates.

**Other**   Coloron comes in a handy 290 gram dispenser. In cold weather the product should be stored in a warm room.

**Supplier**   Alan Haythornthwaite Tel 0772 634782
Price available on request from the supplier.

**Accepted**   Acceptable to most organisations with special permission, but not GCFP.

**Use**

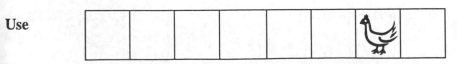

# COLOSTART

Colostart is for use in calves, lambs and pigs of all ages which show dehydration after scouring. It can also be used for bringing stock back on feed and to help overcome growth setbacks such as occurs after transportation.

Colostart contains antibodies from colostrum collected from cows in at least their third lactation. Some of the fat and sugars are removed to concentrate the antibodies which fight against infection in the animals gut. The addition of broad spectrum probiotics which maintain the gut at a pH which inhibits growth of pathogens help to eliminate any bacteria that may be causing scouring and the production of lactic acid by these beneficial bacteria helps to regain appetite. Vitamins and minerals are also included to replace those lost during scouring.

**How to use** Mix the powder in warm milk or water. Feed twice daily for two consecutive days. For animals eating solid feed the powder can be top dressed on to the ration.

**How much** Mix 2 oz (60 gram) in one pint of milk or water per feed. 1 bottle will make approximately 7 feeds.

**Other**
**Supplier** Colostart is supplied as a powder in a 380 gram container.

Alan Haythornthwaite Tel 0772 634782
Price available on request from supplier.

**Accepted** Acceptable to most organisations with special permission, but not GCFP.

**Use**

# COLOSTRUM BOLUS II

Colostrum Bolus II is used to boost the newborn calf's intake of colostrum and by supplementing with a probiotic, vitamins and minerals to give a good start to life that helps to protect the calf against infections. Colostrum Bolus II contains a concentrated form of antibodies obtained from the colostrum of cows in at least their third lactation. A bacterial probiotic of *Streptococcus faecium* is also included to initiate the gut with beneficial bacteria which create conditions in the gut which will kill any pathogens. Vitamins and minerals are also added to enhance the effect of the colostrum antibodies.

**How to use** The bolus can be given at birth and at any time when the animal is stressed for example during transportation, or a change of ration. It is also suitable to use after orally administered antibiotic treatment to restore the balance of bacteria in the gut. Administer through a suitable bolus gun.

**How much** Give the calf one bolus at birth and administer another on the second day if the calf is weak. Administer 1 bolus before any known stress such as transportation, feed ration change or administer after any unforseen stress such as a sudden change in weather conditions.

**Other** Colostrum Bolus II is available as a bottle of 25 bolus each of 6 grams.

**Supplier** Alan Haythornthwaite Tel 0772 634782
Price on application to supplier.

**Accepted** Acceptable to most organisations with special permission, but not GCFP.

**Use**

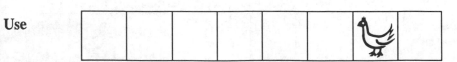

# DE-ODORASE

De-Odorase is a probiotic used for reducing ammonia and odour production from animal manure and is especially useful in housed livestock where animal performance can be suppressed by ammonia production. It can also be used directly in slurry tanks, cess pools and fish ponds.
De-Odorase activity is three fold. It contains saponins, extracted from the Yucca plant (*Yucca shidigera*), which inhibit conversion of urea (the waste product from protein digestion) to ammonia by the enzyme urease. The enzymes cellulase and pentosane are included and these aid the breakdown of the feed fibre in the slurry. The bacteria *Bacillus subtilis* is included to convert any available ammonia into microbial protein.

**How to use**　For use in livestock and pets the probiotic should be included in the feed. For pigs and poultry it can be administered in the drinking water. Use of De-Odorase liquid is best for addition to slurry or cess pits and should be diluted with water before use. De-Odorase liquid can also be used diluted with water and sprayed directly onto bedding.

**How much**　For cattle and horses use 60 grams per tonne of feed. In sheep, pigs, poultry, rabbits and aquaculture include 120 grams per tonne. For pet food include 250 gram per tonne. For use in drinking water for pigs and poultry include 1 ml of De-Odorase in 8 litres of water. For slurry and cess pits use 42 ml De-Odorase liquid per $m^3$. For direct application to bedding apply 240 ml of De-Odorase liquid in 1 - 2 gallons of water per 90m$^2$.

**Other**　De-Odorase is available as a powder or liquid. A concentrated form is available in 25 kg drums for low inclusion. A premix containing 3% deodorase is available in 20 kg bags.

**Supplier**　Alltech (UK) Tel 0978 660198 and from Colborne Dawes Nutrition Ltd Tel 0773 530300 or Belfast (0232) 381434
Prices available on request from suppliers. The approximate cost of inclusion is £1.50 per tonne of feed.

**Accepted**　Acceptable to most with special permission, not GCFP.

**Use**

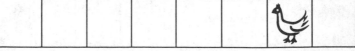

Products for Animals

# DOWNLAND CALF PROBIOTIC GEL

Downlands Calf Probiotic Gel is for improving animal health. By reducing digestive upsets and aiding digestion of the feed liveweight gains can be increased. Meat and Livestock Commission figures show an increase in feed conversion efficiency over animals not fed a probiotic.
Downlands Calf Probiotic Gel contains the bacteria *Lactobacillus acidophilus* and *Streptococcus faecium* which produce lactic acid from the food and therefore acidify the gut making the conditions unfavourable to pathogens which prefer more alkaline conditions. Vitamins are also included to promote the health and disease resistance of the calves.

**How to use** Feed one dose at birth to establish a health gut flora and repeat at times of stress such as transportation, etc.
**How much** Feed one 3 ml dose per head at birth then as required.
**Other** This is supplied as a gel.
**Supplier** Downland Marketing Ltd Tel 0249 817008
Price available on request from supplier.
**Accepted** Acceptable to most organisations with special permission, but not GCFP.

**Use**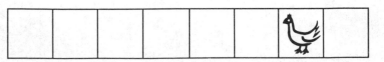

# DOWNLAND CALF PROBIOTIC POWDER

Downlands Calf Probiotic Powder is for improving animal health. By reducing digestive upsets and aiding digestion of the feed liveweight gains can be increased. Meat and Livestock Commission figures show an increase in feed conversion efficiency over animals not fed a probiotic. Downlands Calf Probiotic Powder contains the bacteria *Lactobacillus acidophilus* and *Streptococcus faecium* which produce lactic acid from the food and therefore acidify the gut making the conditions unfavourable to pathogens which prefer more alkaline conditions. Vitamins are also included to promote the health and disease resistance of the calves.

**How to use** Feed with daily whilst receiving milk or at times of stress. Either mix with milk or top dress onto the feed.

**How much** Feed 2.5 grams per head per day.

**Other** This is supplied as a powder and comes with a 2.5 gram scoop.

**Supplier** Downland Marketing Ltd Tel 0249 817008
Price available on request from supplier.

**Accepted** Acceptable to most organisations with special permission, but not GCFP.

**Use**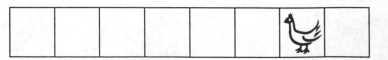

# DOWNLAND PIG PROBIOTIC GEL

Downlands Pig Probiotic Gel is for improving animal health. By reducing digestive upsets and aiding digestion of the feed liveweight gains can be increased. Meat and Livestock Commission figures show an increase in feed conversion efficiency over animals not fed a probiotic.

Downlands Pig Probiotic Gel contains the bacteria *Lactobacillus acidophilus* and *Streptococcus faecium* which produce lactic acid from the food and therefore acidify the gut making the conditions unfavourable to pathogens which prefer more alkaline conditions. Vitamins are also included to promote the health and disease resistance of the piglets. The lactic acid produced also stimulates the appetite.

**How to use** Feed one dose at birth to establish a health gut flora and repeat at times of stress such as transportation, etc.

**How much** Feed one 3 ml dose per head at birth then as required. Runts and weak piglets may require more doses to help build up resistance to pathogens and to encourage appetite.

**Other** This is supplied as a gel.

**Supplier** Downland Marketing Ltd Tel 0249 817008
Price available on request from supplier.

**Accepted** Acceptable to most organisations with special permission, but not GCFP.

**Use**

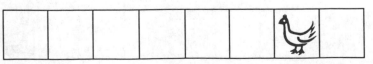

# DOWNLAND SHEEP PROBIOTIC GEL

> Downlands Sheep Probiotic Gel is for improving animal health. By reducing digestive upsets and aiding digestion of the feed liveweight gains can be increased. Meat and Livestock Commission figures show an increase in feed conversion efficiency over animals not fed a probiotic. Downlands Sheep Probiotic Gel contains the bacteria *Lactobacillus acidophilus* and *Streptococcus faecium* which produce lactic acid from the food and therefore acidify the gut making the conditions unfavourable to pathogens which prefer more alkaline conditions. Vitamins are also included to promote the health and disease resistance of the lambs. The lactic acid produced also stimulates the appetite.

**How to use** Feed one dose at birth to establish a health gut flora and repeat at times of stress such as transportation, etc.

**How much** Feed one 3 ml dose per head at birth then as required. Twins and triplets that are weak may require more doses to help build up resistance to pathogens and to encourage appetite.

**Other** This is supplied as a gel.

**Supplier** Downland Marketing Ltd Tel 0249 817008
Price available on request from supplier.

**Accepted** Acceptable to most organisations with special permission, but not GCFP.

**Use**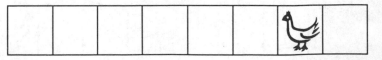

# EQUIBOOST

Equiboost is a probiotic for horses. A probiotic is a selected strain (or strains) of microbe selected for its beneficial effect. As opposed to and antibiotic that kills bacteria a probiotic enhances the conditions for and increases populations of beneficial bacteria while suppressing pathogenic bacteria.

Equiboost has been seen to have a calming effect on horses particularly those that tend to get worked up before or after racing or eventing, etc. It can also be used to help prevent scours in foals and for any horses after antibiotic treatment or purging to re-establish a health gut flora.

Equiboost contains the bacterium *Enterococcus faecium* SF68 which acts in the gut by producing lactic acid from the feed thus reducing gut pH. As pathogenic bacteria prefer more alkaline conditions this reduces the likelihood of gut infection such as scours. Lactic acid also stimulates the appetite. Although the exact mechanism that works to calm the animal is unknown this particular strain is known to adhere very efficiently to the gut wall and therefore allows some protection from acids excreted by the gut that are thought to cause nervousness somewhat similar to people getting "butterflies".

**How to use** Use during periods of stress and before competitions or races when the horse may get worked up. Can also be used to help bring horses back on feed after racing, foaling, etc. Mix the Equiboost with the oats or bran or top dress on nuts.

**How much** Allow 10 - 20 grams per day.

**Other** Equiboost is supplied in an outer cardboard box of 6 sachets each containing 100 grams. A 20 gram measure is also included. The product should be kept in a cool dry place and will last for 12 months.

**Supplier** Tithebarn Ltd Tel 0704 60606
Price for 600 grams - £45.85

**Accepted** Acceptable to most organisations with special permission, but not GCFP.

**Use**

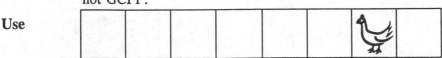

# EQUISTART

Equistart is a probiotic for foals. A probiotic is a strain (or strains) of microbe selected for its beneficial effect. As opposed to and antibiotic that kills bacteria a probiotic enhances the conditions for and increases populations of beneficial bacteria while suppressing pathogenic microbes.

Equistart can be used in foals at birth to establish a healthy gut flora and repeated administration helps maintains the gut balance when the mare comes back on heat and the foal is prone to scour or after antibiotic treatment to re-establish a health gut flora.

Equistart contains the bacterium *Enterococcus faecium* SF68 which acts in the gut by producing lactic acid from the feed thus reducing gut pH. As pathogenic bacteria prefer more alkaline conditions this reduces the likelihood of gut infection such as scours. This particular strain is also known to adhere very efficiently to the gut wall and therefore allows some protection from pathogenic microbes being able to come into contact with the gut lining.

**How to use** Administer the probiotic by placing the end of the syringe on the back of the foal's tongue. Gently squeeze the plunger of the syringe to expel the probiotic.

**How much** Administer 1 syringe as soon after birth as possible. Dose the foal with another syringe at approximately 9 days old when the mare comes back on heat and the foal may show some heat scour. Thereafter administer every 3 days.

**Other** Equistart is supplied as a box of 12 disposable syringes each containing 5 ml of probiotic. Kept in cool dry conditions the product will keep for 12 months.

**Supplier** Tithebarn Ltd Tel 0704 60606
Price for 1 box (12 x 5 ml) - £56.90

**Accepted** Acceptable to most organisations with special permission, but not GCFP.

**Use**

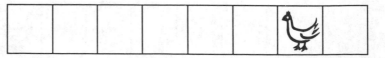

# FEED-ZYME

Feed-Zyme is used to allow the use of low cost feed ingredients without a loss of performance being observed in pigs and poultry. Use will also reduce the incidence of "sticky droppings" in poultry.

Feed-Zyme I contains the enzymes alpha-amylase and proteinase in a cellulase base. The enzymes improve the availability of low grade proteins and so improve the feed value of the feed. Feed-Zyme II contains the same enzymes as Feed-Zyme I but has an addition of beta-gluconase which breaks down the indigestible storage polysaccharides (long chain carbon molecules) that cause sticky droppings in poultry.

**How to use** For poultry include Feed-Zyme at 0.1% of the finished feed. (Mix in 1 kg per tonne of feed.) For pigs include 750 mg per kg of feed.

**How much** 1 drum will treat 25 tonnes of poultry feed, or approximately 33 tonnes of pig feed.

**Other** Feed-Zyme is supplied as free flowing powder in 25 kg drums.

**Supplier** Agil Ltd Tel 0734 785531
Price on application to supplier.

**Accepted** Acceptable to most organisations with special permission, but not GCFP.

**Use**

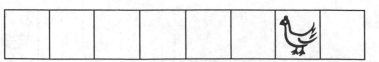

213

# IMULAC

Imulac is for use as a colostrum replacer or supplement for calves when intake of colostrum by the new born calf is in doubt. Imulac can be used to boost the effect of weak colostrum. It can also be used during times of stress such as transportation.

Imulac contains antibodies from colostrum collected from cows in at least their third lactation. Some of the fat and sugars are removed to concentrate the antibodies which fight against infection in the calf.

**How to use**  Feed to the calf as you would milk either from a bucket, bottle or automatic dispenser. Imulac is in a convenient ready to use form.

**How much**  If the calf has received no colostrum from the dam feed 50 ml within 12 hours of birth. If the cow's colostrum is weak or insufficient feed 25 ml within 18 hours of birth.

**Other**  Imulac is supplied as a liquid concentrate in 250 ml bottles. Each pack carries a best before date.

**Supplier**  Alan Haythornthwaite Tel 0772 634782
Price available on request from supplier.

**Accepted**  Acceptable to most organisations with special permission, but not GCFP.

**Use**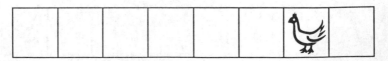

Products for Animals

# KEMPRO DRY

> Kempro Dry is used to improve feed utilisation in all types of animals. It contains the yeast *Saccharomyces cervisiae* at a concentration of 2.5 billion active cells per gram. The yeast accelerate the metabolism of sugars and starch substrates for most animals. In ruminants like cattle and sheep the mopping up of available sugars in the rumen usually at a peak after a feed of concentrates prevents the production of acids that slow the digestion. The feed therefore passes through the rumen more quickly and feed intake is increased.

**How to use** Mix into the feed or add to feed supplements. It is also suitable for top dressing onto the daily ration.

**How much** For mixing into feed include 400 - 1000 grams per tonne. This allows for an intake of 2 kg per day of the mixed feed.

**Other** Kempro Dry is supplied as a powder in 25 kg bags. Store in a cool, dry place preferably in the dark.

**Supplier** Kemin (UK) Ltd Tel 0522 514148
Price on application to supplier.

Use

# KEMZYME DRY

Kemzyme is used to improve animal production in pigs and poultry. More eggs are produced by layers and more meat by pigs and broilers. It also reduces wetness in manure. The use of Kemzyme Dry allows the use of cheaper feeds and so gives more flexibility in feed formulation.

Kemzyme contains a blend of specific enzymes that supplement the animals own enzyme activity to release more nutrients from the feed. The blend includes glucanase which is not produced by the animals and allows the digestion of glucans in the feed that would otherwise pass unaffected through the gut.

**How to use** Kemzyme Dry can be mixed into the feed and is suitable for use with either dry or liquid feed. It has been used with a variety of feed formulations including wheat, barley, sorghum and maize with benefits seen in low fat formulations.

**How much** Include 500 grams per tonne of feed.

**Other** Kemzyme is supplied as a powder.

**Supplier** Kemin (UK) Ltd Tel 0522 514148
Price on application to supplier.)

**Use**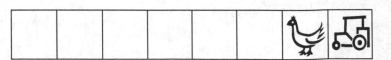

Products for Animals

# LACTOBOOST

Lactoboost for use during rearing of calves to reduce the risk of gut infections which cause scours and other digestive disorders.

Lactoboost contains the bacteria *Enterococcus faecium* (the new name for *Streptococcus faecium*). the bacteria produce lactic acid which reduces the gut pH making conditions unfavourable to pathogens such as *E. Coli*. The bacteria compete directly with pathogen for available nutrients and also coat the lining of the gut making it more difficult for the pathogens to attack the gut wall.

| | |
|---|---|
| **How to use** | Mix with colostrum or milk and feed as you would a normal milk feed either by bucket or machine. Alternatively can be mixed with water and administered as a drench. |
| **How much** | Feed 5 grams per head per day for a minimum of 14 days. |
| **Other** | Lactoboost is supplied as a powder in 100 gram sachets and is sold as 6 sachets in a box. Lactoboost has a shelflife of 12 months if kept in cool dry conditions. |
| **Supplier** | Tithebarn Ltd Tel 0704 60606 |
| | Price for 1 box (600 grams) - £21.00 |
| **Accepted** | Acceptable to most organisations with special permission, but not GCFP. |

Use

# LACTO-SACC

Lacto-sacc is used to prevent of E.Coli scours and to stimulate feed intake in pigs and poultry.

Lacto-sacc contains *Lactobacillus acidophilus, Streptococcus faecium, Lactobacillus bifidus, Saccharomyces cerevisiae* and enzymes. The bacteria produce lactic acid from sugars in the gut which suppress the growth of pathogens which prefer alkaline conditions. The yeast stimulates feed intake and improves digestion.

**How to use** Mix into the finished feed.

**How much** Home mixer pack is less concentrated than compounders pack. For sows, boars and growers mix 2.5 kg of home mix (HM) or 1 kg compound mix (CM) per tonne. For finishers mix in 1.25 kg HM or 0.5 kg per tonne. For piglets include 5 kg HM or 2 kg CM per tonne. For poultry include 2.25 kg HM or 0.9 kg CM per tonne.

**Other** Lacto-sacc is supplied as a powder in 2.5 kg home mixer packs or 40 kg compounders packs. Keep in dry conditions and avoid extremes of temperature. Shelflife is 2 years.

**Supplier** Alltech (UK) Tel 0978 660198
Price for 2.5 kg home mixer pack - 39.50
Price for compounders pack on application to supplier.

**Accepted** Acceptable to most organisations with special permission, but not GCFP.

**Use**

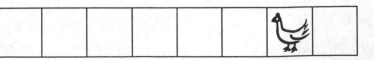

Products for Animals

# MERLICK PURE SEA SALT BLOCKS

Merlick Pure Sea Salt Blocks are used to supply salt and trace elements to all stock. An inadequate supply of sodium (salt) in the plant can have adverse effects on the digestion and production of the stock. The follow-on to a deficiency is usually a loss of appetite and consequent drop in yield or even live weight gain. Fertility can also be affected.

Merlick Pure Sea Salt Blocks provides sodium and contain 55 trace elements. Salt increases the flow of saliva in the mouth and combined with the trace elements has a beneficial effect on the ruminant action. Appetite and forage digestibility are therefore increased.

**How to use** Feed free access.

**How much** Cattle need 3 oz. of salt per day for maintenance and ½ oz. for each gallon of milk produced daily. Sheep need 1 oz. of salt per day. Horses need 2 oz. of salt per day.

**Other** Merlick Pure Sea Salt Blocks are provided in a case of 4 x 5 kg blocks.

**Supplier** Sea Trident Limited Tel 0626 862489
Price on application to supplier.

**Accepted** OFG SA UKROFS GCFP

Use

# ORALIN SFG

> Oralin SFG is for use as an in feed probiotic to replace in-feed antibiotics such as tetracyclines and zinc bacitracin. It will help prevent scours in all livestock without leaving residues.
>
> Oralin SFG contains the bacteria *Enterococcus faecium* (another name for *Streptococcus faecium*) which sticks to the lining of the gut making it difficult for pathogens to attack the gut wall. The *Enterococcus* bacteria compete with pathogenic microbes for available nutrients and produce lactic acid which lowers the gut pH and makes conditions less favourable to pathogens.

**How to use**  Include in the ration by mixing with the feed or milk. As such small amounts are required to be added to a tonne of feed it will be best to make a premix that can be added into the feed at a higher rate to allow more even mixing.

**How much**  For piglets of 6 - 60 kg body weight include 20 grams per tonne of feed. For calves include 40 grams per tonne of feed. For broilers include 80 grams per tonne of feed. For rabbits include 100 -150 grams per tonne of feed.

**Other**  Oralin SFG is supplied packed in 2 kg multi-walled aluminium sachets. Keep cool and dry during storage.

**Supplier**  Agil Ltd Tel 0734 785531
Price on application to supplier.

**Accepted**  Acceptable to most organisations with special permission, but not GCFP.

**Use**

|  |  |  |  |  |  | 🐔 |
|---|---|---|---|---|---|---|

# ORO GLO

Oro Glo is used to pigment egg yolk. Modern consumers generally prefer an egg yolk colour of golden yellow or orange and Oro Glo allow the producer to obtain consistent yolk colour to meet these requirements.

Oro Glo contains a natural pigment called xanthophyll which is collected from the marigold plant. Xanthophylls or carotenoids are chemically related to fats and can suffer from oxidation (which causes rancidity in fats). After harvesting the xanthophylls are processed to protect them from oxidation and bleaching.

**How to use** Oro Glo is suitable for use in solid or liquid feed systems. Mix into the feed at the required rate depending on the level of pigmentation required.

**How much** For layers use a minimum of 100 grams of Oro Glo Layer Dry with 2 grams of yellow xanthophylls added per tonne. A supplement of red xanthophylls will also be required depending on the depth of colour required. Alternatively Oro Glo Liquid can be used. For broilers use Oro Glo Broiler Dry allowing 20 - 25 grams per tonne for slight pigmentation and 25 - 35 grams per tonne for good pigmentation. More than 35 grams per tonne will give high levels of pigmentation. Alternatively use Oro Glo Liquid.

**Other** Oro Glo is available in two powder forms; Oro Glo Layer Dry and Oro Glo Broiler Dry neither of which is water soluble. A liquid form is also available which is water or oil soluble. Oro Glo will keep for about 4 months.

**Supplier** Kemin (UK) Ltd Tel 0522 514148
Price on application to supplier.

**Use**

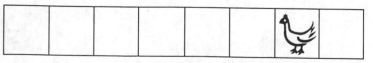

# OVICOL

Ovicol is used to boost the newborn lamb's intake of colostrum and by supplementing with a probiotic, vitamins and minerals to give a good start to life that helps to protect the lamb against infections.

Ovicol contains a concentrated form of antibodies obtained from the colostrum of cows in at least their third lactation. A bacterial probiotic of *Streptococcus faecium* is also included to initiate the gut with beneficial bacteria which create conditions in the gut which will kill any pathogens. Vitamins and minerals are also added to enhance the effect of the colostrum antibodies.

**How to use** The bolus can be given at birth and at any time when the animal is stressed for example during transportation, or a change of ration. It is also suitable to use after orally administered antibiotic treatment to restore the balance of bacteria in the gut. Place the tablet on the back of the tongue and ensure that it is swallowed.

**How much** Give the lamb 1 -2 tablets at birth and administer again on the second day if the lamb is weak.

**Other** Ovicol is supplied as 50 0.8 gram tablets in a resealable bottle.

**Supplier** Alan Haythornthwaite Tel 0772 634782
Price on application to supplier.

**Accepted** Acceptable to most organisations with special permission, but not GCFP.

Use

# POULTRY-LYTE

Poultry-lyte is used to prevent E.Coli scours and promote healthy gut flora in poultry.
   Poultry-lyte contains *Lactobacillus acidophilus, Streptococcus faecium*, Vitamins A, D₃, E, K, and B, organic acids and electrolytes. The bacteria produce lactic acid which acidifies gut promoting beneficial bacteria and suppressing alkali-favouring pathogens. Poultry-lyte also supplies vitamins.

**How to use** Mix into drinking water.

**How much** Mix 1 gram per litre in drinking water and allow for :
            first 7 days after arrival from hatchery.
            1 day per week throughout growing period.
            3-5 days at times of stress or after antibiotic treatment.

**Other**     Poultry-lye is supplied as a powder in 4 kg packs. Keep dry and avoid extremes of temperature. Shelflife 2 years.

**Supplier**  Alltech (UK) Tel 0978 660198
            Price for 4 kg pack - £44.00

**Accepted**  Acceptable to most organisations with special permission, but not GCFP.

**Use**

# SEAQUIM

---

Seaquim is used for improving fertility and production (growth, milk yield, etc) in all classes of livestock. It can also be fed during times of stress to help overcome any setback.

    Seaquim contains the seaweed *Ascophyllum nodosum* which provides the stock with minerals, trace elements and amino acids ensuring that the animal is not deficient of these nutrients. Trace elements have various effects on health, growth, milk production and fertility.

---

**How to use** Feed free access, spread over the ration or incorporate into home mixes.

**How much** For routine feeding, feed daily at a rate of 0.05 % - 0.066 % of the body weight, ie allow 0.5 - 0.66 gram per kg liveweight. For example a 600 kg cow should be fed 300 - 400 grams per day. A 20 kg lamb should receive 10 - 13 grams per day. At times of stress feed at a rate of 0.1 % of body weight ie 1 gram per kg liveweight. The 600 kg cow therefore receives 600 grams per day and the 20 kg lamb receives 20 grams per day.

**Other** Seaquim is supplied as a powdered seaweed meal in 25 kg bags.

**Supplier** Glenside Organics Ltd Tel 0786 816655

Price on application to supplier.

**Accepted** Acceptable to most organisations with special permission, but not GCFP.

**Use**

# SEAWEED MEAL

Seaweed Meal is for use as a health and feed supplement for livestock to supply minerals and trace elements. In cattle fed Seaweed Meal improvements in fertility and coat condition have been seen together with increases in production. It carries Soil Association and Conservation Grade symbols.

Seaweed Meal contains a blend of seaweed collected from unpolluted rivers and oceans. The seaweeds are processed and blended to provide a consistent product. The blend of seaweeds supplies minerals, trace elements and amino acids that are essential to balance the feed ration.

**How to use** Seaweed Meal can be fed free access or mixed with the ration. It is an suitable supplement for hay, silage and concentrate rations.

**How much** Allow 0.25 - 0.5 lb (120 - 240 grams) per head per day. 1 tonne would feed 40 to 80 cattle over the winter period.

**Other** Seaweed Meal is supplied in bulk.

**Supplier** Sea Trident Ltd Tel 0626 862489
Price on application to supplier.

**Accepted** OFG SA UKROFS GCFP

**Use**

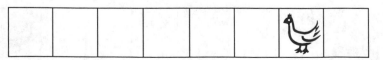

# S/F PLUS

S/F Plus is used to promote a healthier bacterial balance in the gut. It is particularly useful when stock are new born or stressed due to weaning or movement. It is suitable for use in pigs, beef and dairy cattle, sheep, poultry, mink, fox and horses. S/F Plus is also used in mink and fox fur ranching to ensile offals.

S/F Plus contains *Streptococcus faecium* which produces lactic acid from sugars present in the gut which lowers the gut pH and prevents the growth of pathogenic bacteria. When used with offal the production of lactic acid protects the offal from microbial degradation.

**How to use**  S/F Plus can be fed by mixing into the feed, milk or drinking water. Alternatively it can be top dressed onto the ration.

**How much**  Amount to use will depend on the method by which the probiotic is to be fed and also on the animal species concerned. Generally mix in 1 packet per tonne of feed.

**Other**  S/F Plus is supplied as a powder in 1 gram packets.

**Supplier**  Nutrimix Tel 0253 730888
Price on application to supplier.

**Accepted**  Acceptable to most organisations with special permission, but not GCFP.

**Use**

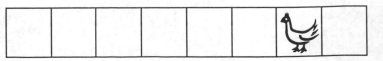

# SMARTE BRAND DCW CONCENTRATE

D

Smarte Brand DCW Concentrate is a colostrum concentrate suitable for use as a total replacer for colostrum in newborn calves, piglets and lambs or as a booster to weak colostrum.

DCW Concentrate has been developed by Smarte International in Canada. Colostrum is collected from dairy cows that are in at least their third lactation. Most of the fat and some of the sugar is removed to leave a whey that is then dried by a process that pasturises the product but leaves the antibodies that pass on immunity intact and in a concentrated form.

**How to use**  Mix the powder with warm water, milk or milk replacer that are unmedicated. Feed either by bucket, bottle or automatic feeder as you would normal colostrum when the quantity or quality of colostrum received by the newborn is in doubt. For all stock feed as soon after birth as possible and for piglets feed for the first two days of life.

**How much**  For newborn calves feed 2 - 3 oz in 1 - 2 pints of milk or replacer. For newborn lambs feed 1 - 2 oz in 1 - 2 pints of milk or replacer. For lambs and calves when some colostrum has been received feed 1 oz in 1 - 2 pints milk or replacer. For newborn piglets allow 0.5 oz (15 gram) per piglet and either mix into milk fed through automatic feeder or mix with 0.5 pint of sow milk replacer and feed by bottle.

**Other**  Smarte Brand DCW Concentrate is supplied in 1 lb, 5 lb, 20 lb and 50 lb quantities and comes with a 2 oz measuring scoop. The product should be stored in dry conditions where extremes of temperature are avoided and will keep for upto two years.

**Supplier**  Alan Haythornthwaite Tel 0772 634782
Price available on request from the supplier.

**Accepted**  Acceptable to most organisations with special permission, but not GCFP.

**Use**

| | | | | | | | |
|---|---|---|---|---|---|---|---|
| | | | | | | 🐓 | |

# SWINE-LYTE

Swine-lyte is used to prevent E.coli scours and to promote a healthy gut flora and replace vitamins at times of stress for piglets and growers.

Swine-lyte contains *Lactobacillus acidophilus* and *Streptococcus faecium*, vitamins A, $D_3$, E, K, B and Organic acids. The bacteria acidify the gut promoting beneficial bacteria and suppressing pathogens that can proliferate in an alkaline gut. The addition of enzymes and organic acids increases digestive enzyme activity.

**How to use**

**How much** Mix 1 gram per litre of drinking water and make available for:
first 7 days after birth.
1 day per week throughout growing period.
3-5 days at times of stress or after antibiotic treatment.

**Other** Swine-lyte is supplied as a powder in 4 kg packs. Keep dry and avoid extremes of temperature. Shelflife is 2 years.

**Supplier** Alltech (UK) Tel 0978 660198
Price for 4 kg pack - £44.00

**Accepted** Acceptable to most organisations with special permission, but not GCFP.

**Use**

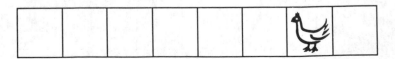

# SURVIVAL PAK

Survival Pak is a feed supplement for newborn pigs and is used to establish a healthy gut flora and give a nutritional boost to the newborn piglet in the first few hours of life.

Survival Pak contains selected trace elements, milk products, vitamins and a combination of micro-organisms (BYM) to start the microbe population of the gut in favour of beneficial bacteria which aid digestion of the feed and prevent the growth of pathogens such as *E. coli*.

**How to use** Mix into water and administer through an oral doser.

**How much** For piglets at birth mix 8 oz with 1.5 pints of water and administer within the first 12 hours of life. For orphaned piglets mix upto a maximum of 1.5 lb per 6 pints of warm water and offer as a free choice.

**Other** Survival Pack id supplied a powder in 5 lb buckets and comes supplied with a measuring cup and doser for oral feeding.

**Supplier** Nutrimix Tel 0253 730888
Price on application to supplier.

**Accepted** Acceptable to most organisations with special permission, but not GCFP.

**Use**

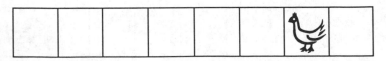

# VITRITION ORGANIC COMPOUND FEEDS

Vitrition Organic Compound Feed are designed to balance homegrown forage to meet the nutritional requirements of livestock under organic, conservation grade or additive free standards. The Managing Director, Angela Bates, has been a member of the Soil Association since 1957 and has recently served on the Producers Committee of the United Kingdom Register of Organic Food Standards (UKROFS).

Vitrition Organic Compound Feeds contain only those products permitted under the specific regulations concerned and the compound feed are individually formulated and produced to balance the requirements of the individual farm and its livestock and the composition of the feed will depend on the production level of the stock, stage of lactation / reproductive cycle, etc.

**How to use**  Feed the compound feed as you would any other - in parlour for dairy cattle and goats, from mangers, etc.

**How much**  The amount to feed will depend on the quality of the forage available as well as the animal species and the level of production or stage of lactation or pregnancy, etc. However Vitrition work within the constraints of the organic regulations that compound feed must be no more than 40% of the dry matter intake. The amount of compound fed is kept to a minimum firstly to comply with the spirit of the organic regulations but also to keep costs down as organic feeds are more expensive to make.

**Other**  VItrition Compound Feeds are available in meal, pellet or nut form. Suitable form of packaging and delivery can be discussed to suit your feeding system.

**Supplier**  Vitrition Ltd 0780 55651
Price will vary depending on formulation and quantity required.

**Accepted**  All

**Use**

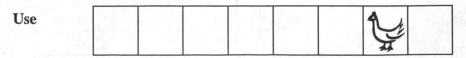

# YEA-SACC

> Yea-Sacc is used for increasing production in livestock either by increasing growth rates or increasing yields of milk and milk solids. It is suitable for use in all ruminants and horses.
> Yea-Sacc contains the yeast *Saccharomyces cerevisiae* which helps to stabilize gut pH. When concentrates are fed for example the rumen becomes very acidic as the sugars released from the feed are turned into acids. The yeast cells utilise the sugars thus preventing acid production. A stable rumen pH stimulates the bacteria that break down the plant cells in the rumen (or caecum in horses) and increases the production of volatile fatty acids which contribute to milk fat production for example. Production of methane gas is reduced increasing in digestibility and feed intake.

**How to use**  Mix in the feed or top dress (sprinkle) onto the ration.

**How much**  For calves before weaning 2 kg per tonne. Beef cattle, sheep and goats should receive between 1 - 2 kg per tonne of feed. Dairy cattle should be allowed 10 grams per head per day and this can be fed top dressed or mixed in the dairy ration at 1 - 1.5 kg per tonne depending on the amount fed. For horses include 2 - 3 kg per tonne of compound feed or top dress 8 grams per head per day on to the oats, bran or cubes.

**Other**  Yea-Sacc is supplied as a powder in 2.5 kg home mixer packs and 40 kg compounder packs. Store in a dry place and avoid exposure to extremes of temperature. In good conditions the product will keep for 2 years.

**Supplier**  Alltech (UK) Tel 0978 660198
Price for 2.5 kg home mixer pack - £8.50
Price for 40 kg compounders pack available on request.

**Accepted**  Acceptable to most organisations with special permission, but not GCFP.

**Use**

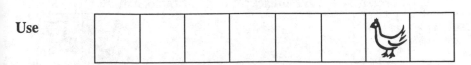

231

# AxpHast

---

AxpHast is a biological silage additive suitable for use on clamp and big bale silage to promote a nutritious and palatable silage. AxpHast is the latest development in biological silage additives from Biotal. AxpHast combines specific strains of bacteria with selected enzymes developed by Enzymatix Ltd. AxpHast contains twice the concentration of bacteria than Supersile Plus. It also includes a nutrient pack that allows the bacteria to begin working before it reaches the crop.

Specific strains of *Pediococcus pentosaceus* and *Lactobacillus plantarum* were selected after extensive screening because they only produce lactic acid from the sugars present in the crop. Enzymes included produce sugars from cellulose material for the bacteria to work on but do not breakdown the cells to release the sap so effluent production is reduced.

---

**How to use** For the premix version - mix with water in a clean container. Mix sachet A and sachet B with 25 litres or 50 litres of water. Spray onto the crop at harvesting. For The granular version - apply the granules through a special granule applicator mounted on the forage harvester.

**How much** For the premix apply 1 litre per tonne if dilution is to 25 litres, or 2 litres per tonne for a dilution to 50 litres. One pack of powder form will treat 25 tonnes of silage. Details for application rates of the granules are not given in the product literature. Enquire from the supplier.

**Other** AxpHast is available either as a soluble powder in 1.6 kg packs for liquid application or as granules for dry application. Store the product in its original container in a cool place (below 15°C) or in a refrigerator or freezer.

**Supplier** Biotal Ltd Tel 0222 766716 and also from
Axis Agricultural Ltd Tel 0785 850941
Price on application and will depend on quantity.

**Accepted** Acceptable to GCFP and SA with special permission. Other organisations are unclear on use of biological additives.

**Use**

| | | | | | |
|---|---|---|---|---|---|

# BIO-DEX

Bio-Dex is a biological silage additive used to create a palatable nutritious silage. It is suited to used on low sugar, low dry matter silages.
  Bio-Dex contains two types of bacteria *Pediococcus* spp and *Lactobacillus* spp selected for their ability to convert sugars quickly to lactic acid. A mix of enzymes are included which increase the level of sugars available to the bacteria and bacteriophages are added to destroy clostridia bacteria that produce butyric acid and cause spoilage.

**How to use** Dissolve 1 sachet of Bio-Dex in 50 litres of water and apply to the crop at the harvester through standard sprayers.

**How much** Apply 2 litres per tonne of the solution as made above. 1 sachet will treat 25 litres of silage.

**Other** Bio-Dex is supplied as a white powder in 125 gram sachets. Stored in a cool dry place Bio-Dex will be active for up to 9 months. Activity levels are guaranteed for 18 months if stored in a deep freeze.

**Supplier** Lever Industrial Ltd Tel 0928 719000
Price on application to supplier.

**Accepted** Acceptable to GCFP and SA with special permission. Other organisations are unclear on use of biological additives.

**Use**

233

# BIO-FERM

Bio-Ferm is a biological silage additive used to promote a rapid fermentation to produce a nutritious palatable silage.

Bio-Ferm contains four strains of lactic acid producing bacteria *Streptococcus faecium*, *Pediococcus* spp and *Lactobacillus plantarum* and *Lactococcus lactis lactis*. Bio-Ferm also contains enzymes that produce sugars for the bacteria to convert to lactic acid which lowers the pH and preserves the crop.

**How to use** This can be applied by powder or liquid application as desired. Apply to the crop at the harvester. For liquid application premix 2 sachets in 4.5 litres of warm water and allow to stand in a warm place to start the bacteria multiplying before further dilution.

**How much** For dry application use 1 bag of powder to 44 tonnes of fresh grass. For liquid application apply 2 sachets (diluted) to 90 tonnes of fresh grass.

**Other** Bio-Ferm is supplied as a powder in 20 kg bags or as a liquid in sachets. After mixing the liquid is stable for 7 days.

**Supplier** Britmilk Tel 0387 75459 also from the following merchants Solway Agriculture; Tarff Valley; Templeton; Pickles; s Gribben; BFS Dunlop; J P Campbell; R McCoull; L S Smellie; Ian Crawford Farm Supplies; Scotts; Tynedale Farm Services; Borderland Supplies and Tom Jefferson.
Price on application to supplier.

**Accepted** Acceptable to GCFP and SA with special permission. Other organisations are unclear on use of biological additives.

**Use**

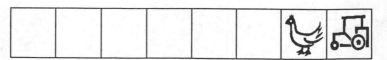

# BIO-SILE

Bio-Sile is a biological silage additive for producing a rapid fermentation and a palatable silage. It is suitable for clamp silage of 15% - 30% dry matter and shows reduced effluent production.

Bio-Sile contains amylase, xylanase and cellulase, enzymes which breakdown the fibrous material to produce sugars. These sugars can then be converted by the added bacteria *Lactobacillus plantarum* and *Pediococcus acidilactica* into lactic acid. The pH drops and the crop is preserved.

**How to use** Apply either as a powder through a suitable powder applicator or as a solution of 1 kg of Bio-Sile liquid into 200 litres of water.

**How much** Apply the powder at a rate of 0.5 kg per tonne of silage. Therefore a 20 kg bag will treat 40 tonnes os silage. Apply the liquid Bio-Sile solution at a rate of 2.5 litre per tonne. 200 litres of mix will treat 90 tonnes of silage.

**Other** Bio-Sile is supplied as a powder in 20 kg bags or as a liquid. Both can be stored for upto 18 months.

**Supplier** Biocon Ltd Tel 0270 665004 and also from
David Nunn Ltd Tel 0939 7555
Price on application and will depend on quantity.

**Accepted** Acceptable to GCFP and SA with special permission. Other organisations are unclear on use of biological additives.

**Use**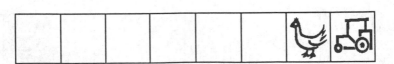

# BIOTAL HAY INOCULANT

---

Biotal Hay Inoculant is used to allow hay to be harvested at higher moisture levels, upto a maximum of 25%, without heating up and preserving more nutrients. It is suitable for use on grass and lucerne hays.

Biotal Hay Inoculant contains two strains of *Pediococcus pentosaceus* bacteria which produce lactic acid which suppresses the growth of spoilage organisms such as moulds that cause heating in the hay.

---

**How to use** Dissolve 100 grams of Hay Inoculant in 20 litres of water and apply 1 litre of solution per tonne of hay. It is best to apply immediately before pick up by the baler or directly into the baling chamber. It is suitable for use with all types of harvesting equipment.

**How much** 1 sachet will treat 20 tonnes of hay.

**Other** Biotal Hay Inoculant is supplied as 100 gram sachets.

**Supplier** Biotal Ltd Tel 0222 766716 and from
Axis Agricultural Ltd Tel 0785 850941
Price on application and will depend on quantity.

**Accepted** Acceptable to GCFP and SA with special permission. Other organisations are unclear on the use of biological additives.

**Use**

Silage Inoculants

# ECOSYL

Ecosyl is a biological silage additive from the agrochemical giant ICI. It is used to improve the feed value and palatability of grass silage.

Ecosyl contains the bacteria *Lactobacillus plantarum* which produces lactic acid from available sugars in the crop. The lactic acid lowers the pH of the silage making conditions unfavourable to spoilage organisms such as *Clostridia* bacteria.

After many years of insisting that silage inoculants were ineffective and that only the acids sold by ICI and others were of benefit in silage making, the company claims to have identified a truly useful product. Trials data is available showing this product to perform better than some of its competitors.

This product is significant in that ICI is one of the world's largest chemical companies and this is their only contribution to Green Growing at present, although the company is working on its own versions of other Green Products.

**How to use** Dilute with water and spray onto the crop at the harvester. If preferred Ecosyl can be applied as a powder.

**How much** For liquid application dilute one bottle of Ecosyl with 100 litres of water and apply to 33 tonnes of fresh forage. For powder application apply 0.5 kg per tonne 1 bag therefore treats 40 tonnes of silage.

**Other** Ecosyl is supplied as a liquid in 33 tonne treatment packs. It will retain activity for 6 months in an unopened bottle if kept in a cool place. If frozen it will keep for 2 years. After mixing the liquid will keep for 3 days. Ecosyl powdered for is supplied in 20 kg bags. It will keep for 12 months in sealed bags, use within 7 days of opening.

**Supplier** ICI Ltd Tel 0642 523680
Price on application to supplier.

**Accepted** All

**Use**

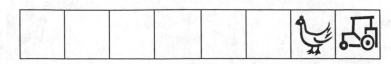

# EXCELLEX

Excellex is an enzyme silage additive for increasing sugar levels in grass and other ensiled crop so that naturally present bacteria can reduce pH more rapidly and so that the silage is sweet and therefore palatable. It is suitable for clamp and bale silage and for material of the dry matter range 15% - 40%.

Excellex contains sugar releasing enzymes which breakdown the cellulose and other fibrous material to produce sugars which can then be converted by bacteria into lactic acid which in turn reduces the pH and preserves the crop. Excess sugars are also produced making the silage sweet and very palatable. The enzyme activity also makes the fibre more digestible. If the naturally present bacteria are inefficient the pH may not be stabilized allowing the fermentation to be taken over by bacteria that produce a butyric acid and ammonia which raise the pH and render the silage unpalatable. Big bale silage and the clamp face are vulnerable to spoilage by mould and the fungus will grow more rapidly when there is free sugar available.

**How to use**  Apply through a clean calibrated applicator preferably during the chopping stage on a precision chopper. Accuracy of application will be increased by diluting with water. Mix 1 part of Excellex to 7 parts of water. For example empty 25 litres into a 200 litre tank and top up with water.

**How much**  A 25 litre drum will treat 100 tonnes of silage. Apply 2 litres per tonne of the 17 Excellex solution.

**Other**  Excellex is supplied in 25 litre drums. Once diluted it is ready for immediate use and will remain stable for upto 90 days if stored as directed on the drum. Undiluted it is stable for 1 year.

**Supplier**  Berk Ltd Tel 0256 64711

Price on application and will depend on quantity. treatment will cost approximately £2 per tonne.

**Accepted**  Acceptable to GCFP and SA with special permission. Other organisations are unclear on the use of biological additives.

**Use**

|  |  |  |  |  | 🐓 | 🚜 |
|--|--|--|--|--|--|--|

# FORAGER<sup>+</sup>

Forager<sup>+</sup> is for use on all silage crops under UK conditions to produce a good quality silage. The attractive spiral bound product literature warns us that Forager<sup>+</sup> "cannot be expected to improve hopelessly poor grass" which of course is true of all silage additives whether biological or acid.

Forager<sup>+</sup> contains three strains of bacteria, namely *Lactobacillus plantarum*, *Streptococcus faecium* and *Pediococcus acidilacti*. The bacteria are microencapsulated (coated) to ensure viability for longer storage time. Forager<sup>+</sup> also contains enzymes to release sugars for the bacteria to make into lactic acid; Vitamin B and yeast extracts to promote rapid bacterial growth and clostridophages to kill the clostridia bacteria that cause butyric spoilage.

**How to use**  Mix Forager<sup>+</sup> powder with water in a clean bucket and make up to the required amount in the spray tank. Mix 1 sachet with 100 litres of water. As most applicators have 200 litre tanks use two sachets with a full tank of water. Apply to the crop at the harvester through standard applicator that have been calibrated to apply 2.5 litres of mix per tonne. Alternatively Forager<sup>+</sup> can be applied as a solid via a granule applicator.

**How much**  1 sachet will treat 40 tonnes of silage. For granular application apply 0.5 kg per tonne. 1 bag of granules will treat 40 tonnes of silage.

**Other**  Forager<sup>+</sup> is supplied as a powder for liquid application in 400 gram sachets or as a granule in 20 kg bags. It will remain effective for 18 months in sealed containers. Once opened all the contents should be used.

**Supplier**  Shell Chemicals UK Ltd Tel 0480 414140
Price on application to supplier.

**Accepted**  Acceptable to GCFP and SA with special permission. Other organisations are unclear on use of biological additives.

**Use**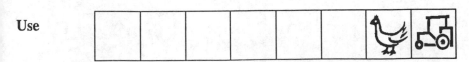

# GRASS-SILE

Grass-Sile is a biological silage additive suitable for use on clamp and big bale silage to promote a nutritious and palatable silage. Grass-Sile combines a specific strain of bacteria with selected enzymes developed by Enzymatix Ltd. Grass-Sile contains a lower total concentration of bacteria than Supersile Plus or AxpHast even when allowing for the inclusion of only one strain of bacteria.

The bacteria chosen is a strain of *Pediococcus pentosaceus*, selected after extensive screening because it only produces lactic acid from the sugars present in the crop and rapidly reduces pH to about 4.. Enzymes included produce sugars from cellulose material for the bacteria to work on but do not breakdown the cells to release the sap so effluent production is reduced.

| | |
|---|---|
| **How to use** | Mix the contents of the sachet with water in a clean container. Use 25 litres or 50 litres of water for each sachet. Apply to the forage through a suitable applicator fixed to the harvester. |
| **How much** | Apply 1 litre per tonne if dilution is to 25 litres, or 2 litres per tonne for a dilution to 50 litres. One sachet will treat 25 tonnes of silage. |
| **Other** | Grass-Sile is available as a soluble powder in 150 gram packs for liquid application. If required it can also be supplied in granular form for dry application. Store the product in its original container in a cool place (below 15°C) or in a refrigerator or freezer. |
| **Supplier** | Biotal Ltd Tel 0222 766716 and also from Axis Agricultural Ltd Tel 0785 850941 Price on application and will depend on quantity. |
| **Accepted** | Acceptable to GCFP and SA with special permission. Other organisations are unclear on use of biological additives. |

**Use**

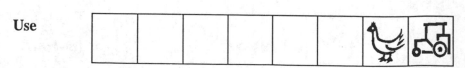

# H/M INOCULANT

H/M Inoculant is used to reduce effluent and conserve dry matter for better silage that is higher in nutrient value and more palatable.

H/M Inoculant contains strains of bacteria, *Streptococcus faecium* and *Lactobacillus plantarum* and *Pediococcus acidlactica* that multiply rapidly and produce lactic acid resulting in a fast and effective fermentation.

**How to use** Apply as a solid through granule applicators or as a liquid after mixing with water through a suitable sprayer mounted on the harvester. Mix with sufficient water to give even coverage of the crop foe example mix 1 sachet with 10 litres of water and apply at a rate of 1 litre per tonne.

**How much** For solid application apply 0.5 kg per tonne of forage. For liquid application 1 sachet of powder will treat 10 tonnes of silage.

**Other** H/M Inoculant is supplied as a granule in 20 kg plastic lined paper bags, or as a powder in sachets.

**Supplier** Nutrimix Tel 0253 730888
Price on application to supplier.

**Accepted** Acceptable to GCFP and SA with special permission. Other organisations are unclear on use of biological additives.

**Use**

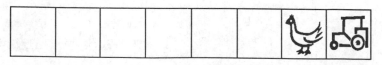

# KEM LAC

> Kem Lac is used to allow a good quality, palatable silage to be made even in poor weather conditions and to allow a short wilt period.
>
> Kem Lac contains the bacteria *Lactobacillus plantarum*, *Lactobacillus acidophilus* and *Lactobacillus bulgaricus*. All three strains of bacteria produce lactic acid from sugars present in the crop. A nutrient mix is included to get the bacteria off to a good start and amylase and cellulase enzymes are added to increase the supply of sugars to the bacteria. Lactic acid produced by the bacteria lowers the pH of the forage and prevents the growth of spoilage organisms.

**How to use**    Dissolve Kem Lac in warm water (25 - 30°C) as this will stimulate the bacteria to begin growing. Apply by spraying onto the forage crop in the harvester.

**How much**    Mix 1 sachet of Kem Lac with 25 litres of water and apply 2 litres per tonne of forage. One sachet will therefore treat 12.5 tonnes of forage and the sachets contents have been measured to treat 1 hectare of crop as the average yield of grass for silage cropping in Holland is 12.5 tonnes per hectare.

**Other**    Kem Lac is supplied as a soluble powder in 125 gram sachets which are further packed in 200 gram boxes. The presence of the nutrient mix allows the bacteria to remain active for three days after the mix has been made. Unopened the bacteria will be viable for 18 months.

**Supplier**    Kemin (UK) Ltd Tel 0522 514148
Price on application to supplier.

**Accepted**    Acceptable to GCFP and SA with special permission. Other organisations are unclear on use of biological additives.

**Use**

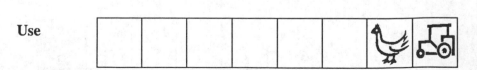

# LACTOMOL

Lactomol is a biological silage additive for use with molasses on all silage crops to produce a rapid fermentation and a palatable silage. Not surprisingly this product comes from Rumenco a division of Tate and Lyle.
  Lactomol contains lactic acid producing bacteria *Lactobacillus plantarum* and *Pediococcus acidilactica*. The application of molasses with Lactomol provides sugars for the bacteria to convert to lactic acid. In trials activity of the Lactomol bacteria was shown to be limited by insufficient sugar levels. Inclusion of molasses allowed the bacteria to lower clamp pH in 4 days and the resultant silage was very palatable due to the high sugar levels. Clostridiaphages are also included to kill the clostridia bacteria that cause butyric spoilage.

**How to use** Dissolve 1 pack of Lactomol with 4.5 - 9 litres of water (1 - 2 gallons). Mix this premix solution into 200 litres of molasses (44 gallons) in the molasses applicator. Stir the mix to ensure even distribution of the bacteria. The mix can be sprayed onto the crop at the harvester or in the clamp.

**How much** Apply 9 litres per tonne of the Lactomol molasses mix. 1 pack will treat 22 tonnes of silage, and will require 200 litres of molasses. 9 packs will treat approximately 200 tonnes of silage, and will require 1800 litres of molasses.

**Other** Lactomol is supplied as a powder in 1 kg packs.

**Supplier** Rumenco Tel 0283 511211
Price on application to supplier.

**Accepted** Acceptable to GCFP and SA with special permission. Other organisations are unclear on use of biological additives.

**Use**

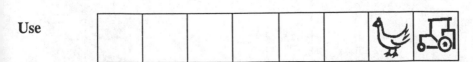

243

# LACTOSILE

Lactosile is a biological silage additive suitable for use on clamp and big bale silage to promote a nutritious and palatable silage. Lactosile has been developed to be suitable for European weather conditions specifically low dry matter and low sugar content grass. Lactosile combines specific strains of bacteria with selected enzymes developed by Enzymatix Ltd and was re-launched in 1990 following further development of the enzyme component and trialing by ADAS of the new mix.

Specific strains of *Pediococcus pentosaceus* and *Lactobacillus plantarum* were selected after extensive screening because they only produce lactic acid from the sugars present in the crop. Enzymes included produce sugars from cellulose material for the bacteria to work on but do not breakdown the cells to release the sap so effluent production is reduced.

**How to use** Mix the contents of both sachets with water and apply to the fresh crop at the harvester. Use either 25 litres or 50 litres of water per sachet set and apply 1 or 2 litres per tonne respectively.

**How much** 1 set of sachets will treat 25 tonnes of silage. An outer pack will treat 100 tonnes of forage.

**Other** Lactosile is supplied as an enzyme mix sachet and a bacterial agent sachet, combined weight 500 grams. Four of each sachet are packed into a box. Lactosile will keep for 18 months if kept sealed in the original container in a cool dry place.

**Supplier** Tithebarn Ltd Tel 0704 60606
Price per 2 kg pack - £135.00

**Accepted** Acceptable to GCFP and SA with special permission. Other organisations are unclear on use of biological additives.

**Use**

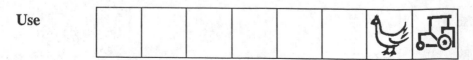

# LIVE SYSTEM SILAGE INOCULANT

Live system silage inoculant is used to Boost bacteria levels on grass to promote rapid pH drop and preservation of the feed material.
Live system silage inoculant contains *Lactobacillus plantarum* a lactic acid producing bacteria. The lactic acid lowers the pH of the crop preventing the growth of spoilage organisms such as clostridia and moulds.

**How to use** Activate culture in 200 ml water and incubate for 20 hours. You will need at least one heater. Transfer to 25 litre drum for further incubation to give $4 \times 10^9$ cfu per ml. Apply through a standard additive applicator at the harvester.

**How much** Apply 2 litres per tonne after diluting with 175 litres of water.

**Other** Live silage inoculant is supplied as a freeze dried culture with a growth medium. Store in a cool dry place. If unopened will keep for 2 years. Once activated will keep for 6-8 weeks if refrigerated.

**Supplier** Genus Animal Health Tel 0905 424940 and also through the Milk Marketing Board.
Price for a pack to treat 100 tonnes of crop - £80.00
Price for a pack to treat 200 tonnes of crop - £160.00

**Accepted** Acceptable to GCFP and SA with special permission. Other organisations are unclear on use of biological additives.

**Use**

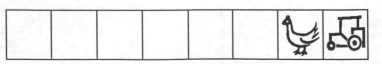

# SAFE-SILE 4

---

Bio-Sile is a biological silage additive for producing a rapid fermentation and a palatable silage. It is suitable for low dry matter silage and shows reduced effluent production.

Bio-Sile contains enzymes which breakdown the fibrous material to produce sugars. These sugars can then be converted by the added bacteria into lactic acid. The pH drops and the crop is preserved. Safe-Sile also includes phages that kill the clostridia bacteria present in the silage. There is some controversy over the effectiveness of these phages. In the clamp the phages will only be active if they are close to the clostridia bacteria and low levels can be brought under control by a rapid pH drop. High levels of clostridia are only likely to occur in silage where soil has inadvertently been included and are unlikely to be kept in check by the phages.

---

**How to use** Apply through standard additive applicators fixed on to the forage harvester.

**How much** Amount to apply are not specified in the literature.

**Supplier** Downland Marketing Ltd Tel 0249 814700
Price on application and will depend on quantity.

**Accepted** Acceptable to GCFP and SA with special permission. Other organisations are unclear on use of biological additives.

**Use**

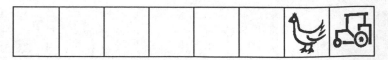

# SIL-ALL

> Sil-All is a biological silage additive used to produce a nutritious and palatable silage. It is suitable for use on grass or legume silage.
> Sil-All contains *Lactobacillus plantarum* and *Streptococcus faecium* bacteria that convert available sugars to lactic acid which preserves the crop. Enzymes which breakdown the cellulose of the plant material to release sugars are included to provide food for the bacteria to work on and another type of enzyme that attacks clostridia bacteria is included.

**How to use**   Mix with water and spray onto the fresh crop at the chopper or blower of the harvester. Alternatively it can be mixed with a carrier and applied as a solid.

**How much**   For liquid application allow 11 grams per tonne of crop, for example a mix of 11 grams of Sil-All per litre of water should be applied at a rate of 1 litre per tonne of crop. For solid application blend with the chosen carrier at a rate of 14 kg per tonne (of carrier) and add to the silage at a rate of 0.5 - 1 kg per tonne. A 90 tonne clamp will require 1 kg of Sil-All.

**Other**   Sil-All is supplied as a powder. Pack sizes vary to meet customer requirements.

**Supplier**   Alltech (UK) Tel 0978 660198
Price on application to supplier and will depend on quantity.

**Accepted**   Acceptable to GCFP and SA with special permission. Other organisations are unclear on use of biological additives.

**Use**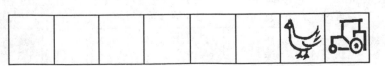

# SUPERSILE PLUS

Supersile Plus is a biological silage additive suitable for use on clamp and big bale silage to promote a nutritious and palatable silage. Supersile Plus has been developed to be specifically suitable for European weather conditions specifically low dry matter and low sugar content grass. Supersile Plus combines specific strains of bacteria with selected enzymes developed by Enzymatix Ltd and was re-launched in 1990 following further development of the enzyme component and trialing by ADAS of the new mix.

Specific strains of *Pediococcus pentosaceus* and *Lactobacillus plantarum* were selected after extensive screening because they only produce lactic acid from the sugars present in the crop. Enzymes included produce sugars from cellulose material for the bacteria to work on but do not breakdown the cells to release the sap so effluent production is reduced.

**How to use** For the premix version - mix with water in a clean container. Mix sachet A and sachet B with 25 litres or 50 litres of water. Spray onto the crop at harvesting. For The granular version - apply the granules through a special granule applicator mounted on the forage harvester.

**How much** For the premix apply 1 litre per tonne if dilution is to 25 litres, or 2 litres per tonne for a dilution to 50 litres. One pack of powder form will treat 25 tonnes of silage. For the granules apply 400 grams per tonne of fresh forage.

**Other** Supersile Plus is available either as a soluble powder in 500 gram packs for liquid application or as granules for dry application. Store the product in its original container in a cool place (below 15°C) or in a refrigerator or freezer.

**Supplier** Biotal Ltd Tel 0222 766716 and also from
Axis Agricultural Ltd Tel 0785 850941
Price on application and will depend on quantity.

**Accepted** Acceptable to GCFP and SA with special permission. Other organisations are unclear on use of biological additives.

**Use**

| | | | | | | |
|---|---|---|---|---|---|---|

# ACTIVE GREEN

---

Active Green is 100% seaweed extract with added trace elements and has been designed for use on all agricultural and horticultural crops and pasture. Active Green is imported by Botanic Ltd a sister company of May and Dawson.

    Active Green is made from specially selected seaweeds gathered off the coast of New Zealand. The area is free from pollution. The seaweed contains a balance of cytokinins, amino acid, sugars, starches and growth regulators which promote plant growth. A stabiliser is added to prevent degradation of the product during storage.

---

**How to use**  Apply by spraying or trickle irrigation. It is best to apply during the spring as the plants begin to grow. Do not apply in hot sunlight.

**How much**  For normal spraying apply 5 - 10 litres per ha ( 3.5 - 7 pints per acre) at a dilution of 1:20 or 1:40. For trickle irrigation add to the system at a dilution of 1:100. For forestry apply at a dilution of 1:50.

**Other**  Active Green is supplied as a liquid in 10 litre containers. Store in warm, dry, frost free conditions.

**Supplier**  Botanic Ltd Tel 0377 71039 and from
WBC Technology Ltd Tel 0799 30146
Price on application to supplier.

**Use**

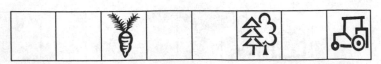

# BASIC SLAG

Basic Slag is used to supply phosphate and lime (calcium) and is suitable for use on all plants but especially root crops which have high phosphorus and calcium requirements. It helps promote a healthy green colouration. Basic Slag is a waste product from the iron and steel industry and was once readily available in the Uk. With the closing of many of the steel works and changes to the processes involved in British steel making has resulted in most of the basic slag now available being from imported sources. When the iron ore is heated to release the metal the minerals are made more available. The rock is then crushed which increases the surface area of the rock available for release of the minerals.

**How to use**  Sprinkle onto the soil and hoe or rake in. Apply to lawns after the last cut of the year to promote a good colour and strong root for next year. Be careful not to over dose as too much phosphate can lock up other minerals.

**How much**  For root crops apply 4 - 8 oz per square yard. For lawns apply 2 - 4 oz per square yard. A 25 kg bag will therefore cover 200 - 400 square yards.

**Other**  Basic Slag is supplied as ground rock in 3 kg, 6 kg and 25 kg bags.

**Supplier**  Chempak Products Tel 0992 441888
Price for 3 kg - £2.20
Price for 6 kg - £3.85
Price for 25 kg - £9.50

**Accepted**  All

Use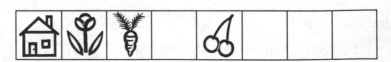

# BIO FRIENDLY BONE MEAL

Bio Friendly Bone Meal is a new product from Pan Britannica Industries Ltd which claims to be a 100% organic fertiliser but the actual ingredients are not included in the product literature. It releases its nutrients slowly into the soil and can be used on all plants in the garden. Bone Meal was one of man's first fertilisers and its effectiveness has been proved over many generations.

**How to use**  This fertiliser is ideal for soil preparation and should be dug or worked into the soil before planting any garden plants.

**How much**  For general use 1 kg would treat 9 - 18 sq yd, 3 kg would treat 26 - 53 sq yd and 6 kg would treat 53 -106 sq yd.

**Other**  Bio Friendly Bone Meal is supplied as a powder in a 1 kg carton and a 3 or 6 kg polybag.

**Supplier**  Pan Britannica Industries Limited Tel 0992 23691
Bio Friendly products are also available by many garden centres and department stores.
Price for 1 kg - £1.99 (1990 price)
Price for 3 kg - £3.75 (1990 price)
Price for 6 kg - £6.89 (1990 price)

**Accepted**  All

**Use**

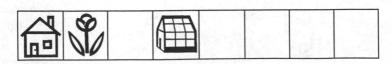

# BIO FRIENDLY PLANT FOOD

Bio Friendly Plant Food is a new product from Pan Britannica Industries Ltd which claims to be a 100% organics and minerals, but the actual ingredients are not included in the product literature. It is fortified with 2 natural minerals; Rock Potash and Gypsum, which are mined from the earth.

Bio Friendly Plant Food provides humus, nitrogen and phosphate by including in this Plant Food; Fish Meal, Blood Meal, Bone Flour & Seaweed - all heat treated or steam sterilised to make them safe and to make handling more pleasant.

**How to use**  Sprinkle  on surface of soil and hoe into the ground.
**How much**  Application rates will vary depending on the plants and soil.
**Other**  Bio Friendly Plant Food is supplied as a powder in a 1 kg carton and a 3 or 6 kg polybag.
**Supplier**  Pan Britannica Industries Limited Tel 0992 23691
Bio Friendly products are also available by many  garden centres and department stores.
Price for 1 kg - £1.99 (1990 price)
Price for 3 kg - £3.75 (1990 price)
Price for 6 kg - £6.89 (1990 price)
**Accepted**  All

**Use**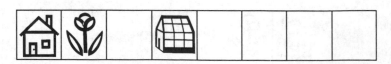

# BIO FRIENDLY UNIVERSAL COMPOST

F

Bio Friendly Universal Compost is a new product from Pan Britannica Industries Ltd which claims to be a 100% natural, but the actual ingredients are not included in the product literature. It contains all major plant foods - nitrogen, phosphate and potash in a peat base. These elements together with magnesium and calcium are sourced entirely from organics and minerals. It can be used for sowing seeds, potting-up, growing in tubs and in hanging baskets.

**How to use** Mix the required amount of compost into the soil surrounding the plant.

**How much** Application rates will vary depending on the plants and soil.

**Other** Bio Friendly Universal Compost is supplied as a loose material in 3 sizes of pack. These are a No.1 size polybag which is 3.5 litres when packed, a No.2 size polybag which is 10 litres when packed and a No.3 polybag which is 20 litres when packed.

**Supplier** Pan Britannica Industries Limited Tel 0992 23691
Bio Friendly products are also available by many garden centres and department stores.
Price for No.1 size - £1.22 (1990 price)
Price for No.2 size - £2.95 (1990 price)
Price for No.3 size - £4.75 (1990 price)

**Accepted** All

**Use**

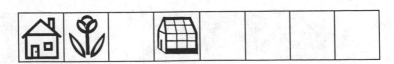

253

# BLOOD FISH AND BONE MEAL

> Blood Fish and Bone Meal is for use as general fertiliser for annual plants.
> It can also be used as a lawn feed in spring or early summer, and to top
> dress shrubs and fruit, etc where compost or manure is not available.
> Blood Fish and Bone Meal provides nitrogen and phosphate and has an
> analysis of 3.5% nitrogen and 8% phosphate. The nutrients will be
> released by microbial activity in the soil with the nitrogen from blood
> being released fairly rapidly as it is in a soluble form while the nutrients
> released from the fish and bone meal will be released more slowly.

| | |
|---|---|
| How to use | Apply not more than two weeks before sowing or planting. Sprinkle onto the surface of the soil and hoe or fork into the surface. Can also be top dressed later on in the season by sprinkling along close to the plants and gently hoeing in. |
| **How much** | Apply 4 - 6 oz per square yard. |
| **Other** | Blood Fish and Bone Meal is supplied as a powder in 2 kg and 20 kg bags. |
| **Supplier** | HDRA Sales Ltd Tel 0203 303517 (Ryton shop only) and from Suffolk Herbs Ltd Tel 0787 227247<br>Price for 2 kg from HDRA shop - £2.79 (1990 price)<br>Price for 20 kg from HDRA shop - £22.00 (1990 price)<br>Price for 2 kg from Suffolk Herbs - £3.10 |
| **Accepted** | All |

Use

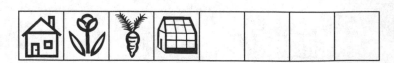

# BONE MEAL

Bone meal is for use as a slow release source of phosphate. It can be used to grow vegetables on poor, light soil. The main use is when planting fruit, vines, roses and shrubs especially where phosphate levels are low. Bone Meal is produced by crushing bones and heat treating to sterilise it, this also serves to make the phosphate more available. Bone meal is broken down slowly in the soil by microbial activity and by acids leached out of the plant roots.

**How to use**  Apply to the surface of the soil and gently work into the top soil. When planting roses or shrubs, etc sprinkle some meal into the hole before placing the plant in position.

**How much**  For vegetables on poor light land apply 3 -4 oz per square yard. For fruit, vines, roses and shrubs apply 2 - 6 ox per square yard.

**Other**  Bone meal is supplied as a granular powder in 3 kg, 6 kg and 25 kg bags.

**Supplier**  Chempak Products Tel 0992 441888
Price for 3 kg - £3.15
Price for 6 kg - £5.50
Price for 25 kg - £18.50

**Accepted**  OFG SA UKROFS GCFP

**Use**
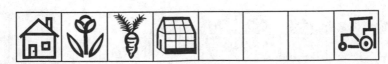

# BONE MEAL AND BONE FLOUR

Bone meal and Bone flour are for use as slow release sources of phosphate. Both products can be of use to vegetables grown on poor light soil and their main use is when planting fruit, vines, roses and shrubs especially where phosphate levels are low.

Both products contain bone but the two products are ground to a different fineness. The flour, being finer particles, begins to release phoshate at an earlier stage of approximately one month after application. The meal takes longer to release the phosphate but will have a longer term effect. This is because the flour has a larger surface area for microbes to attack so breakdown occurs quicker. Some nitrogen will also be released.

**How to use**  Apply to the surface of the soil and gently work into the top soil. When planting roses or shrubs, etc sprinkle some meal or flour into the hole before placing the plant in position.

**How much**  For vegetables on poor light land apply 3 -4 oz per square yard. For fruit, vines, roses and shrubs apply 2 - 6 ox per square yard.

**Other**  Bone meal is supplied as a granular powder in 1.5 kg and 20 kg bags. Bone flour is supplied as a fine powder in 1 kg and 3 kg bags. Both products are produced in the UK from the bones of animals raised in Britain and have been steam sterilised.

**Supplier**  HDRA Sales Ltd Tel 0203 303517 (Ryton shop only) and from Suffolk Herbs Tel 0787 227247 (supply 1.5 kg bone meal only)
Price for 1.5 kg bone meal from Suffolk Herbs - £3.10
Price for 1.5 kg bone meal from HDRA - £1.99 (1990 price)
Price for 20 kg of bone meal - £20.00 (1990 price)
Price for 1 kg bone flour - £1.94 (1990 price)
Price for 3 kg bone flour - £2.39 (1990 price)

**Accepted**  All

**Use**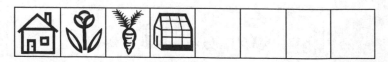

# CALCIFIED SEAWEED

Calcified Seaweed can be used as a soil conditioner. It helps to maintain pH and increase soil friability. The dry matter content of plants is increased and palatability of grass is improved.

Calcified seaweed contains numerous trace elements and minerals which of course includes calcium. The calcium acts as a buffer to Ph change ie it helps the soil resist any change in pH either towards acidity or alkalinity. As the calcium provides this buffering it is only necessary to apply the calcified seaweed every 3 years.

Breakdown of the seaweed in the soil to form humus helps the soil structure formation by holding mineral particles. The trace elements and other nutrients released by microbes in the soil improve plant health and growth.

**How to use**  Calcified seaweed can be applied at any time of the year for most plants and can be used in potting mixes. For lawns apply in spring or autumn.

**How much**  Apply as required. Amount will vary depending on the crop or plant concerned. Generally apply 4 - 8 oz per square yard.

**Other**  Calcified Seaweed is supplied as a fine grade fertiliser in 3 kg, 6 kg and 25 kg bags.

**Supplier**  Chempak Products 0992 441888
Price for 3 kg - £2.20
Price for 6 kg - £3.85
Price for 25 kg - £9.50

**Accepted**  OFG SA UKROFS

**Use**

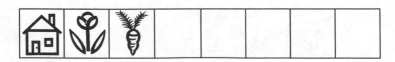

# CALCIFIED SEAWEED

Calcified Seaweed can be use as a soil conditioner. It helps to maintain pH and increase soil friability. The dry matter content of plants is increased and palatability of grass is improved.

Calcified seaweed contains numerous trace elements and minerals which of course includes calcium. The calcium acts as a buffer to pH change ie it helps the soil resist any change in pH either towards acidity or alkalinity. As the calcium provides this buffering it is only necessary to apply the calcified seaweed every 3 years.

Breakdown of the seaweed in the soil to form humus helps the soil structure formation by holding mineral particles. The trace elements and other nutrients released by microbes in the soil improve plant health and growth.

**How to use** Calcified seaweed can be applied at any time of the year to beds and lawns and can be used in potting mixes.

**How much** Apply as required. Amount will vary depending on the crop or plant concerned. Generally apply 66 grams per m².

**Other** Calcified Seaweed is supplied as a fine grade fertiliser in 2 kg, 10 kg and 20 kg bags. It is only available from the HDRA shop at Ryton.

**Supplier** HDRA Sales Ltd Tel 0203 303517 (Ryton shop only) and from Suffolk Herbs Ltd Tel 0787 227247 (2 kg pack only)
Price for 2 kg from Suffolk Herbs - £2.20
Price for 2 kg from HDRA - £1.99 (1990 price)
Price for 10 kg - £9.42 (1990 price)
Price for 20 kg - £21.00 (1990 price)

**Accepted** All

**Use**

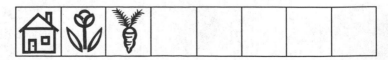

# CALCIFIED SEAWEED

> Calcified Seaweed can be use as a soil conditioner. It helps to maintain pH and increase soil friability. The dry matter content of plants is increased and palatability of grass is improved.
>
> Calcified seaweed contains numerous trace elements and minerals which of course includes calcium. The calcium acts as a buffer to pH change ie it helps the soil resist any change in pH either towards acidity or alkalinity. As the calcium provides this buffering it is only necessary to apply the calcified seaweed every 3 years.
>
> Breakdown of the seaweed in the soil to form humus helps the soil structure formation by holding mineral particles. The trace elements and other nutrients released by microbes in the soil improve plant health and growth.

**How to use**  Calcified seaweed can be applied as any granular (graded pearl) fertiliser. Ground seaweed for powder application may be available on request.

**How much**  2 Oz per square yard
70 grams per
1 small bag per 29 square meters (24 sq yd)
1 medium bag per 140 square meters (116 sq yd)
1 large bag per 285 square meters (236 sq yd)

**Supplier**  Cumulus Organics Ltd Tel 0452 305814 and also
Gala (Broker) Ltd Tel 0244 390712
2kg  (Gala)  10kg  20kg
£1.99 (£2.45)  £8.10   £14.50 + carriage for Cumulus

**Accepted**  All

**Use**

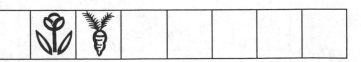

# CALCIFIED SEAWEED

Calcified Seaweed can be use as a soil conditioner. It helps to maintain pH and increase soil friability. The dry matter content of plants is increased and palatability of grass is improved.

Calcified seaweed contains numerous trace elements and minerals which of course includes calcium. The calcium acts as a buffer to pH change ie it helps the soil resist any change in pH either towards acidity or alkalinity. As the calcium provides this buffering it is only necessary to apply the calcified seaweed every 3 years.

Breakdown of the seaweed in the soil to form humus helps the soil structure formation by holding mineral particles. The trace elements and other nutrients released by microbes in the soil improve plant health and growth.

**How to use** Calcified seaweed can be applied as any granular (graded pearl) fertiliser. Ground seaweed for powder application may be available on request.

**How much** For most crops 6 cwt (300 kg) per acre every three years is sufficient.

**Other** Calcified Seaweed is supplied as a graded pearl granule in 50 kg bags and bulk.

**Supplier** Organic Farmers and Growers Ltd Tel 0449 720838
Price 1 tonne in 50 kg bag - £44.00
Price 1 tonne in bulk - £33.00
Delivery is charged extra on these prices.

**Accepted** OFG

**Use**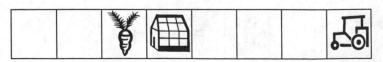

# CARBONATE OF LIME (GROUND CHALK)

**F**

Carbonate of Lime is used to neutralise acid soils and to supply calcium where the soil is deficient.

Carbonate of Lime is made from chalk quarried in the UK. It is crushed and the level of effectiveness will depend on how finely the chalk has been crushed. The finer the particles, the larger the surface area and therefore the quicker the calcium will be released into the soil.

**How to use** Sprinkle onto the soil and hoe or rake into the surface.

**How much** For neutralising acidic soils apply 0.5 - 1 lb per square yard to increase the soil pH by 0.5 units ie from pH 6 to pH 6.5. Amount required will depend on the soil type.

**Other** Carbonate of Lime is supplied as ground rock in 3 kg, 6 kg and 25 kg bags.

**Supplier** Chempak Products Tel 0992 441888
Price for 3 kg - £2.20
Price for 6 kg - £3.85
Price for 25 kg - £7.25

**Accepted** All

**Use**

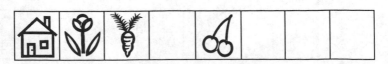

Fertilisers

# CARPHOS

Carphos is a general phosphate and calcium fertiliser and is a useful source of phosphate for acidic soils as the calcium will also help to buffer the soil against a low pH.

As this product will give a slow release of phosphorus as breakdown of the mineral rock in the soil is slow. Both phosphorus and calcium can be held in the soil in association with the electrically charged soil particles either clay or organic matter.

Carphos contains 30.5% $P_2O_5$, 48.1% CaO, 3.7% Fluoride, 0.7% $Fe_2O_3$, 0.4% $Al_2O_3$. Moisture content is 1.3%.

**How to use** Apply through standard spreader.
**How much** An application of 3 - 7 cwt (150 - 350 kg) per acre is recommended. As the phosphate and calcium will be slowly released from the rock and can be held in the soil application need only be repeated every three years.
**Other** Carphos is available in 500 kg big bags or in bulk.
**Supplier** Organic Farmers and Growers Ltd Tel 0449 720838
Price 1 tonne in 500 kg big bags - £99.00
Price 1 tonne in bulk - £89.00
Delivery is charged extra on this price.
**Accepted** OFG

Use

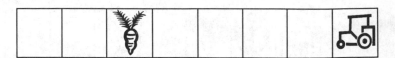

# Carr's Organic Compost

**F**

> This material supplies good rooting material and nutrients. A blend of composts, it keeps indefintiely and is a good general compost. It is supplied as a powder.

**How to use** As normal with compost
**How much** As normal
**Supplier** Cumulus Organics Ltd  Telephone  0452 305814
40 litres for £6.00 + carriage
**Accepted** All

Use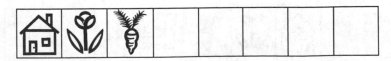

# CHEMPAK MORGRO

> Chempak Morgro is used as a fertiliser and soil conditioner and is suitable for use vegetables, flowers, lawns, roses, greenhouse plants, shrubs, fruit trees and soft fruit.
>
> Chempak Morgro is made in Norfolk and contains dried and composted manures ensuring that it is weed free and sterilised. The addition of manures to the soil stimulates microbial activity in the soil and increases the amount of nutrients available for uptake by the plant. Humus formed by microbial breakdown of the manure helps give structure to the soil by holding particles together.

**How to use** Apply by sprinkling onto the soil and hoe or rake in. Alternatively digest some Morgro in water for a few days and use the resulting liquor as a liquid feed. This can be applied as a foliar spray or as a root feed.

**How much** For general use apply 4 - 6 oz per square yard.

**Other** Chempak Morgro is supplied as a powder in bags.

**Supplier** Chempak Products Tel 0992 441888

Price for 2 - 4 bags - £6.25 each (+ £1.50 carriage)

Price for 5 - 9 bags - £5.75 each (carriage included)

Price for 10 bags or more - £5.50 each (carriage included)

If placing an order over £30  - £4.75 each bag

If placing an order over £10.30 - £5.25 each bag

**Accepted** All

**Use**

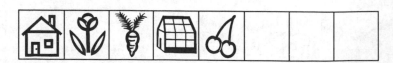

264

# CHILEAN NITRATE OF POTASH

F

---

Chilean Nitrate of Potash is used as a nitrogen and potassium fertiliser and is suitable for use on all plants.

Chilean Nitrate of Potash is produced from natural salt deposits and contains soluble nitrate and potassium. As the nitrogen and potassium are in soluble form they are readily available for uptake by the plants. It also contains chlorine.

---

**How to use** Sprinkle onto the soil and hoe or rake into the surface. Apply early in the year. It can also be used as a liquid feed by making a weak solution in water.

**How much** For general use apply 2 - 4 oz per square yard. For liquid use dissolve 0.5 oz per gallon of water.

**Other** Chilean Nitrate of Potash is supplied in 3 kg, 6 kg and 25 kg bags.

**Supplier** Chempak Products Tel 0992 441888
Price for 3 kg - £2.50
Price for 6 kg - £4.40
Price for 25 kg - £14.50

**Accepted** GCFP

**Use**

# COIR COMPOST

Coir Compost is for use as a peat replacer and is suitable for use in all situations such as sowing and potting composts, tubs and hanging baskets where peat would otherwise be used.

Coir Compost is made entirely from coconut fibres and husks and therefore comes from a completely renewable source. The fibre is very absorbent and so improves the water holding capacity of soils and has an ideal pH for most plants.

**How to use** Reconstitute the Coir block with water to make a workable medium. If required mix with other composts or manures or use a liquid feed when reconstituting.

**How much** Rate of use will depend on the use to which the compost is put, pot size, etc.

**Other** Coir Compost is supplied as compressed fibre blocks about the size of a house brick and weighing 1.5 lb. Each block will swell up to 8 times its original size when moistened. The blocks are available with or with out a nutrient feed in packs of 2, 8 or 24 blocks.

**Supplier** Chempak Products Tel 0992 441888
Price for 2 blocks - £3.95
Price for 8 blocks - £11.95
Price for 24 blocks (without nutrient pack) - £21.20

**Use**

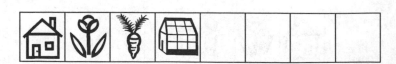

# COMPLETE ORGANIC FERTILISER

Organic complete fertiliser is for use as a slow release nitrogen, phoshorus and potassium fertiliser. It is particularly suitable for top dressing of brassica crops such as cabbage.

Organic complete fertiliser contains a mixture of organic nutrient sources including feather down, hoof and horn, bone flour, chicken manure, ash and rock potash. It has an NPK analysis of 4.8:5.8:2.1 and the nutrients are released gradually by microbial activity in the soil.

**How to use** Spread over the required area and lightly fork into the top soil. For top dressing of for example brassicas sprinkle along the row of plants and gently hoe into the soil.

**How much** Apply 4 - 8 oz per square yard.

**Other** Organic complete fertiliser is supplied as granules in 1.5 kg and 20 kg bags.

**Supplier** HDRA Sales Ltd Tel 0203 303517 (Ryton shop only) and from Suffolk Herbs Ltd Tel 0787 227247 (1.5 kg pack only)
Price for 1.5 kg from Suffolk Herbs - £3.10
Price for 1.5 kg bag from HDRA shop - £2.79 (1990 price)
Price for 20 kg bag HDRA shop - £22.00 (1990 price)

**Accepted** All

**Use**

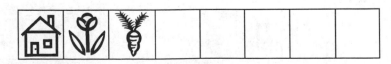

Fertilisers

# CORNISH CALCIFIED SEAWEED

Cornish Calcified Seaweed is used for improving soil fertility and structure. It can also be used to decrease soil acidity and encourage microbial activity in the soil. Calcified seaweed can also be fed to livestock and horses to improve bone growth and fertility.

Cornish Calcified Seaweed contains the red seaweed called *Lithothamnium calcareum* which grows in a hard coral-like structure and contains a high proportion of calcium and magnesium as well as other minerals and trace elements. The seaweed is broken down in the soil by the soil microbes to release these nutrients. Similarly livestock benefit from the range of nutrients supplied.

**How to use** Calcified seaweed can be applied through standard spreaders at any time of the year. On cultivated land apply after ploughing and then worked into the seedbed. For livestock either top dress onto the ration, mix into feed or feed "through the grass" by applying to the pasture before grazing. For quick release of nutrients use a ground form.

**How much** For grassland and cereals apply 5 cwt (250 kg) per acre. For brassicas and root crops apply 6 - 8 cwt (300 - 400 kg) per acre. Due to the relatively slow release of the nutrients in the soil one application should be sufficient every three years. For orchards, soft and top fruits, apply 6 - 8 cwt (300 - 400 kg) per acre every year. For livestock the amount to include in the feed will depend on the composition of the ration and should be discussed with the supplier.

**Other** Cornish Calcified Seaweed is available as a graded granule which consists of a range of granule sizes from the size of a pinhead to that of a pearl. A ground form suitable for feed to livestock is also available. Pack sizes are 50 kg & bulk/big bag.

**Supplier** Cornish Calcified Seaweed Co Ltd Tel 0872 78878 or 40272 Price available on request from supplier.

**Accepted** GCFP SA OFG

**Use**

# COWPACT

Cowpact is a peat free product for use as a low level fertiliser to provide all plant nutrients including trace elements and will also supply humus to the soil helping to aceive or maintain a good soil structure.

Cowpact contains cow pats and includes no bedding such as straw or sawdust and is also weed free. The cow pats break down in the soil and stimulate microbial activity making nutrients more available to the plants.

**How to use** Use preplanting and during the growing season to supply a tick over supply of nutrient. Sprinkle onto the soil and hoe or fork into the surface.

**How much** For general use apply 4 oz per square yard. 1 bag will treat 160 square yards. For poor soils higher rates should be applied.

**Other** Cowpact is supplied as a powder in 50 litre bags.

**Supplier** HDRA Sales Ltd Tel 0203 303517 (Ryton shop only) and from Suffolk Herbs Ltd Tel0787 227247

Price for a minimum order of 5 bags from HDRA shop - £28.50 (1990 price)

Prices for 1 bag from Suffolk Herbs - £8.25

Price for 2 bags from Suffolk Herbs - £7.50 each

Price for 3 - 9 from Suffolk Herbs - £6.50 each

Price for 10 - 19 bags from Suffolk Herbs - £6.00 each

Price for 20 - 49 bags from Suffolk Herbs - £5.50 each

Price for 50 bags from Suffolk Herbs - £5.00 each

Suffolk Herbs prices include delivery from the maker.

**Accepted** All

**Use**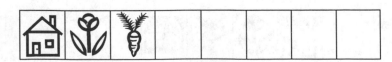

# COWPOST

> Cowpost is a multi-purpose potting compost. It is ideal for sowing, seedlings,small plants and light feeders.
> Cowpost contains organic material and perlite priviging nutrients and a suitable rooting material for most plants.

**How to use** Use as per standard compost.
**How much** Rate of use will depend on the use, ie potting, sowing, etc and on the plant species concerned.
**Other** Cowpost is supplied as a powder in 40 litre bags.
**Supplier** Suffolk Herbs Ltd TEl 0787 227247
Price fir 1 bag  - £8.25
Price for 2 bags - £7.50 each
Price for 3 - 9 bags - £6.50 each
Price for 10 - 19 bags - £6.00 each
Price for 20 -49 bags - £5.50 each
Price for 50 bags - £5.00 each
Prices include delivery from maker.
**Accepted** All

**Use**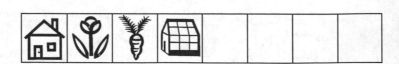

# CROP PLUS

Crop Plus is used to increase yields and improve crop quality. It will maximise root development which increases resistance to stress and disease. It is suitable for use on broad leave crops and cereals.

Crop Plus contains hydrolysed protein complexes that provide amino acid nutrients to the seedling. Selected enzymes are included to breakdown compounds in the soil that inhibit germination. Nutrient uptake is therefore maximised and allows maximum yields and quality.

**How to use** Dilute with water and apply as a foliar feed.

**How much** For cereals, maize, potatoes, sugarbeet, oil seed rape, peas, beans, root vegetables and tomatoes apply 425 ml per ha diluted in 175 - 300 litres of water. For vegetables (other than root vegetables), soft fruit and fruit trees apply 600 ml per hectare diluted in 175 - 300 litres of water.

**Other** Crop Plus is supplied as a liquid in bottles to treat 2 ha.

**Supplier** Cytozyme (UK) Ltd 0733 238545
Price on application to supplier. Cost is approximately £9 per acre.

**Use**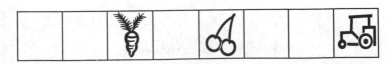

# CROP UP AND METALOSATE FOLIARS

Crop Up is a foliar feed containing a mixture of trace elements that have been chelated to amino-acids derived from hydrolysed soya protein.

Metalosate Foliars are a range of products designed to rebalance a specific trace element deficiency. The trace elements are biological in content and activity and these products allow effective remedy of trace element imbalance under the standards of Organic Farmers & Growers.

Chelate comes from the Greek "chelae" meaning claw. When a trace element is chelated it means it is held by another molecule or substance which acts like a claw and can be readily broken down in the animal, plant or soil. In this instance the chelating substances are amino acids (the building blocks of proteins) which in the soil will be broken down by soil microbes to form soluble nitrates which can be taken up by the plant.

Trace elements available either individually as Metalosate single or in combination as a Metalosate Combined are Iron, Manganese, Magnesium, Copper, Zinc, Calcium and Boron.

**How to use** Crop Up and Metalosate Foliars should be applied as foliar feeds.

**How much** Generally application rate is 0.5 - 1 pints per acre. If two foliar feeds are combined no more than 1 pint per acre should be applied.

**Other** Crop Up and Metalosate Foliars are supplied in 6.66 pint (3.75 litre) drums.

**Supplier** Organic Farmers and Growers Ltd Tel 0449 720838
Price for 1 drum Crop Up (3.75 litres) - £38.00
Price for 1 drum Metalosate combined (3.75 litres) - £38.00
Price for 1 drum Metalosate single (3.75 litres) - £36.00
Delivery is included for orders in England and Wales.

**Accepted** OFG

**Use**

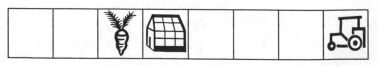

# CUMULUS COMPLETE ORGANIC FERTILISER

Cumulus Complete Organic Fertilizer (Grosafe) is used for promoting strong healthy plants.It contains hoof and horn, bonemeal and rock potash, which break down in the soil to release nutrients.

**How to use** Sprinkle onto the soil and hoe or rake in.

**How much** Apply 4 oz per sq yd 140g per m$^2$.

**Other** Cumulus Complete Organic Fertiliser is supplied as granules and can be stored indefinitely. Requirements are 1 small bag per 11m$^2$ (9sq yd), 1 medium bag per 70m$^2$ (60sq yd), 1 large bag per 140m$^2$ (120sq yd).

**Supplier** Cumulus Organics Ltd Tel 0452 305814 and also from Gala (Brokers) Ltd 0244 390712
Price for 1.5 kg from Cumulus - £2.85 (+ carriage)
Price for 1.5 kg from Gala (Brokers) - £3.20
Price for 10 kg from Cumulus - £13.00 (+ carriage)
Price for 10 kg from Gala (Brokers) - £14.99
Price for 20 kg from Cumulus - £18.50 (+ carriage)

**Accepted** All

Use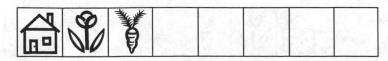

# CUMULUS CONCENTRATED FOLIAR FEED

> Cumulus Concentrated Foliar Feed (Plant Builda) is used to promote healthy growth in young plants.
>  Cumulus Concentrated Foliar Feed contains nitrogen, phosphorus, potassium and trace elements from organic sources which provide nutrients for the plants in liquid form.

**How to use**   Mix with water and spray onto the crop or plant. Follow the directions on the bottle.

**Other**   Cumulus Concentrated Foliar Feed is supplied as a liquid in 0.5 litre containers. It will keep indefinitely.

**Supplier**   Cumulus Organics Ltd Tel 0452 305814 and from
Gala Brokers Limited Tel 0244 390712
Price for 0.5 litres - £2.56 (+ carriage)

**Accepted**   Foliar feeds containing trace elements are 'natural' but are often made in factories by chemical processes. This product is from wholly natural sources and should therefore be acceptable to most green growers.

**Use**

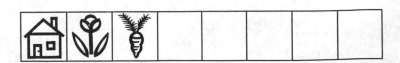

Fertiliser

# CUMULUS PURE BLOOD AND FISH MEAL

F

Cumulus Pure blood fish and bone is used for promoting strong root development in spring and summer.

Cumulus Pure blood fish and bone contains blood, fish and bone which break down in the soil to release nitrogen rapidly and phosphate slowly. Blood contains protein nitrogen which is readily soluble in water and so is rapidly available in the soil. Fish and bone both contain phosphorus in complex molecules that are broken down more slowly by microbial activity.

**How to use** Sprinkle onto the soil and hoe or rake in.

**How much** For general use apply 4oz per sq yd or 100g per $m^2$. Requirements are 1 small bag per $20m^2$ (17sq yd), 1 medium bag per $100m^2$ (83sq yd), 1 large bag per $100m^2$ (83sq yd).

**Other** Cumulus Pure Blood Fish and Bone Meal is supplied as a powder in 2 kg, 10 kg and 20 kg bags. It can be stored indefinitely in a dry place.

**Supplier** Cumulus Organics Ltd Tel 0452 305814 and from Gala Brokers Ltd Tel 0244 390712

Price for 2kg from Culmulus - £2.80 (+ carriage)

Price for 2 kg from Gala - £3.20

Price for 10 kg from Cumulus - £12.95 (+ carriage)

Price for 20 kg from Gala - £18.11 (+ carriage)

**Accepted** All

Use

275

# DINGLEY'S ORGANIC FERTILISERS

Dingley's Organic Fertilisers are produced by W.L Dingley & Co which has been established since 1921. They have been producing Organic Base Fertilisers for many years which contain the natural forms of the trace elements. Dingley's Organic Fertiliser helps to promote bacterial action, improve the worm count and puts the soil in good heart so making locked up plant food available.

Dingley's Organic Fertiliser is a complete and balanced plant food which is pelletted. These pellets are uniform in size thus making it easier to spread by hand or all types of spreader, giving an efficient pattern of distribution. This fertiliser is ideal for flowers shrubs and young trees because of the gradual release of nutrients over a long period of time.

**How to use** Spread either by hand or by all types of spreader.

**How much** One bag contains 40g. For new seed beds use 3-5 bags/acre, on vegetable crops use 4-8 bags/acre, in seed beds use 4-6 oz/Sq yard raked in, for established beds use 3-5 oz/Sq yard hoed into soil spring and summer, roses and shrubs 2-4 oz per plant in spring before leaves fully open and in the summer, June - July (not later), use 1-2 oz per plant and for lawns; top dress in spring 2 oz/Sq yard and the second application in autumn 2 oz/Sq yard.

**Other**
**Supplier** Dingley's Organic Fertiliser is supplied as pellets in 40 kg bags.
W.L Dingley & Co Tel 0386 830242
Price for 1 bag is approximately £12, list price £205 per tonne + VAT (ex works).
Price reduction depending on size of order. (Normally sold by tonne).

**Accepted** All

**Use**

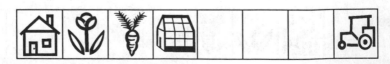

# DOLOMITE LIMESTONE

> Dolomite limestone is used for neutralising acid soil and maintain healthy plant colour.
> Dolomite lime contains calcium which neutralises acidity in soil. It also supplies magnesium which is required for chlorophyll the green pigment in plants.

**How to use** Apply to the soil in autumn or winter.

**How much** Apply at a rate of 8 oz per square yard. This is equal to 200 grams per m². 1 small bag will treat 30m² (25 square yards).

**Other** Dolomite limestone is supplied as a powder in 6 kg and 20 kg bags. Will keep indefinitely but best kept under cover.

**Supplier** Cumulus Organics Ltd Tel 0452 305814 and also from HDRA Sales Ltd Tel 0203 303517 (Ryton shop only) and from Suffolk Herbs Tel 0787 227247 (6 kg pack only)
Price for 6 kg from Suffolk Herbs - £4.35 (+P&P)
Price for 6 kg from Cumulus - £3.95 (+ carriage)
Price for 6 kg from HDRA shop only - £3.95 (1990 price)
Price for 20 kg from Cumulus - £9.00 (+ carriage)
Price for 20 kg from HDRA shop only - £13.00 (1990 price)

**Accepted** All

Use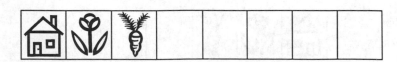

# DOLOMITE LIMESTONE

> Dolomite limestone is used for neutralising acid soil and maintain healthy plant colour.
> Dolomite limestone, also known as magnesium limestone, contains calcium which neutralises acidity in soil. It also supplies magnesium which is required for chlorophyll the green pigment in plants.

**How to use** Apply to the soil in autumn or winter.

**How much** Apply at a rate of 8 oz - 1 lb per square yard. This is equal to 200 grams per m². 1 small bag will treat 30m² (25 square yards).

**Other** Dolomite limestone is supplied as a powder in 3 kg, 6 kg and 25 kg bags. Will keep indefinitely but best kept under cover.

**Supplier** Chempak Products Tel 0992 441888

**Accepted** All

**Use**

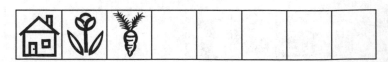

# DRIED BLOOD

Dried Blood is used as a readily available source of nitrogen and is suitable for use on all plants.

Dried Blood is produced from slaughterhouse waste products that are dried and coloured almost black. Because the dried components of blood are readily soluble in water they are easily available for uptake by microbes and plant roots.

| | |
|---|---|
| **How to use** | Sprinkle onto the soil surface and hoe or rake in. Apply to boost growth in the spring and again in summer to maintain growth. Do not apply in winter when plants are growing very little as the nitrogen will readily be leached out of the soil. |
| **How much** | For general use apply 1 - 2 oz per square yard. |
| **Other** | Dried Blood is supplied as a black powder in 1 kg, 2 kg, 4 kg and 25 kg bags. |
| **Supplier** | Chempak Products Tel 0992 441888 |
| | Price for 1 kg - £1.80 |
| | Price for 2 kg - £3.15 |
| | Price for 4 kg - £5.50 |
| | Price for 25 kg - £27.50 |
| **Accepted** | All |

Use

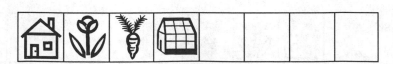

# DUG (CONCENTRATED ORGANIC DUNG)

F

---

DUG is used to provide a balance of nutrients to all plants and to provide a rich easily worked soil.

DUG contains composted and processed dung from organically reared animals which encourages microbial activity around the plant roots and breaks down to release nutrients and humus into the soil. It is free from harmful microbes and weeds and contains no chemicals.

---

**How to use**    Spread onto the soil and gently hoe or fork in to the topsoil. Full directions are given on each bag.

**How much**    One sack (25 kg) will treat 165 - 665 m² (200 - 800 square yards). Amount will vary depending on the plant species and soil status.

**Other**    DUG is supplied as a powder in 25 kg bags.

**Supplier**    Suffolk Herbs Ltd Tel 0787 227247

Price for 1 bag - £11.95

Price for 2 bags - £10.00 each

Price for 3 - 5 bags - £8.50 each

Price for 6 or more bags - £8.00

All above prices include carriage.

**Accepted**    All

**Use**

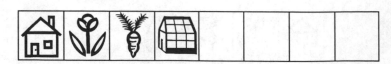

# FARMURA LIQUID ORGANIC FERTILISER

Farmura Liquid Organic Fertiliser is suitable for use as a liquid feed for all plants. Use as a foliar feed on vegetables, fruit and flowers and as a tonic for tomatoes. It is also suitable for feed house plants.

Farmura Liquid Organic Fertiliser is made from farmyard manure and supplies nitrogen, phosphorus, potassium and trace elements.

| | |
|---|---|
| **How to use** | Dilute with water and apply as a foliar feed or water onto the soil. |
| **How much** | Mix 1 part of Farmura with 30 parts of water. Make up 5 litres of solution with 150 ml of Farmura topped up to 5 litres with water. 5 litres of mix will treat 40m². (1 gallon will treat 10 square yards.) |
| **Other** | Farmura is supplied as a liquid in 1 litre and 2.5 litre containers. It will keep almost indefinitely. |
| **Supplier** | Cumulus Organics Ltd Tel 0452 305814 and from HDRA Sales Ltd Tel 0203 303517 (HDRA shop only) and from Suffolk Herbs Ltd Tel 07878 227247 (1 litre pack only) Price for 1 litre from Cumulus - £3.90 (+ carriage) Price for 2.5 litre from Cumulus - £5.60 (+ carriage) Price for 1 litre from HDRA shop - £3.90 Price for 25 litres from HDRA shop - £33.00 Price for 1 litre from Suffolk Herbs - £4.30 (+ P&P) |
| **Accepted** | All |

**Use**

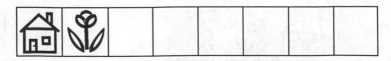

# FLORA MOOR

> Flora Moor is used for promoting plant health.  It contains plant extracts
> of Austrian origin which provide trace elements.

**How to use** As a foliar feed. Particularly when the plant is stressed such as
wilted.  Apply as directed  on bottle.
**How much** Information not available.
**Other** Storage, indefinite.
Supplied as liquid
Pack Size, 0.5 litre
**Supplier** Cumulus Organics Ltd
Tel.(0452)305814
Price £2.50 + carriage
**Accepted** All

**Use**

# GENERAL FERTILISER

General Fertiliser is used to provide general or specific fertiliser. It contains calcium ammonium nitrate, single super phosphate, sulphate of potash, etc. as per list of permitted products of GCFP.

**How to use** Apply nitrogen in spring; phosphate and potassium in autumn; nitrogen, phosphate and potassium mix in spring. N.B. Minimum order for special formulation 4 tonnes.

**How much** Depends on crop species, soil type and condition etc.

**Other** Storage, indefinite.
Supplied as solid or granular
Pack Size 50kg 100kg 500kg or bulk.

**Supplier** J&H Bunn Ltd
Tel.(0493)441111
Price Varies with requirements and order size.

**Accepted** GCFP only

**Use**

# GOË-MAR BASE

Goë-Mar Base is used to increase yields and promote evenness of the crop for example to promote even size of tubers in potatoes. Improvements in keeping quality and the quality of skins in potatoes and fruit are also seen. It is suitable for use on all crops.

Goë-Mar Base is produced by the latest method of processing fresh seaweed from the leafy state to a liquid. It contains plant activating hormones, the cytokinins, auxins and gibberellins together with the vitamin, amino acid and betaine content of the fresh seaweed in an unimpaired form. The mix of contents assist the uptake, transfer and utilisation of nutrients to promote strong healthy growth.

**How to use** Apply as a spray for foliar feeding. It can applied with most fungicides and insecticides if mixed spraying is required. Timing of application will depend on the crop.

**How much** Apply 1 litre per acre. Number of applications will vary depending on the crop species being treated.

**Other** Goë-Mar Base is supplied as a sprayable liquid.

**Supplier** Sea Trident Tel 0626 862489
Price on application to supplier.

**Accepted** SA GCFP

**Use**

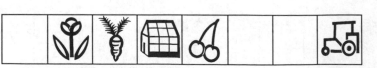

# GOË-MAR BM 86

Goë-Mar BM 86 is used to increase yields and promote evenness of the crop for example to promote even size of tubers in potatoes. Improvements in keeping quality and the quality of the skin of potatoes and fruit is also seen. It is suitable for use on all crops.

Goë-Mar BM 86 is produced by the latest method of processing fresh seaweed from the leafy state to a liquid. It contains plant activating hormones, the cytokinins, auxins and gibberellins together with the vitamin, amino acid and betaine content of the fresh seaweed in an unimpaired form. The mix of contents assist the uptake, transfer and utilisation of nutrients to promote strong healthy growth. Goë-Mar BM 86 contains added boron, sulphur, magnesium and nitrogen.

**How to use** Apply as a spray for foliar feeding. It can be applied with most fungicides and insecticides if mixed spraying is required. Timing of application will depend on the crop.

**How much** Apply 1 litre per acre. For cabbage, field peas and potatoes spray twice. For apples, vines and soft fruit spray three times.

**Other** Goë-Mar BM 86 is supplied as a sprayable liquid.

**Supplier** Sea Trident Tel 0626 862489
Price on application to supplier.

**Accepted** GCFP

**Use**

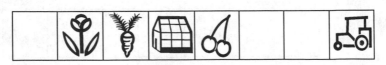

# GOË-MAR C+

> Goë-Mar C+ is used to increase yields and promote evenness of the crop for example to promote even size of beans. It is designed to increase disease resistance of cereals and correct mineral deficiencies in the soil. It is suitable for use on all cereals and beans.
>
> Goë-Mar C+ is produced by the latest method of processing fresh seaweed from the leafy state to a liquid. It contains plant activating hormones, the cytokinins, auxins and gibberellins together with the vitamin, amino acid and betaine content of the fresh seaweed in an unimpaired form. The mix of contents assist the uptake, transfer and utilisation of nutrients to promote strong healthy growth. Goë-Mar C+ contains added sulphur, magnesium, manganese, zinc and nitrogen.

**How to use** Apply as a spray for foliar feeding. It can be applied with most fungicides and insecticides if mixed spray if is required. For cereals apply at the second node stage. For beans apply at early leaf, early flower and after flowering stages.

**How much** Apply 1 litre per acre. For cereals apply once. For beans apply three times at the stages of growth quoted above.

**Other** Goë-Mar C+ is supplied as a sprayable liquid.

**Supplier** Sea Trident Tel 0626 862489
Price on application to supplier.

**Accepted** GCFP

**Use**

# GOË-MAR SPECIAL GRASS

> Goë-Mar Special Grass is used to increase grass growth and as it stimulates through the leaves rather than the root it is particularly useful in drought conditions. It is suitable for use on grass for grazing or cutting.
>
> Goë-Mar Special Grass is produced by the latest method of processing fresh seaweed from the leafy state to a liquid. It contains plant activating hormones, the cytokinins, auxins and gibberellins together with the vitamin, amino acid and betaine content of the fresh seaweed in an unimpaired form. The mix of contents assist the uptake, transfer and utilisation of nutrients to promote strong healthy growth. Goë-Mar Special Grass contains added magnesium, copper and nitrogen.

**How to use**  Apply as a spray for foliar feeding. It can be applied with most fungicides and insecticides if mixed spray if is required. Apply in early spring and if required make a further application after grazing or the first silage or hay cut.

**How much**  Apply 1 litre per acre. Apply 1 or 2 applications per season.

**Other**  Goë-Mar Special Grass is supplied as a sprayable liquid.

**Supplier**  Sea Trident Tel 0626 862489
Price on application to supplier.

**Accepted**  GCFP

**Use**

287

# GROW-VEG

Grow-Veg is for use as a general fertiliser for use on vegetables. It contains 8% nitrogen, 8.5% total phosphates and 14% potash. Trace elements are also added to promote strong, healthy growth. Grow-Veg increases microbial activity in the soil and makes nutrients more available to the plant.

**How to use** Apply through standard applicators.
**How much** Amount to apply will depend on the vegetable being grown.
**Other** Grow-Veg is supplied as a granule.
**Supplier** Tony Ashmore Ltd Tel 0270 586671
Price on application to supplier.
**Accepted** GCFP

**Use**

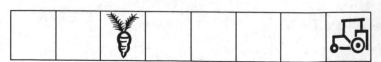

# GYPSUM

Gypsum is well known for its soil improving qualities and has numerous uses. In clay soils it can be used as a flocculate ie it "settles" the clay particles into a friable structure. Gypsum can reduce salinity (salt content) of soils and it can also help reduce alkalinity.

Gypsum contains calcium sulphate which mainly acts in the soil by changing the particles held in association with the soil. By replacing the sodium in a salty soil with calcium the sodium ions can move into the soil moisture and can be leached out of the soil.

In a clay soil the clay particles are electrically charged and attract particles of an opposite charge which act as links between soil particles. This results in a heavy soil that clings to itself and tools, boots, etc. In wet conditions the clay can become suspended as the charged particles around the soil become disassociated from the clay particles which then repel each other due to their like charge. The calcium in gypsum helps to neutralise some of this charge and the soil then forms into aggregates allowing water and air to enter the soil more easily and making the soil more manageable.

**How to use**  The gypsum should be applied to ploughed soil and cultivated into the top 2 - 3 inches (5 - 8 cms) Thorough incorporation into the soil is essential for the flocculation of heavy clay soils. Even the heaviest of soils will succumb to cultivation and will be helped by regular applications of manure or compost.

**How much**  An application of 2 tonnes per acre should be suffice for most soils if followed annually by liberal manure or compost applications.

**Other**  Gypsum is supplied in 50 kg and 1000 kg bags

**Supplier**  Organic Farmers and Growers Ltd Tel 0449 720838
Price 1 tonne in 50 kg bag - £37.00
Price 1 tonne in 1 tonne bags - £39.00
Delivery is charged extra on these prices.

**Accepted**  OFG and all others

**Use**

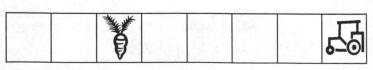

# GYPSUM

Gypsum is well known for its soil improving qualities and has numerous uses. In clay soils it can be used as a flocculate ie it "settles" the clay particles into a friable structure. Gypsum can reduce salinity (salt content) of soils and it can also help reduce alkalinity.

This particular Gypsum from HDRA contains 80% calcium sulphate and 20% dolomite. The calcium sulphate acts in the soil by changing the particles held in association with the soil. By replacing the sodium in a salty soil with calcium the sodium ions can move into the soil moisture and can be leached out of the soil.

In a clay soil the clay particles are electrically charged and attract particles of an opposite charge which act as links between soil particles. This results in a heavy soil that clings to itself and tools, boots, etc. In wet conditions the clay can become suspended as the charged particles around the soil become disassociated from the clay particles which then repel each other due to their like charge. The calcium in gypsum helps to neutralise some of this charge and the soil then forms into aggregates allowing water and air to enter the soil more easily and making the soil more manageable.

**How to use** Scatter over the surface of bare soil and hoe well in. On lawns apply in the spring after spiking or slitting and brush it into the soil.

**How much** Apply 8 oz per square yard.

**Other** Gypsum is supplied as ground rock in 6 kg and 20 kg bags. It is best kept under cover.

**Supplier** HDRA Sales Ltd Tel 0203 303517 (Ryton shop only) and from Suffolk Herbs Ltd Tel 0787 227247 (6 kg pack only)
Price for 6 kg from Suffolk Herbs - £4.35
Price for 6 kg bag from HDRA shop only - £3.95 (1990 price)
Price for 20 kg bag from HDRA shop only - £13.00 (1990 price)

**Accepted** All

**Use**

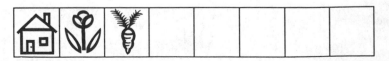

# GYPSUM

Gypsum is well known for its soil improving qualities and has numerous uses. In clay soils it can be used as a flocculate ie it "settles" the clay particles into a friable structure. Gypsum can reduce salinity (salt content) of soils and it can also help reduce alkalinity.

Gypsum contains calcium sulphate which acts by changing the particles held in association with the soil. By replacing the sodium in a salty soil with calcium the sodium ions can move into the soil moisture and can be leached out of the soil.

In a clay soil the clay particles are electrically charged and attract particles of an opposite charge which act as links between soil particles. This results in a heavy soil that clings to itself and tools, boots, etc. In wet conditions the clay can become suspended as the charged particles around the soil become disassociated from the clay particles which then repel each other due to their like charge. The calcium in gypsum helps to neutralise some of this charge and the soil then forms into aggregates allowing water and air to enter the soil more easily and making the soil more manageable.

**How to use** Scatter over the surface of bare soil and hoe well in. On lawns apply in the spring after spiking or slitting and brush it into the soil.

**How much** Apply several applications of 1 lb per square yard to improve structure of clay and sandy soils.

**Other** Gypsum is supplied as ground rock in 3 kg, 6 kg and 25 kg bags. It is best kept under cover.

**Supplier** Chempak Products Tel 0992 441888

**Accepted** All

Use

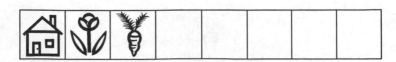

# HEADSTART

> Headstart is used as a seed dressing to ensure that seedlings are given the good start.
> Headstart contains natural extract of cytokinins, plant growth hormones, combined with trace elements and other growth factors. The combination of ingredients stimulates nutrient uptake and promotes photosynthesis which provides the 'fuel' for growth.

**How to use**  Headstart should be applied as a seed dressing by spraying on to the seed.

**How much**  Rates of application will depend on the crop as different sized seeds will require different amounts of Headstart to ensure that all the seed surface is covered.

**Other**  Headstart is supplied in 25 litre drums and has a shelf life of 12 months.

**Supplier**  Microbial Developments Ltd Tel 0684 568434
Price on application to supplier.

**Use**

# HIGHLAND POTASH

> Highland Potash is used to encourage strong even growth and earlier ripening.
> Highland Potash contains Adularia shale and fine grained dolomite which are slowly broken down in the soil by to microbial activity and acids excreted by the plant roots to release potassium, calcium and magnesium.

**How to use** Highland Potash can be applied through most hoppers. Use of an agitator is recommended to ensure even application. Highland Potash has a low moisture content and can be dampened down if required.

**How much** Application rates vary depending on plant species and soil type and status. For cereals apply approximately 1 bulk bag per ha. For potatoes apply approximately 2 bulk bags per ha.

**Other** Highland Potash is supplied as a powder of ground rock. \It is available in 25 kg and 500 kg bags. It is also available in bulk. Store in a dry place if possible.

**Supplier** Glenside Organics Ltd Tel 0786 816655
Price on application to supplier.

**Accepted** All

**Use**

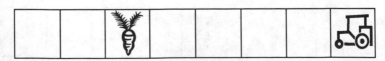

# HIGHLAND SLAG

Highland Slag is used for encouraging vigorous plant growth and neutralising acidic soil.
Highland Slag contains a mix of phosphate, calcified seaweed, potassium and trace elements which encourages microbial activity in the soil and makes nutrients more available. Rooting activity of the plant is therefore promoted.

**How to use** Highland Slag can be spread through most types of hopper. Use of an agitator will ensure a more even application. This product has a low moisture content and can be dampened down if required.

**How much** Normal rates are 5 - 10 cwt per acre. This is equal to 550 - 1100 kg per hectare. Apply 1 - 2 bulk bags per ha, or 0.5 - 1 bulk bags per acre.

**Other** Highland Slag is available in 25 kg and 500 kg bags. It is also available in bulk. Store in a dry place if possible.

**Supplier** Glenside Organics Ltd Tel 0786 816655
Price on application to supplier.

**Accepted** All

**Use**

# HOOF AND HORN

Hoof and Horn is used as a slow release source of nitrogen and is particularly useful where supplies of manure and compost are limited. Hoof and Horn contains nitrogen that is held in complex arrangements of protein in the hoof and horn structure and so the nitrogen is released slowly by microbial breakdown.

**How to use**   Apply to the soil as required. Use on leafy crops in spring and summer and also for fruit trees when planted on poor soils.

**How much**   For leafy plants apply 4 ox per square yard. For fruit trees use approximately 1 lb (0.5 kg) per tree.

**Other**   Hoof and Horn is supplied as a powder in 4.5 kg and 20 kg bags.

**Supplier**   HDRA Sales Ltd Tel 0203 303517 Ryton shop only.
Price for 4.5 kg from HDRA shop - £6.50 (1990 price)
Price for 20 kg from HDRA shop - £25.00 (1990 price)

**Accepted**   All

**Use**

# HOOF AND HORN MEAL

> Hoof and Horn Meal is used as a slow release source of nitrogen and is particularly useful where supplies of manure and compost are limited.
> Hoof and Horn Meal is made by crushing and sterilising the waste products. It contains nitrogen that is held in complex arrangements of protein in the hoof and horn structure and so the nitrogen is released slowly by microbial breakdown.

**How to use**  Apply to the soil as required. Use on leafy crops in spring and summer and also for fruit trees when planted on poor soils.

**How much**  For leafy plants apply 2 - 4 oz per square yard. For fruit trees use approximately 1 lb (0.5 kg) per tree.

**Other**  Hoof and Horn is supplied as a powder in 1 kg, 2 kg, 4 kg and 25 kg bags.

**Supplier**  Chempak Products Tel 0992 441888

**Accepted**  All

Use

# HUMBER ORGANIC FERTILIZER

Humber Organic Fertilizer is for use as a slow release source of plant nutrients. This product has Soil Association symbol status.
Humber Organic fertilizer contains mostly vegetable matter with a small addition of municipal waste. The material breaks down in the soil to release nutrients and will add some organic matter (humus) to the soil. Nutrients will be released over a period of several months.

**How to use**    Apply to the soil surface and hoe or fork into the top of the soil. For best results apply before sowing or planting.

**How much**    Apply at a rate of 6 - 8 oz per square yard but allow up to 12 oz per square yard on poor soils.

**Other**    Humber Organic Fertilizer is supplied as a dry compost in bags.

**Supplier**    HDRA Sales Ltd Tel 0203 303517 Ryton shop only
Price for 1 bag from shop - £15.65 (1990 price includes carriage)
Price for 2 bags from shop - £26.85 (1990 price includes carriage)

**Accepted**    All

**Use**

Fertilisers

# J Arthur Bower's Bone Meal

J Arthur Bower's Bone Meal is for use as a phosphate and nitrogen fertiliser when planting trees or shrubs and when preparing or feeding borders and bedding plants. It is used to promote strong root growth. J Arthur Bower's Bone Meal contains sterilised bone meal that is slowly broken down in the soil by microbial activity and plant enzymes leached into the soil from the plant roots. Phosphate and nitrogen are released into the soil and can be taken up by the plant. It also contains phosphorus pentoxide that raises the phosphate contribution but prevents the product being totally organic.

**How to use** For trees and shrubs, etc at planting mix the bone meal with a generous portion of peat or soil and scatter around the hole into which the shrub will be planted. For beds and borders scatter the bone meal on the soil surface and hoe or fork into the surface of the soil. Always water well in after applying.

**How much** When planting trees or shrubs mix 60 grams (2 oz) per plant with a generous portion of peat or soil and evenly distribute around the hole into which the tree will be planted. For preparing the soil for planting scatter 70 grams per m² (2 oz per square yard). For herbaceous borders, rose beds and vegetable plots apply 135 grams per m² (4 oz per square yard).

**Other** J Arthur Bower's Bone Meal is supplied in 1.2 kg, 2 kg and 4 kg boxes and also in 10 and 25 kg packs.

**Supplier** Sinclair Horticulture & Leisure Ltd Tel 0522 537561 and from most wholesalers and garden centres.
Price for 1.2 kg - £1.83
Price for 2 kg - £2.75
Price for 4 kg - £4.87
Price for 10 kg - £9.53
Price for 25 kg - £23.44

**Use**

298

# J ARTHUR BOWER'S DRIED BLOOD

F

J Arthur Bower's Dried Blood is for use as a nitrogen fertiliser to promote rapid plant growth. Use when planting trees or shrubs and when preparing or feeding borders and bedding plants.
J Arthur Bower's Dried Blood contains dried blood that is readily soluble in water and so is directly available for uptake by the plants' roots. The blood contains proteins that can be broken down to release nitrogen and also minerals that encourage healthy plant growth. As the product is soluble it gives a relatively rapid release of nitrogen.

**How to use** Generally scatter over the soil as a top dressing and lightly hoe into the top soil. Water well in after application.

**How much** Apply 35 grams per $m^2$ (1 oz per square yard). For strong growing vegetables it is best to repeat the application at monthly intervals.

**Other** J Arthur Bower's Dried Blood is supplied in a 1.2 kg box or in 2.5 kg, 5 kg, 10 and 25 kg bags.

**Supplier** Sinclair Horticulture & Leisure Ltd Tel 0522 537561 and from most wholesalers and garden centres.
Price for 1.2 kg - £1.70
Price for 2.5 kg - £2.63
Price for 5 kg - £4.27
Price for 10 kg - £7.17
Price for 25 kg - £13.91

**Accepted** All

**Use**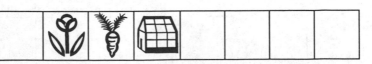

# J ARTHUR BOWER'S HOOF AND HORN

# F

---

J Arthur Bower's Hoof and Horn is for use as a nitrogen fertiliser to promote plant growth. Use for green and root vegetables and for flowers. J Arthur Bower's Hoof and Horn contains 13% nitrogen that is released slowly into the soil by microbial breakdown of the complex protein structures making up hoof and horn.

---

**How to use** Generally scatter over the soil as a top dressing and lightly hoe into the top soil. Water well in after application.

**How much** For brassica plants such as cabbage apply 135 grams per m² (4 oz per square yard) a week to 10 days before planting. For root crops apply 35 grams per m² (1 oz per square yard) and twice this amount for flower borders.

**Other** J Arthur Bower's Hoof and Horn is supplied in 0.9 kg box and 2 kg or 25 kg bags.

**Supplier** Sinclair Horticulture & Leisure Ltd Tel 0522 537561 and from most wholesalers and garden centres.
Price for 0.9 kg - £2.34
Price for 2 kg - £3.71
Price for 25 kg - £36.35

**Accepted** All

**Use**

# J ARTHUR BOWER'S ORGANIC FERTILISER

F

J Arthur Bower's Organic Garden All-Purpose Fertiliser is for use as a base or top dressing and is suitable for use on vegetables and flowers. J Arthur Bower's Organic Garden All-Purpose Fertiliser contains only natural vegetable and animal matter (unspecified) that will supply nitrogen phosphorus and potassium that will be released slowly by microbial action in the soil.It will also supply trace elements and organic matter that will increase the fertility and structure of the soil.

**How to use** As a base dressing spread the recommended amount onto the soil and dig in to the soil.As a top dressing scatter over the soil as a top dressing and lightly hoe into the top soil. Water well in after application.

**How much** For roses apply 200 grams per m² (6 oz per square yard) if applied as a base dressing or 140 grams per m² top dressed. For vegetables apply a base dressing of 140 - 200 grams per m² (4 - 6 oz per square yard) or a top dressing of 70 - 140 grams per m² (2 - 4 oz per square yard). For trees, shrubs, hedges, herbaceous borders, lawns, flowers and bedding areas apply either a base dressing of 140 grams per m² (4 oz per square yard) or a top dressing of 70 grams per m² (1 oz per square yard).

**Other** J Arthur Bower's Organic Garden All-Purpose fertiliser is supplied in 3 kg or 6 kg bags.

**Supplier** Sinclair Horticulture & Leisure Ltd Tel 0522 537561 and from most wholesalers and garden centres.
Price for 3 kg - £2.32
Price for 6 kg - £3.99

**Accepted** All

**Use**

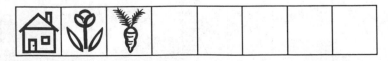

# K MORE +

K More+ is for use as a P.K fertiliser to provide a quick but long lasting response in grasses for grazing or cutting.

K More+ contains soluble phosphates, basic slag, magnesium, potash and eight added trace elements to ensure immediate availability of nutrients to the grass. It also contains a high level of organic matter.

**How to use** Apply through standard spreaders in late summer. Follow with a straight nitrogen application in the spring.

**How much** Apply 3 - 5 cwt (150 - 250 kg) per acre.

**Other** K More+ is supplied as a prill.

**Supplier** Tony Ashmore Ltd Tel 0270 586671

Price on application to supplier.

**Accepted** GCFP

**Use**

# LAWN AND GARDEN GYPSUM

Lawn and Garden Gypsum (Reclaym) is used for conditioning clay soils. Lawn and Garden Gypsum contains gypsum, calcium and sulphur. Clay particles in the soil are negatively charged and when wet are held together by positively charged hydrogen ions giving the characteristic heavy, sticky consistency. The gypsum and calcium loosen clay soils by counter acting the negative charge on the clay particles and prevent the particles being so strongly drawn together. This allows deeper root penetration and easier access for air and water. Sulphur is a natural growth promoter.

**How to use** Sprinkle onto soil surface and hoe in, or rake into lawns.

**How much** For general use apply 8 oz per sq yd or 200 grams per m². 1 small bag will treat 30 m². 1 large bag will 100 m².

**Other** Lawn and garden gypsum is supplied as a powder in 6 kg and 20 kg bags. It will keep indefinitely.

**Supplier** Cumulus Organics Ltd Tel 0452 305814
Price for 6 kg bag - £4.00 (+ carriage)
Price for 20 kg bag - £9.00 (+ carriage)

**Accepted** All

Use

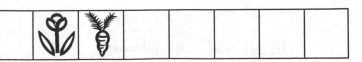

# LIMESTONE CHIPPINGS

**F**

> Limestone Chippings are used to provide a constant background of "limey water" for plants such as carnations, sweet peas and brassicas that like alkaline conditions. It can also be used in very free draining acidic soils to raise the soil pH.
>
> Limestone Chippings are small lumps of rock that release calcium slowly from the surface of the rock. In the soil microbial activity and acids leached from the plant roots will increase the rate of release of calcium into the soil.

**How to use** Place a few chippings in or around plant pots. For treatment of acidic soils sprinkle over the top soil and hoe or rake in.

**How much** For acidic soils use 1 lb or mare per square yard depending on soil acidity.

**Other** Limestone Chippings are available in 3 kg, 6 kg and 25 kg bags.

**Supplier** Chempak Products Tel 0992 441888
Price for 3 kg - £2.20
Price for 6 kg - £3.85
Price for 25 kg - £10.50

**Accepted** All

**Use**

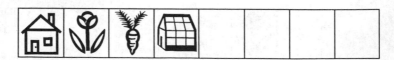

# LIQUID SEAWEED EXTRACT (FOLIA FEED)

Liquid Seaweed Extract (Folia Feed) is used to encourage vigorous, healthy and disease resistant plants and is suitable for use on all plants and crops.

Liquid Seaweed Extract contains a pure extract of seaweed which provide 60 minerals and trace elements that provide nutrients for growth and raise disease resistance. Seaweed extract also contains plant hormones that stimulate growth.

**How to use** Dilute with water and apply as a foliar spray.
**How much** Mix 4 bottle caps full of extract with 5 litres of water. 1 bottle makes 50 litres of spray.
**Other** Liquid Seaweed Extract is supplied as a liquid in 0.5 litre bottles. It will keep indefinitely.
**Supplier** Cumulus Organics Ltd Tel 0452 305814 and from Gala Brokers Ltd Tel 0244 390712
Price for 0.5 litre bottle from Cumulus - £2.50 (+ carriage)
Price for 0.5 litre bottle from Gala Brokers - £3.09
**Accepted** All

**Use**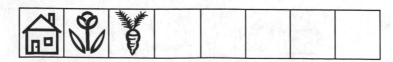

# LIQUID SEAWEED EXTRACT

> **Liquid Seaweed Extract** is used for encouraging vigorous, healthy and disease resistant plants. It is suitable for use on all plants.
>
> Liquid Seaweed Extract contains a pure extract of seaweed which provides 60 minerals and trace elements in soluble form. Seaweed extract also contains plant growth hormones that have a direct effect on plant growth.

**How to use**  Apply as a foliar feed by spraying. Can also be used as a root feed.

**How much**  For vegetables, fruit, shrubs, flowers and lawns apply 1 fluid oz per 6 square yards. 1 litre will treat 200 square yards.

**Other**  Liquid Seaweed Extract is supplied in 1 litre, 2.5 litre and 5 litre plastic containers.

**Supplier**  Chempak Products Tel 0992 441888
Price for 1 litre - £3.95
Price for 2.5 litres - £8.00
Price for 5 litre - £15.00

**Accepted**  OFG SA UKROFS GCFP

**Use**

# MARINURE ★ ★ ★

---

Marinure ★ ★ ★ is used to encourage root development and photosynthesis. It can also be used to overcome stress for example in drought. Marinure ★ ★ ★ contains the seaweed *Ascophyllum nodosum* which provides plant hormones (cytokinins, gibberellins and auxins) that have a direct effect on plant growth and minerals and trace elements that are nutrients for the plant.

---

**How to use** Apply with water through a sprayer; it is suitable for use with CDA machines. It can also be used as a root dip during transplanting. Timing of application depends on the plant species but can often coincide with application of other products. Consult the supplier for details. Dilute 1:50 for root dipping and 1:1000 for overhead irrigation systems.

**How much** Requirements vary depending on the plant species, number and timing of applications. For root crops apply 4 - 5 litres per acre. For cereals apply 1 - 3 litres per acre. For soft fruit apply 3 - 5 litres per acre. For details on other plants contact supplier.

**Other** Marinure ★ ★ ★ is supplied as a water soluble concentrate in 20 litre and 200 litre containers.

**Supplier** Glenside Organics Ltd Tel 0786 816655
Price on application to supplier.

**Accepted** SA OFG UKROFS

**Use**

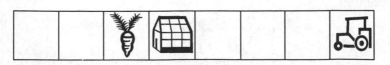

# MASCOT ORGANIC LIQUID COCKTAIL

# F

Mascot Organic Liquid Cocktail is suitable for use on all fine turf and lawns where stimulation of growth and colour is required. This includes golf courses, race courses, sports and polo fields, bowling greens and lawns in parks and gardens. It is particularly useful for aiding establishment of seed in sandy soils.

Mascot Organic Liquid Cocktail contains pure liquid cow manure mixed with seaweed extract at a ratio of 7:3. The cow manure has been anaerobically fermented and separated and is aged for more than 12 months. It contains no additives. Both the cow manure and seaweed extract provide plant nutrients including nitrogen, phosphate, potash and trace elements in a soluble form and will be readily taken up by the grass. The addition of wetting agent (Hydro-Wet) aids soil penetration and makes this product particularly suitable for use on areas of turf suffering from thatch.

**How to use** This can be applied through conventional spraying equipment either tractor mounted or knapsack sprayer. It is best to use fan jets and to remove filters. Always mix the product with water by adding the water first and ensure that the container is well shaken before use. Mix the required amount of fertiliser with twice as much water. When using with other products test mix a small amount of the materials to check for compatibility. It is recommended to apply fertiliser 3 times a year preferably in spring, summer and Autumn.

**How much** Apply 100 litres per hectare (9 gallons per acre). This is equivalent to 5 litres per 500 m². A full size bowling green will require 15 litres (3 gallons). For small lawns apply 1 litre per 100 m².

**Other** Mascot Organic Liquid Cocktail is supplied in 25 litre containers.

**Supplier** Rigby Taylor Ltd Tel 0483 34058
Price available on request from supplier.

**Accepted** All

**Use**

# MASCOT ORGANIC LIQUID FERTILISER

F

---

Mascot Organic Liquid Fertiliser is suitable for use on all turf and lawns. This includes golf courses, race courses, sports and polo fields, bowling greens, parks and gardens. It can also be use on newly sown areas and land reclamation sites.

Mascot Organic Liquid Fertiliser contains a pure anaerobically (i.e. without air) fermented and separated liquid cow manure which has aged for more than 12 months and contains no additives. It provides plant nutrients including nitrogen, phosphate, potash and trace elements in a soluble form and will be readily taken up by the grass.

---

**How to use** This can be applied through conventional spraying equipment either tractor mounted or knapsack sprayer. It is best to use fan jets and to remove filters. Always mix the product with water by adding the water first. Mix the required amount of fertiliser with an equivalent or double volume of water, for example for use with a 200 litre tank half fill with water and add 100 litres of Mascot Organic Liquid Fertiliser. When using with other products test mix a small amount of the materials to check for compatibility. It is recommended to apply fertiliser 3 times a year preferably in spring, summer and Autumn.

**How much** For golf courses, bowling greens, cricket squares, tennis courts and ornamental lawns apply 100 litres per ha (9 gallons per acre). This is equivalent to 5 litres per 500 m$^2$. A full size bowling green will require 15 litres (3 gallons). For small lawns apply 1 litre per 100 m$^2$.

**Other** Mascot Organic Liquid Fertiliser is supplied in 25 litre containers.

**Supplier** Rigby Taylor Ltd Tel 0483 34058
Price available on request from supplier.

**Accepted** All

**Use**

# MASCOT ORGANIC LIQUID GREEN

> Mascot Organic Liquid Green is suitable for use on all fine turf and lawns where a bright green grass is required with out producing excessive growth. This includes golf courses, bowling greens and lawns in parks and gardens.
>
> Mascot Organic Liquid Green contains a pure anaerobically (i.e. without air) fermented and separated liquid cow manure which has aged for more than 12 months and contains no additives. Iron has been added to improve plant colour and also helps harden the turf against fungal diseases. It provides plant nutrients including nitrogen, phosphate, potash and trace elements in a soluble form and will be readily taken up by the grass.

**How to use** This can be applied through conventional spraying equipment either tractor mounted or knapsack sprayer. It is best to use fan jets and to remove filters. Always mix the product with water by adding the water first. Mix the required amount of fertiliser with twice as much water, in dry conditions higher volumes of water should be used. When using with other products test mix a small amount of the materials to check for compatibility. It is recommended to apply fertiliser 3 times a year preferably in spring, summer and Autumn. Over application may result in a temporary blackening of the grass.

**How much** Apply 100 litres per hectare (9 gallons per acre). This is equivalent to 5 litres per 500 m². A full size bowling green will require 15 litres (3 gallons). For small lawns apply 1 litre per 100 m².

**Other** Mascot Organic Liquid Green is supplied in 25 litre containers.
**Supplier** Rigby Taylor Ltd Tel 0483 34058
Price available on request from supplier.

**Accepted** All

**Use**

# MAXICROP NATURAL SEAWEED EXTRACT

Maxicrop Natural Seaweed Extract is for use on fruit, vegetables, lawns and other plants to promote healthy growth of the plant and its roots. This particular Maxicrop product has Soil Association Symbol status.

Maxicrop Natural Seaweed Extract contains the bladder seaweed *Ascophyllum nodosum* which is harvested off the coast of Norway. It breaks down slowly in the soil to release nutrients and stimulates microbial activity in the soil.

**How to use** Generally should be applied as a foliar feed or as a liquid feed by watering onto the soil.

**How much** For general use dilute 10 ml in 2 litres of water.

**Other** Maxicrop Natural Seaweed Extract is supplied as a liquid in 500 ml containers.

**Supplier** HDRA Sales Ltd Tel 0203 303517 (Ryton shop only)
Price for 500 ml - £2.39

**Accepted** SA Symbol but accepted by all

Use

# MAXICROP ORIGINAL SEAWEED EXTRACT

F

Maxicrop Original Organic Seaweed is claimed to be the World's biggest selling organic seaweed growth stimulant. Like its competitor seaweed products it has a beneficial effect on plant growth and health by providing minerals and trace elements. It contains the bladder seaweed *Ascophyllum nodosum* which is harvested off the coast of Norway. It breaks down slowly in the soil to release nutrients and stimulates microbial activity in the soil. Maxicrop produce a range of products based on seaweed many of which contain added fertiliser or chemical pesticides and so are not suitable for use by the organic or conservation grade producer, but may be suitable for some low input systems.

**How to use** Apply as a foliar spray through standard sprayers or by root watering. Timing will vary with crop treated. Application early in the season is generally recommended to promote root growth and strengthen the plant. For cereals, potatoes and grassland apply as a solution of 11 litres of seaweed extract in 100 - 400 litres of water. For fruit and vegetable crops the strength of the solution is not critical. Soft fruit and vegetables should receive 4 applications a year. Top fruit should receive 8 applications a year. In glasshouses it can also be applied through drip irrigation systems at a dilution of 1:600, or as a weekly applied foliar spray diluted 1:500.

**How much** For cereals, potatoes and grassland apply 11 litres of extract per acre diluted as above. For vegetables apply 6 litres per hectare. For soft fruit apply 11 l/ha. For top fruit apply 5.5 l/ha.

**Other** Maxicrop Original Seaweed Extract is supplied as liquid in 500 ml, 1 litre, 5 litre and 25 litre containers.

**Supplier** Maxicrop International Ltd Tel 0536 402182 and from
Gala (Brokers) Ltd Tel 0244 390712
Price for 500 ml - £2.55, 1 litre - £4.29, 5 litre - £12.85
Price for 25 litre containers to trade only on application.

**Accepted** SA

**Use**

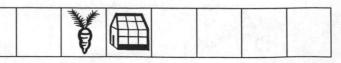

# MERMIN

Mermin is used to supply minerals and organic matter to the soil and is suitable for use on all crops. It carries both Soil Association and Conservation Grade symbols.

Mermin contains a calcareous magnesium algae with a hard coral-like structure known to marine botanists as Lithothamnium calcareum. The seaweed is lifted from the seabed, screened, dried and ground into a fine powder for easy assimilation into the soil. Supplying calcium, magnesium and a wide range of minerals and trace elements, Mermin encourages bacterial action and worm population, thus assisting in the breakdown of dung, slurry and old root systems.

**How to use** Apply through standard fertilizer spreaders.
**How much** For general use apply 5 bags per acre (250 kg) every 3 years. Applications from 3 bags per acre (150 kg) annually to 7 bags per acre (350 kg) every three years can be made as an alternative where circumstances dictate.
**Other** Mermin is supplied in 50 kg bags.
**Supplier** Sea Trident Limited Tel 0626 862489
Price on application to supplier.
**Accepted** OFG SA UKROFS GCFP

**Use**

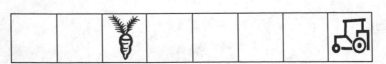

# MERMINFOS 18

Merminfos 18 is a combination of fine ground Mermin calcareous seaweed mixed with microground Gafsa phosphate in an easy-to-spread granular form. Merminfos 18 supplies calcium, magnesium and a wide range of minerals and trace elements to encourage bacterial action and worm population, thus assisting in the breakdown of dung, slurry and old root systems. It also provides the necessary elements for good plant production.

**How to use** Apply through standard fertiliser spreaders.
**How much** A standard dressing of 5 bags/acre (250kg.) every three years is suggested. Applications from 3 bags/acre (150kg.) annually to 7 bags/acre (350kg.) every three years can be made as an alternative where circumstances dictate.
**Other** Pack Size: 50 and 500kgs
**Supplier** Sea Trident Limited  Tel.: (0626)862489
**Accepted** SA GCFP

**Use**

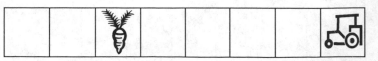

# MERMINFOS 18 AND G27

Merminfos is used to supply minerals and organic matter to the soil and is suitable for use on all crops.

Merminfos contains a calcareous magnesium algae with a hard coral-like structure known to marine botanists as Lithothamnium Calcareum. The seaweed is lifted from the seabed, screened, dried and ground into a fine powder for easy assimilation into the soil. Supplying calcium, magnesium and a wide range of minerals and trace elements, Merminfos encourages bacterial action and worm population, thus assisting in the breakdown of dung, slurry and old root systems.

Gafsa, a soft phosphate rock is added to provide phosphorus to the soil. Merminfos 18 and G27 provide 18 and 27 units of phosphorus respectively. Both products carry Soil Association and Conservation Grade symbols.

**How to use** Apply through standard fertilizer spreaders.

**How much** For general use apply 5 bags per acre (250 kg) every 3 years. Applications from 3 bags per acre (150 kg) annually to 7 bags per acre (350 kg) every three years can be made as an alternative where circumstances dictate.

**Other** Mermin is supplied in 50 kg bags.

**Supplier** Sea Trident Limited Tel 0626 862489

Price on application to supplier.

**Accepted** OFG SA UKROFS GCFP

Use

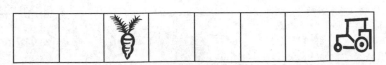

# Natgro Planting & Mulching Compost F

> Natgro Tree Planting and Mulching Compost is used for improving soil structure around trees and other plants when planting or to maintain soil structure around established plants.
>
> Natgro Tree Planting and Mulching Compost contains animal manure and fully composted straw which are broken down in the soil by microbes to release nutrients and provide humus. Humus acts in the soil by holding the mineral particles together in a crumb structure which allows free passage of air and water and deeper root penetration.

**How to use** Mix with the soil at a ratio of 1 part of compost to 3 parts of soil. Use when trees are planted and back filled.

**How much** Mix 1 bag with 240 litres of soil.

**Other** Natgro Tree Planting and Mulching Compost is supplied as a loose compost in 80 litre bags. It is best used within 30 days.

**Supplier** Hensby Biotech Ltd Tel 0487 842562
Price for 80 litre bag - £2.40
Price for bulk - £27.00 per m³.

**Accepted** GCFP and all others

**Use**

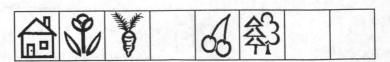

# NITRA-MIN

Nitra-Min is for use as a nitrogen fertiliser and is suitable for use on all crops. It carries Conservation Grade symbol approval.

Nitra-Min contains 21% nitrogen all of which is present in the ammoniacal form, ie as ammonium ions. Ammonium ions are charged particles and so are held in the soil structure resulting in minimal losses due to leaching. Eight trace elements and sulphur are added and promote strong, healthy growth.

**How to use** Apply through standard applicators.
**How much** Amount to apply will depend on the crop and number of applications being made.
**Other** Nitra-Min is supplied as a prill and due to the mix of added minerals is yellow in colour.
**Supplier** Tony Ashmore Ltd Tel 0270 586671
Price on application to supplier.
**Accepted** GCFP

**Use**

# NITRATE OF SODA

Nitrate of Soda is used as a nitrogen fertiliser and is suitable for use at low levels on most crops. It is particularly suitable for use on autumn root crops such as beetroot that also benefit from the sodium content.

Nitrate of Soda is also known as Chilean Nitrate and its correct chemical name is sodium nitrate. It contains about 16% nitrogen which is quick acting as it is soluble in water and so readily available for plants to take up from the soil. Some trace elements are also added to the soil.

**How to use** Sprinkle on to the soil and hoe or rake in. it is mostly applied in the spring to give an early boost to growth.

**How much** For general use apply 1 - 2 oz per square yard.

**Other** Nitrate of Soda is supplied in 3 kg, 6 kg and 25 kg bags.

**Supplier** Chempak Products Tel 0992 441888
Price for 3 kg - £2.20
Price for 6 kg - £3.85
Price for 25 kg - £14.05

**Accepted** GCFP

**Use**

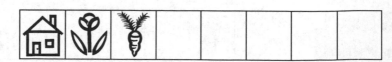

# OCEAN HARVEST

> Ocean Harvest is used as an organic mineral feed supplement for cattle, sheep and goats. It carries the Conservation Grade symbol.
> Ocean Harvest contains sea kelp, calcareous seaweed, phosphorus, vitamins, bicarbonate of soda, calcined magnesite and cod liver oil. Ocean Harvest improves utilisation and the digestion of food. Trace elements and amino acids provided by the seaweed improve fertility, skin condition and toughen hooves.

**How to use** Feed free access or mix into home mixed rations.
**How much** Feed at rates of 2 - 8 oz free access or include 30 - 40 kg per tonne of mixed feed.
**Other** Ocean Harvest is supplied as a powder in 25 kg bags.
**Supplier** Sea Trident Ltd Tel 0626 862489
Price on application to supplier.
**Accepted** GCFP

**Use**

# OFG No.4 Fertiliser Pellets

> OFG Fertiliser Pellets are suitable for use on most crops including cereals, grass, fruit and vegetables.
> This fertiliser supplies nitrogen, phosphate and potassium and has an analysis of 5.3.3. The source of these nutrients is not detailed in the product information it is assumed to be of organic origin. The pellets are available in two sizes allowing application through most spreaders although the smaller size tends to include more mealy powder than the larger size.

**How to use**  Select the pellet size best suited to the spreader to be used. Apply as per usual fertiliser. Splitting the application particularly in grass will be beneficial.

**How much**  In winter wheat apply up to 400 kg per acre. In spring wheat apply up to 250 kg per acre. For winter barley up to 300 kg per acre is recommended and for spring barley a maximum of 250 kg per acre. In oats apply a maximum of 250 kg per acre. For rye the maximum recommended is 200 kg per acre. Potatoes should receive up to 500 kg per acre. Applications for grass should not exceed 600 kg per acre and split application is recommended.

**Other**  OFG Fertiliser Pellets are supplied in 4 mm and 6 mm sizes. Pellets can be supplied in 25kg, 500 kg and bulk.

**Supplier**  Organic Farmers and Growers Ltd Tel 0449 720838
Price for 1 tonne in 25 kg bags - £105.00 ex works, orders by special arrangement only.
Price for 1 tonne delivered in 500 kg bags - £118.00
Price for 1 tonne delivered in bulk available by special order.
Members obtain a 3% discount on the above prices.

**Accepted**  OFG

**Use**  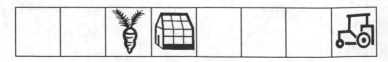

# OFG SEAWEED

> OFG Seaweed is produced exclusively for Organic Farmers and Growers Ltd by fermenting the seaweed and removing the liquid produced. It is concentrated and filtered before packaging. No external input of heat or chemicals is used during this process.
>
> OFG Seaweed contains natural growth stimulants which encourage root growth and in turn this stimulates the microbial activity around the root making more nutrients available. At least 60 minerals and trace elements are present in the liquid ensuring a bio-chemical balance is maintained. Disease and frost resistance is raised in all plants and application to grass gives a more palatable sward.

**How to use** Apply in autumn and spring to improve winter hardiness of crops particularly oats. Use in spring at the start of growth. In cereals extra benefit is to be gained from an application at flag leaf emergence.

**How much** Apply 3 litres per acre for cereals and grass. In fruit and vegetable crops use 6 litres per acre split into two applications.

**Other** OFG Seaweed is supplied as liquid in 20 litre plastic containers.

**Supplier** Organic Farmers and Growers Tel 0449 720838

Price for 20 litres - £50.40 with a £5 discount to members

**Accepted** OFG

**Use**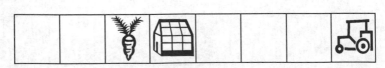

# ORGANIC BASED FERTILISER

> Organic Based Fertilisers are a range of fertilisers from Sea Trident. The fertilisers are suitable for use on cereals, oil seed rape, grass, potatoes, vegetables and fruit. The complete organic fertiliser carries Soil Association symbol approval and products S12, S14, S15, S17, S18, S21, BF and B carry Conservation Grade symbol approval.
>
> Organic Based Fertilisers contain a valuable amount of sulphur which assists the maximum utilisation of nitrogen, whilst the healthy soil action created makes soil based phosphates and potash more available to the plant. It gives a better growth, a greater resistance to leaching, a higher resistance to drought and a better keeping quality of the produce.

**How to use** Apply through standard spreaders.

**How much** For grass apply 3 - 5 bags per acre. For cereals apply 2 - 4 bags per acre. For potatoes apply 10 - 15 bags per acre. For oil seed rape apply 3 - 6 bags per acre. For sugar beet apply 3 - 9 bags per acre. For salad crops, brassicas, root crops, onions or leeks apply 8 - 10 bags pe acre. For fruit apply 6 -12 bags per acre.

**Other** Sea Trident Organic Based Fertilisers are supplied in 25 kg bags.

**Supplier** Sea Trident Limited Tel 0626 862489
Price on application to supplier.

**Accepted** SA GCFP

**Use**

# ORGANIC POTTING COMPOST

Organic Potting Compost is used for potting out and is suitable for use in all pot plants, hanging baskets, etc.

Organic Potting Compost contains wormcasts and perlite which together supply a good rooting material and a range of nutrients. Wormcasts are know to increase soil microbe activity to very high levels which in turn makes nutrients more available.

**How to use** Use as you would a normal potting compost.
**How much** Amount used will depend on the situation to which the compost is put and will depend on pot size, etc.
**Other** Organic Potting Compost is supplied as a powder in 35 litre bags. It will keep indefinitely.
**Supplier** Cumulus Organics Ltd Tel 0452 305814
Price for 35 litre bag - £6.50 (+ carriage)
**Accepted** All

**Use**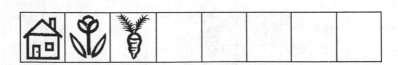

# ORGANIC SEEDING COMPOST

> Organic Seeding Compost is used for germination and seed beds and is particularly suitable for use with untreated seeds.
> Organic Seeding Compost contains a blend of composts which supply a variety of nutrients required by the seeds.

**How to use** For general us as a seed compost mix with peat to make a suitable ready to use compost.

**How much** Mix 1.5 kg of Organic seeding compost with 45 litres of peat. 1 bag will therefore mix with 1350 litres peat.

**Other** Organic Seeding Compost is supplied as a powder in 45 litre bags. It will keep indefinitely.

**Supplier** Cumulus Organics Ltd Tel 0452 305814
Price for 45 litre bag - £8.50 (+ carriage)

**Accepted** All

**Use**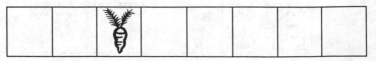

# ORIGINS FLOWER AND SHRUB FOOD

F

---

Origins Organic Flower and Shrub Food is a new product from Fisons which contains completely organic plant foods and trace elements plus a natural soil nutrient booster. It has an active ingredient of processed animal manure. It can be used in any planting areas where plants or shrubs are deficient of food.

---

**How to use** Scatter the tiny pellets evenly around plants. When sowing or planting; For shrubs - mix the pellets with the soil or compost that will refill the planting hole. For flowers - scatter the pellets onto the flower bed and work into the soil. Feeding during the growing season; Scatter pellets evenly around the plants and hoe into soil applying twice during the growing season from March onwards.

**How much** Application rates vary with time of year and species of plant or shrub.

**Other** Origins Organic Flower and Shrub Food must be watered into the soil if it does not rain within a week of application.

**Supplier** Fisons plc  Tel 0473 830492 and also supplied by most garden centres or department stores.
Price for 1 kg pack - £2.25 including VAT.
Price for 3.5 kg pack - £4.99 including VAT.

**Accepted** **All, is approved by the** Draft European Community Directive on producing organic food.

**Use**

# ORIGINS ORGANIC LAWN FOOD

---

Origins Organic Lawn Food is a new product from Fisons which has been developed through extensive research and uses only naturally occurring plant, animal and mineral materials. This new range of products called the Origins Organic are non toxic and effective to use.

Origins Organic Lawn Food fertilises the lawn and due to the nutrients being in organic form the nutrients are released slowly by microbial action. Effects will normally take 2 weeks to show but for a faster response, water the pellets in immediately after application.

---

**How to use** Scatter the pellets evenly onto the lawn. One feed will give the lawn enough nutrients to make a good start for the year.

**How much** Apply at the rate of 70 g per sq metre during March to April and 50 g per sq metre in June, August and October to November .

**Other** Origins Organic Lawn Food can be also used for establishing new lawns by before laying turf or seeding apply the lawn food at a rate of 100 g per sq metre and rake in. The new lawn can be fed again 3 months later, at a rate of 70 g per sq metre.

**Supplier** Fisons plc  Tel 0473 830492 and also supplied by most garden centres or department stores.
Price for 1.6 kg pack - £4.69 including VAT.
Price for 3.3 kg pack - £7.99 including VAT.
Price for 10 kg pack - £19.99 including VAT.
Price for 15 kg pack - £27.99 including VAT.

**Accepted** All, is approved by the Draft European Community Directive on producing organic food.

**Use**

Fertiliser

# ORIGINS ORGANIC SEAWEED EXTRACT

Origins Organic Seaweed Extract is a new product from Fisons which is a completely organic concentrated liquid plant fertiliser that is ideal for all types of plants.
Origins Organic Seaweed Extract contains plant hormones and trace elements. It enhances nutrient uptake, plant development and resistance to adverse conditions. It can be used as either a foliar feed or a root drench and it is possible to use in dry weather.

**How to use** Apply as a diluted solution to plants depending on size and species.

**How much** To use for root drenching dilute 4 measures (4 bottle caps which are 10 ml each) into 4.5 litres (1 gallon) of water. Apply every 1 - 2 weeks to all types of plants young or mature. To use for foliar feeding dilute 2 measures in 4.5 litres of water. Spray every 1 - 2 weeks. Ensure leaves are thoroughly wetted but do not apply to open flowers or in the direct sunlight.

**Other** Origins Organic Seaweed Extract is supplied as a concentrated liquid in two standard sized bottles, 1 litre and 500 ml. It must be diluted before using on any plant and can be applied using any standard spray gun.

**Supplier** Fisons plc  Tel 0473 830492
Also supplied by most garden centres or departments.
Price available on application.

**Accepted** **All, is approved by the** Draft European Community Directive on producing organic food.

Use

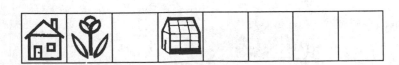

# ORIGINS ORGANIC SOIL TONIC

Origins Organic Soil Tonic is a new product from Fisons which unlocks soil nutrients and makes them more available for plants to use therefore improving soil fertility. It is one of the products from the new range of products called the Origins Organic. It can be used on all types of soil and its active ingredients are organic materials.

Origins Organic Soil Tonic contains organic material that promotes microbial activity and increases availability of minerals and trace elements.

**How to use** Scatter the granules evenly around the planting area and rake into the soil. It can be applied at any time of the year but especially effective when used in early spring.

**How much** Apply at the rate of 35 g per sq metre.

**Other** Origins Organic Soil tonic is supplied in one standard size pack which contains 350 g of granules.

**Supplier** Fisons plc  Tel 0473 830492 and also supplied by most garden centres or department stores.
Price for a 350 g shaker bottle - £2.99 inc.VAT

**Accepted** All is approved by the Draft European Community Directive on producing organic food.

**Use**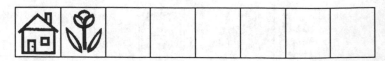

# ORIGINS ORGANIC TOMATO FOOD

Origins Organic Tomato Food is a new product from Fisons which is a completely organic compound fertiliser that is a balanced food for growing tomatoes, courgettes, green peppers and aubergines.
It contains only naturally occurring plant, animal and mineral materials. Origins Organic Tomato Food contains processed animal manures and minerals from natural sources as the active ingredients. The manures stimulate microbial activity in the soil which increases the availability of nutrients to the plant.

**How to use** Scatter the pellets evenly around the base of a plant.

**How much** For feeding in growing bags, once the first truss has set, apply 50 g or 2 oz per growing bag per week and push the pellets down inside the bag. For feeding in containers and borders, before planting - prepare the soil by forking in 150 g m² or 4 oz per sq yard. After planting - once the first truss has set, apply 25 g or 1 oz per plant two weeks and work into soil.Apply at the rate of 70 g per sq metre during March to April and 50 g per sq metre in June, August and October to November .

**Other** Origins Organic Tomato Food is added when the first truss has set, this is when small green fruits have appeared.

**Supplier** Fisons plc  Tel 0473 830492 and also supplied by most garden centres or department stores.
Price for 1 kg pack - £2.25 including VAT.

**Accepted** **All, is approved by the** Draft European Community Directive on producing organic food.

**Use**

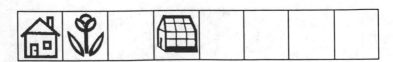

# ORIGINS ORGANIC VEGETABLE FERTILISER F

Origins Organic Vegetable Fertiliser is a new product from Fisons which as the name suggests it is an organic fertiliser that is recommended for feeding vegetables. It boosts plant growth and strengthens long term soil fertility.

Origins Organic Vegetable Fertiliser contains processed animal manure which breaks down slowly in the soil to release nutrients. The product is pelleted to prevent an unpleasant smell and to increase its handling efficiency thus preventing wastage.

**How to use** It can be used by scattering the pellets evenly around the plant.

**How much** When planting or sowing; Scatter the pellets on to the soil and work into the top 4 inches of the soil. Ffor feeding during the growing season; When the crop is well established, scatter the pellets and hoe into the soil. Apply when sowing, 100 - 150 g per sq metre, when planting 150 -250 g per sq metre and during the season 70 - 100 g per sq metre.

**Other** It is available in pellets in two sizes of box, a 1 kg or 5 kg box. Water Origins Organic Vegetable Fertiliser into the soil if it does not rain a week after application.

**Supplier** Fisons plc  Tel 0473 830492
Also supplied by most garden centres or departments.
Price for 1 kg pack - £1.99 including VAT.
Price for 5 kg pack - £3.99 including VAT.

**Accepted** All, it is approved by the Draft European Community Directive on producing organic food.

**Use**

# PERLKA

Perlka is a nitrogen fertiliser which can also be used for a variety of other purposes. As a fertiliser it provides a slow release of nitrogen with minimal risk of nitrate pollution. It also has a liming effect on the soil. Due to its strong pesticidal properties it can be used as a herbicide, fungicide and nematicide and will also help to control parasites of livestock such as liver fluke.

Perlka is totally broken down in the soil by a complex system of interacting factors (plants, microbes, etc) and to which the product can attribute its many features. Perlka is based on calcium cyanamide ($CaCN_2$) and contains approximately 20% nitrogen and 50% lime. In contact with the soil moisture the calcium cyanamide becomes cyanamide ($H_2CN_2$) which has pesticidal properties.

**How to use** Perlka can be applied through standard spreaders. For control of clubroot use Perlka before planting. Avoid planting the crop too soon after application of Perlka so that germination is not impaired. A waiting period of two days is recommended for every 100 kg of Perlka applied per hectare. If plants are transplanted in blocks of peat the waiting period can be reduced by about 7 days. Post-emergence application is possible for some crops, eg cereals and oilseed rape however the plant leaves must be dry.

**How much** Generally in cereals apply 300 - 400 kg per ha for weed and eye spot control. For weed control in maize and potatoes apply 300 - 500 kg per hectare. For control of weeds and root-rot in sugar beet apply 400 - 600 kg per ha. For fruit trees apply 400 - 800 kg per ha. Rates for vegetables vary.

**Other** Perlka is supplied as a grey coloured granule in 25 kg and 50 kg bags or in a 1 kg tin.

**Supplier** Robin Appel Ltd Tel 0489 896388
Price available on request from supplier.

**Accepted** GCFP

**Use**

# PURE BLOOD FISH AND BONE

Pure Blood Fish and Bone is a completely organic product made by W.L. Dingley who have been producing organic Base Fertiliser for many years. It is used for market garden and glass house crops.

Pure Blood Fish and Bone is made from a careful blend and selection of organic substances and minerals resulting in a balanced fertiliser of Nitrogen, Phosphate and Potash (potash is the sulphate form of potassium thus minimalising chlorine content), as well as trace elements. The resulting mixture is pelleted which means that not only the efficiency of the product is increased but the handling and spreading is cleaner, quicker and more accurate, which reduces both time and wastage. All the compounds contained by the fertilisers are approved by The Conservation Grade and The Soil Association.

**How to use**  Can be applied with the use of any standard pellet fertiliser spreader.

**How much**  For use in a glasshouse or polytunnel the application is 3 - 5 bags/acre.

**Other**  The Pure Blood Fish and Bone fertiliser is supplied as pellets in 50 kg or 500 kg bags. The contained trace elements are obtained from natural organic sources therefore it is not possible to guarantee the quantities present in each fertiliser as variations can occur.

**Supplier**  W.L. Dingley & Co.Tel 0386 830242
Price for 1 tonne at list price is £255 + VAT but is reduced depending on the quantity purchased.

**Accepted**  All

**Use**

# PURE ENGLISH BONEMEAL

Pure English Bonemeal is used to provide phosphate for strawberries, fruit trees, shrubs, roses and herbaceous plants.
The bone is broken down slowly in the soil by microbial action and acids leached from plant roots to release phosphate. The bonemeal is sterilised and also provides 3.5% nitrogen.

**How to use** Sprinkle on the soil surface and hoe or rake in.

**How much** For general use apply 4 oz per sq yd, 100 grams per m². Use 1 small bag per 15 m² (12 sq yd). 1 medium bag will treat 100 m² (83 sq yd). 1 large bag will treat 200 m² (166 sq yd).

**Other** Pure English Bonemeal is supplied as a powder in 1.5 kg, 2 kg, 10 kg and 20 kg. It will keep indefinitely.

**Supplier** Cumulus Organics Ltd Tel 0452 305814 and from Gala Brokers Ltd 0244 390712
Price for 1.5 kg from Cumulus - £2.79 (+ carriage)
Price for 2 kg from Gala Brokers - £3.20
Price for 10 kg from Cumulus - £12.90 (+ carriage)
Price for 20 kg from Cumulus - £16.50 (+ carriage)

**Accepted** All

**Use**

# REDDZLAAG

---

Reddzlaag - "the natural successor to basic slag" is produced in a similar process to its predecessor. Quarried calcium alumino ore is heated to form a granular phosphate fertiliser.

Reddzlaag is suitable for use in any soil and is especially useful in alkaline soils due to its relatively low calcium content. Reddzlagg contains a useful range of trace elements as well as 32% $P_2O_5$ and 11% $Fe_2O_3$. The granules will breakdown gradually in the soil to release the mineral nutrients.

---

**How to use** This can be applied at any time of the year through standard applicators. A spreading service is available in most parts of the U.K.

**How much** Apply 250 kg per acre or 550 kg per ha, every 3 years.

**Other** Reddzlaag is supplied as granules or solid in 50 kg bags or in bulk. It will keep indefinitely.

**Supplier** Gale & Mount / Rhone Poulenc Ltd Tel 061 7873337 and also from local agents. The national Coordinator is Eric Wigg.

Price on application to supplier - will depend on order size.

**Accepted** OFG GCFP

**Use**

# REDDZLAAG

Reddzlaag - "the natural successor to basic slag" is produced in a similar process to its predecessor. Quarried calcium alumino ore is heated to form a granular phosphate fertiliser.

Reddzlaag is suitable for use in any soil and is especially useful in alkaline soils due to its relatively low calcium content. Reddzlagg contains a useful range of trace elements as well as 32% $P_2O_5$ and 11% $Fe_2O_3$. The granules will breakdown gradually in the soil to release the mineral nutrients.

**How to use** Apply through standard spreader.

**How much** An application of 4 - 6 cwt (200 - 300 kg) per acre is recommended. Requirements will vary depending on the current soil reserves and the crop grown. As the phosphate and calcium will be slowly released from the rock and can be held in the soil application need only be repeated every three years.

**Other** Reddzlagg is available in 50 kg bags or in bulk.

**Supplier** Organic Farmers and Growers Ltd Tel 0449 720838
Price for 1 tonne in 50 kg bags - £146.50
Price for 1 tonne in 10 tonnes bulk - £136.50
Price for 1 tonne in 10 tonne bulk spread - £149.50
Delivery is included for England and Wales.

**Accepted** OFG GCFP

**Use**

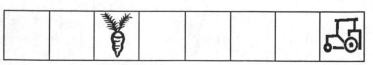

335

# RHIZOKIN

Rhizokin is used encourage growth and nutrient uptake in crops and other plants to ensure maximum yields and health.

Rhizokin contains natural extract of cytokinins, plant growth hormones, combined with trace elements and other growth factors. The combination of ingredients stimulates nutrient uptake and promotes photosynthesis which provides the 'fuel' for growth.

**How to use** Apply as a foliar feed by spraying on to the plants.
**How much** Application rates will depend on the crop concerned.
**Other** Rhizokin is supplied in 10 litre and 20 litre containers. Shelf life is 12 months.
**Supplier** Microbial Developments Ltd Tel 0684 568434
Price on application to supplier.
**Accepted** All

**Use**

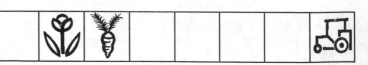

Fertilisers

# ROCK PHOSPHATE

Rock phosphate is used to supply a very slow release phosphate and to give long term improvement to soil phosphorus status.

Rock phosphate is a pure ground rock that contains 26% $P_2O_5$. The rock will be broken down slowly in the soil by microbial activity and by acids leached from the plant roots and mineral nutrients will be released.

**How to use** Scatter over the soil surface and hoe well in.
**How much** Apply 6 - 8 oz per square yard.
**Other** Rock phosphate is supplied as a powder of ground rock in 20 kg bags.
**Supplier** HDRA Sales Ltd Tel 0203 303517
Price for 20 kg bag from HDRA shop only - £17.00 (19910 price)
**Accepted** All

Use

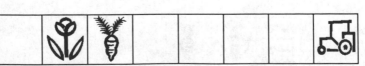

# ROCK PHOSPHATE

Rock phosphate is used to supply a very slow release phosphate and to give long term improvement to soil phosphorus status.

Rock phosphate is a pure ground rock that contains 26% $P_2O_5$. The rock will be broken down slowly in the soil by microbial activity and by acids leached from the plant roots and mineral nutrients will be released.

**How to use** Scatter over the soil surface and hoe well in. It is best applied in autumn or winter to be effective the next summer.

**How much** Apply 2 - 4 oz per square yard.

**Other** Rock phosphate is supplied as a powder of ground rock in 3 kg, 6 kg and 25 kg bags.

**Supplier** Chempak Products Tel 0992 441888
Price for 3 kg - £2.25
Price for 6 kg - £3.95
Price for 25 kg - £11.90

**Accepted** All

**Use**

# ROCK POTASH

Rock potash as its name implies is a crushed rock source of potash. It can be used as a slow release potassium fertiliser. The presence of some calcium and magnesium will also aid build up of these minerals in the soil. It is suitable for use on all crops.

Rock potash is made from adularia shale and analysis may vary as with all products from natural sources. Most of the rock is silicate with the average analysis for this product showing it to contain 55% $SiO_2$, 11% $K_2O$, 6% CaO, 5% MgO, 3% $Fe_2O_3$ and a mixture of other minerals.

Rock potash is insoluble in water and therefore cannot be leached from the soil. Release of the potash from the mineral rock is achieved by acids leached into the soil by the plant's root hairs which gradually break down the rock structure and convert the potash to a water soluble form that can be taken up by the plant.

**How to use** Apply through standard spreader. It is best to apply in autumn or winter to be effective the following summer.

**How much** For horticultural or garden plants apply 4 - 8 oz per square yard. For grass and cereals apply 250 kg per acre, this will provide approximately 55 units of $K_2O$. For potatoes, other root crops and vegetables apply 500 kg - 1 tonne per acre. Requirements will vary depending on the current soil reserves and the specific crop grown. As the potash will be slowly released from the rock and can be held in the soil application need only be repeated every three years.

**Other** Rock Potash is supplied as a powder in 3 kg, 6 kg and 25 kg bags.

**Supplier** Chempak Products Tel 0992 441888
Price for 3 kg - £2.70
Price for 6 kg - £4.75
Price for 25 kg - £15.65

**Accepted** OFG

**Use**

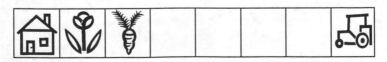

# ROCK POTASH

Rock potash as its name implies is a powdered rock source of potash. It can be used as a slow release potassium fertiliser. The presence of some calcium and magnesium will also aid build up of these minerals in the soil. Rock potash is made from adularia shale and analysis may vary as with all products from natural sources. Most of the rock is silicate with the average analysis for this product showing it to contain 55% $SiO_2$, 11% $K_2O$, 6% CaO, 5% MgO, 3% $Fe_2O_3$ and a mixture of other minerals.

Rock potash is insoluble in water and therefore cannot be leached from the soil. Release of the potash from the mineral rock is achieved by acids leached into the soil by the plant's root hairs which gradually break down the rock structure and convert the potash to a water soluble form that can be taken up by the plant.

**How to use** Sprinkle on to the soil and hoe or rake in.

**How much** For general use apply 6 - 8 oz per sq yd, 200g per $m^2$ every 2-3 years. 1 small bag treats 15 $m^2$ (13 sq yd), 1 large bag treats 100 $m^2$ (83 sq yd).

**Other** Rock potash is supplied as a powder in 3 kg and 20 kg bags. it will keep indefinitely.

**Supplier** Cumulus Organics Ltd Tel 0452 305814 and from HDRA Sales Ltd Tel 0203 303517 (Ryton shop only) and from Suffolk Herbs Ltd Tel 0787 227247 (3 kg pack only).
Price for 3 kg from Suffolk Herbs - £2.90 (+P&P)
Price for 3 kg from Cumulus - £2.65 (+ carriage)
Price for 3 kg from HDRA shop - £2.65 (1990 price)
Price for 20 kg from Cumulus - £10.35 (+ carriage)
Price for 20 kg from HDRA shop - £14.00 (1990 price)

**Accepted** All

**Use**

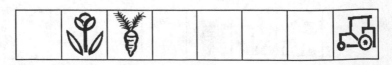

# ROCK POTASH

Rock potash as its name implies is a powdered rock source of potash. It can be used as a slow release potassium fertiliser. The presence of some calcium and magnesium will also aid build up of these minerals in the soil.

Rock potash is made from adularia shale and analysis may vary as with all products from natural sources. Most of the rock is silicate with the average analysis for this product showing it to contain 55% $SiO_2$, 11% $K_2O$, 6% CaO, 5% MgO, 3% $Fe_2O_3$ and a mixture of other minerals.

Rock potash is insoluble in water and therefore cannot be leached from the soil. Release of the potash from the mineral rock is achieved by acids leached into the soil by the plant's root hairs which gradually break down the rock structure and convert the potash to a water soluble form that can be taken up by the plant.

**How to use**  Apply through standard spreader.

**How much**  For grass and cereals apply 250 kg per acre, this will provide approximately 55 units of $K_2O$. For potatoes, other root crops and vegetables apply 500 kg - 1 tonne per acre. Requirements will vary depending on the current soil reserves and the specific crop grown. As the potash will be slowly released from the rock and can be held in the soil application need only be repeated every three years.

**Other**  Rock Potash is supplied as a powder in bags of 25 kg or 500 kg and also in bulk.

**Supplier**  Organic Farmers and Growers Ltd Tel 0449 720838
Price for 1.5 tonne in 25 kg bags - £76.00
Price for 1 tonne in 500 kg bags - £69.00
Price for 1 tonne in bulk - £56.70
Delivery is charged extra on these prices.

**Accepted**  All

**Use**

# Root Dip & Transplant Aid

Root Dip & Transplant Aid is used to improve survival and establishment of bare rooted trees (including bonsai), whips, shrubs and roses.

Root Dip & Transplanting Aid is derived from seaweed and contains natural trace elements and plant hormones cytokinins, auxins and giberellins which stimulate growth and root formation. Stress caused by damage to the rooting system and problems of dehydration are major factors influencing the success of transplanting. The gelatinous form of the root dip provides a temporary seal around the plant root providing nutrients and allowing water to be taken up by the plant.

**How to use** During transplanting dip the root in to the gel and ensure that all the root surface is covered.

**How much** Amount used will depend on the size of the plant and the extent of the rooting system.

**Other** Root Dip & Transplanting Aid is supplied as a gel in 1 litre, 2.5 litre and 5 litre plastic containers.

**Supplier** Chempak Products Tel 0992 441888
Price for 1 litre - £7.50
Price for 2.5 litres - £16.00
Price for 5 litres - £27.00

**Use**

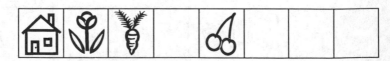

Fertiliser

# SEAWEED MEAL

> Seaweed Meal is for use as soil conditioner and fertiliser. The seaweed in this product from HDRA is collected off the West coast of Ireland where there is little pollution of the sea and coastlines.
> Seaweed Meal contains nitrogen, potassium, and a wide range of trace elements. The seaweed also adds a variety of organic compounds to the soil which encourage microbial activity in the soil and combined with the nutrients released during breakdown in the soil stimulate plant growth.

**How to use** Apply in winter. Sprinkle on to the soil and hoe or rake in.

**How much** For general use apply 4 - 6 oz per sq yd, 100 - 200 grams per m². Apply 1 small pack per 8 - 15 m² (6 - 12 sq yd). Use 1 medium pack per 50 - 100 m² (40 - 83 sq yd). 1 large pack will treat 100 - 200 m² (85 - 165 sq yd).

**Other** Seaweed Meal is supplied as a powder in 1.5 kg, 10 kg and 20 kg bags.

**Supplier** Cumulus Organics Ltd Tel 0452 305814 and from Gala Brokers Tel 0244 390712
Price for 1.5 kg from Cumulus - £2.99 (+ carriage)
Price for 1.5 kg from Gala Brokers - £3.50
Price for 10 kg from Cumulus - £17.60 (+ carriage)
Price for 20 kg from Cumulus - £25.46 (+ carriage)

**Accepted** All

Use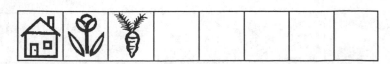

# SEAWEED MEAL

Seaweed Meal is for use as soil conditioner and fertiliser. The seaweed in this product from HDRA is collected off the West coast of Ireland where there is little pollution of the sea and coastlines.

Seaweed Meal contains nitrogen, potassium, and a wide range of trace elements. The seaweed also adds a variety of organic compounds to the soil which encourage microbial activity in the soil and combined with the nutrients released during breakdown in the soil stimulate plant growth.

**How to use** Scatter over bare soil in autumn and hoe or fork into the soil surface. it is suitable for use on lawns and can be scattered into the compost heap to activate microbial activity.

**How much** For use as a top dressing apply 4 - 6 oz per square yard.

**Other info** Seaweed Meal is supplied a powder in 1.5 kg, 4.5 kg and 20 kg bags.

**Supplier** HDRA Sales Ltd Tel 0203 303517 (Ryton shop only) and from Suffolk Herbs Ltd Tel 0787 227247 (1.5 kg pack only)
Price for 1.5 kg bag from Suffolk Herbs - £3.25
Price for 4.5 kg bag from HDRA shop - £5.90 (1990 price)
Price for 20 kg bag from HDRA shop - £25.50 (1990 price)

**Accepted** All

Use

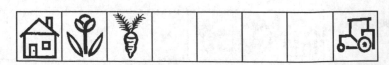

# SEAWEED MEAL

Seaweed meal is available in two grades. The poorer of the two is for application to soil and can be used to improve soil structure and supply trace elements. The higher grade is of feed quality and can be used to supply minerals, trace elements, vitamins and amino acids to all livestock.

Seaweed meal applied to the soil will encourage microbial activity and be broken down to release minerals, trace elements and other nutrients. The result of the microbial breakdown is humus which is broken down much more slowly in the soil and acts similarly to clay particles as they are electrically charged. Organic gums are also produced and together with the humus help to hold the soil mineral particles together in aggregates giving structure to sandy soils and allowing easier passage of air and water in clay soil.

**How to use**   Seaweed Meal should be spread over the soil before or during the winter and allowed to breakdown on the surface. The meal should then be incorporated into the soil in the spring.

High quality Seaweed Meal should be fed to stock during the winter and can be top dressed (sprinkled) on the daily ration or fed free access.

**How much**   For soil conditioning an application of 100 - 200 kg per acre is recommended.

For use as a feed supplement allow 2 oz (60 grams) per day. Therefore 1 bag will treat approximately 100 animals for 4 days.

**Other info**   Seaweed Meal is supplied for both soil application and feed supplement use in 25 kg paper bags.

**Supplier**   Organic Farmers and Growers Ltd Tel 0449 720838

Price 1 tonne for soil conditioning - £340.00

Price 1 tonne for use as a feed supplement - £400.00

Delivery is charged extra on this price.

**Accepted**   OFG

**Use**

345

# SEAWEED MEAL

> Seaweed Meal is for use as soil conditioner and fertiliser. It strengthens and thickens growth and improves colour and so is ideal for lawns, golf courses, etc.
>
> Seaweed Meal contains seaweed that has been dried and crushed to form a meal. It supplies nitrogen, potassium, and a wide range of trace elements. The seaweed also adds a variety of organic compounds to the soil which encourage microbial activity in the soil and combined with the nutrients released during breakdown in the soil stimulate plant growth. An alginate gel and other organic material released during breakdown helps improve soil structure.

**How to use** Scatter over bare soil in autumn and hoe or fork into the soil surface. It is suitable for use on lawns and can be scattered into the compost heap to activate microbial activity.

**How much** For general use as a top dressing apply 4 oz per square yard. for lawns apply 2 oz per square yard, 2 - 3 times a year if necessary.

**Other** Seaweed Meal is supplied as a powder in 3 kg, 6 kg and 25 kg bags.

**Supplier** Chempak Products Tel 0992 441888
Price for 3 kg - £3.50
Price for 6 kg - £6.15
Price for 25 kg - £17.25

**Accepted** All

**Use**

# SILVAPERL HORSE MANURE

Silvaperl Horse Manure is for use as a soil conditioner to improve soil structure and fertility. Use in light soils improve water holding capacity and to provide better drainage and aeration in clay soils. It is not suitable for use for lime hating plants such as rhododendrons, azaleas and heathers.

Silvaperl Horse Manure contains composted sterilised horse manure blended with peat and ground chalk. The horse manure will add humus to the soil which helps bind the particles into aggregates and so gives the soil structure and the chalk will supply calcium that counteracts acidity in the soil.

**How to use** For improving the soil dig the manure into the top 15 - 25 cm (6 - 9 inches) of soil in spring or autumn. Use at planting around the roots of crops or use as a surface mulch.

**How much** For mulching or during laying of new lawns spread a layer of manure approximately 5 cm (2 inches) deep on the required area. One 50 litre bag will cover an area of 1 m². For planting out mix the manure with an equal quantity of soil.

**Other** Silvaperl Horse Manure is supplied in a 50 litre bag.

**Supplier** Sinclair Horticulture & Leisure Ltd Tel 0522 537561 and from most wholesalers and garden centres.
Price for 50 litres - £3.88

**Accepted** All

Use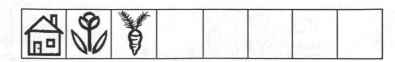

# SILVAPERL SEAGOLD

> Silvaperl Seagold is for use as a soil conditioner and to encourage soil microbial activity and vigorous root development in all plants.
>   Silvaperl Seagold contains the coral like seaweed *Lithothamnium calcareum* which accumulated calcium during its growth. The seaweed is broken down in the soil by microbial activity to release minerals and trace elements and the residual humus helps add structure to the soil.

**How to use** Apply the recommended amount to the soil surface and lightly rake into the top soil.

**How much** For lawns apply 70 grams per m² (2 oz per square yard). For flowers apply 140 grams per m² top dressed. For vegetables and soft fruit apply 200 grams per m² (6 oz per square yard). For fruit trees apply 350 grams per m² (10 oz per square yard). Apply once a year. Annual applications will continue to improve the soil.

**Other** Silvaperl Seagold is supplied in 5 lb, 10 lb, 20 lb and 50 lb bags. (2.3 kg, 4.5 kg, 9.1 kg and 22.7 kg respectively)

**Supplier** Sinclair Horticulture & Leisure Ltd Tel 0522 537561 and from most wholesalers and garden centres.
Price for 5 lb - £1.84
Price for 10 lb - £3.43
Price for 20 lb - £6.39
Price for 50 lb - £12.18

**Accepted** All

**Use**

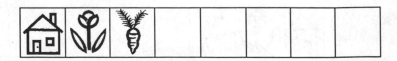

# SM3 LIQUID SEAWEED EXTRACT

SM3 Liquid Seaweed Extract is used as a soil conditioner and as a potassium and trace element fertiliser. It will stimulate plant growth and reduce the effects of stress.

SM3 Liquid Seaweed Extract contains alginic acid which binds sand particles together and separates clay particles helping to give all soils better structure. Alginic acid also encourages microbial activity in the soil around the plant roots and the seaweed releases nutrients that can be absorbed by the plant and so health growth is promoted.

**How to use** This is a very concentrated feed and must be diluted with water before use. Apply as a foliar feed or apply directly to the soil.

**How much** Mix 10 ml per 4.5 litres of water and apply as desired. Amount to use will depend on plant species and soil status.

**Other info** SM3 Liquid Seaweed Extract is supplied in 125 ml, 500 ml and 1 litre containers.

**Supplier** HDRA Sales Ltd Tel 0203 303517 (Ryton shop only) - 125 ml and 1 litre packs and from
Suffolk Herbs Ltd Tel 0787 227247 (500 ml and 1 litre only)
Price for 125 ml from HDRA shop - £1.15 (1990 price)
Price for 500 ml from Suffolk Herbs - £5.30 (Inc P&P)
Price for 1 litre from HDRA shop - £5.25 (1990 price)
Price for 1 litre from Suffolk Herbs - £5.25 (+ P&P)

**Accepted** All

Use

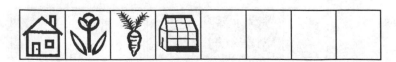

# STIMGRO MULTI-PURPOSE COMPOST

Stimgro Multi-Purpose Compost can be used as an alternative to conventional composts.

Stimgro Multi-Purpose Compost contains a blend of cow manure and peat which has been matured for at least 2 years. The manure supplies nutrients that increase plant growth as well as stimulating microbial activity around the plant roots. The inclusion of peat provides a medium for the plants to root in that can hold water very efficiently however this makes it a less than optimal environmental friendly product in terms of conservation of threatened habitats.

**How to use** Use as you would any other general purpose compost.

How much      Amount used will vary with the plant species and the pot size used, etc. 1 small pack will fill 10 0.5 litre pots.

**Other**      Stimgro Multi-Purpose Compost is supplied as a loose fibrous material in 5 litre, 15 litre and 40 litre bags.

**Supplier**      Stimgro Natural Organic Garden Foods Tel 0536 402182 and from Gala (Brokers) Ltd Tel 0244 390712

         Price for 5 litres - £1.49

         Price for 15 litres - £3.69

         Price for 40 litres - £6.89

Accepted      All

**Use**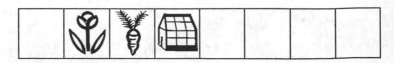

# STIMGRO ORGANIC COW MANURE

Stimgro Organic Cow Manure is a humus rich odour free manure making it very convenient and pleasant to use. It is used as a soil conditioner and to improve soil structure.
Stimgro Organic Cow Manure contains a blend of cow manure and peat which has been matured for at least 2 years. The mix supplies nutrients that increase plant growth as well as microbes and humus that improves soil structure. Although the source of this product is organic its peat content makes it a less than optimal environmental friendly product in terms of conservation of threatened habitats.

**How to use** Stimgro Cow Manure can be applied through standard spreaders. In gardens sprinkle onto the soil and incorporate into the soil.

**How much** Apply 40 litres (20 kg) per 10 m². A small bag (15 litres) will treat approximately 4 m². An area of 100 m² will require 10 large bags.

**Other info** Stimgro Organic Cow Manure is supplied as a loose fibrous material in 15 litre, 40 litre, and 20 kg bags.

**Supplier** Stimgro Natural Organic Garden Foods Tel 0536 402182 and from Gala (Brokers) Ltd Tel 0244 390712
Price for 15 litres - £3.69
Price for 40 litres - £6.89
Price for 20 kg economy bag - £4.99

**Accepted** All

**Use**

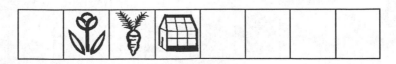

# STIMGRO ORGANIC GROWING BAG

Stimgro Organic Growing Bag is suitable as an organic alternative to conventional grow bags and makes a convenient way for gardeners and those with restricted space be able to grow food organically.

Stimgro Organic Growing Bag contains a blend of cow manure and peat which has been matured for at least 2 years. The manure supplies nutrients that increase plant growth as well as stimulating microbial activity around the plant roots. The inclusion of peat provides a medium for the plants to root in that can hold water very efficiently however this makes it a less than optimal environmental friendly product in terms of conservation of threatened habitats.

**How to use** Use as you would any other grow bag. The crops are planted directly into the growing bag by cutting holes into the upper surface of the bag. Full instructions for use are printed onto the growing bag.

**How much** The number of plants that can be planted into the growing bag will depend on the crop species chosen and its rooting requirements.

**Other info** Stimgro Organic Growing Bag is supplied as a loose fibrous material in a plastic bag ready for use.

**Supplier** Stimgro Natural Organic Garden Foods Tel 0536 402182 and from Gala (Brokers) Ltd Tel 0244 390712
Price per growing bag - £3.69

**Accepted** All

**Use**

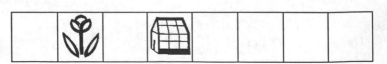

352

# STIMGRO ORGANIC PLANTING MIXTURE

Stimgro Organic Planting Mixture is designed to give a healthy start to trees, shrubs and roses when planted out.

Stimgro Organic Planting Mixture contains a blend of cow manure and peat which has been matured for at least 2 years. The manure supplies nutrients that increase plant growth as well as stimulating microbial activity around the plant roots. The inclusion of peat provides a medium for the plants to root in that can hold water very efficiently however this makes it a less than optimal environmental friendly product in terms of conservation of threatened habitats.

**How to use**  Use as you would any other planting compost. Sprinkle in around the roots of the plant when planted. Suitable for use for as a planting medium for shrubs in pots.

**How much**  Amount used will vary with the plant size and species. A 5 litre bag will be sufficient from two medium sized shrubs.

**Other**  Stimgro Organic Planting Mixture is supplied as a loose fibrous material in 5 litre 15 litre and 40 litre bags.

**Supplier**  Stimgro Natural Organic Garden Foods Tel 0536 402182 and from Gala (Brokers) Ltd Tel 0244 390712
Price for 5 litres - £1.45
Price for 15 litres - £3.29 (+33% extra = 20 litres)
Price for 40 litres - £5.99 (+33% extra = 52 litres)

**Accepted**  All

**Use**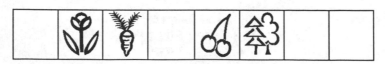

# STIMGRO ORGANIC SEED COMPOST

F

Stimgro Organic Seed Compost can be used as an alternative to conventional seed composts.

Stimgro Organic Seed Compost contains a blend of cow manure and peat which has been matured for at least 2 years. The manure supplies nutrients that increase plant growth as well as stimulating microbial activity around the plant roots. The inclusion of peat provides a medium for the plants to root in that can hold water very efficiently however this makes it a less than optimal environmental friendly product in terms of conservation of threatened habitats.

| | |
|---|---|
| **How to use** | Use as you would any other seed compost. |
| **How much** | Amount used will vary with the plant species and the seed tray size used, etc. |
| **Other** | Stimgro Organic Seed Compost is supplied as a loose fibrous material in 5 litre and 15 litre bags. |
| **Supplier** | Stimgro Natural Organic Garden Foods Tel 0536 402182 and from Gala (Brokers) Ltd Tel 0244 390712 |
| | Price for 5 litres - £1.49 |
| | Price for 15 litres - £3.69 |
| **Accepted** | All |

Fertilisers

# SULPHATE OF POTASH

Sulphate of Potash is used as a potassium fertiliser and is suitable for use on all plants. Potassium imparts flavour to tomatoes, colour to flowers and aids ripening in fruit.

Sulphate of Potash contains 50% $K_2O$ and also provides useful amounts of sulphur. The potash breaks down in the soil to release potassium that can be taken up by the plant.

**How to use** Sprinkle onto the soil and hoe or rake into the surface.

**How much** For use as a straight fertiliser apply 1 oz per square yard. Do not over apply as potassium tends to lock up other minerals especially calcium.

**Other** Sulphate of Potash is supplied in 3 kg, 6 kg and 25 kg bags.

**Supplier** Chempak Products Tel 0992 441888
Price for 3 kg - £2.50
Price for 6 kg - £4.40
Price for 25 kg - £14.95

**Accepted** OFG SA UKROFS GCFP

Use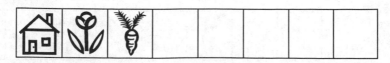

# SUPERLIME 'COMPLETE', 'P' AND 'K'

Superlime products are used for reducing soil acidity whilst maintaining phosphate and potassium levels and supplying trace elements.

Superlime contains lime and fertiliser. 'P' contains no potassium, 'K' contains no phosphorus while 'Complete' contains both potassium and phosphorus.

**How to use** Superlime can be spread through most types of hopper. Depending on pH and requirement for potassium or phosphorus choose the appropriate Superlime type. Apply 0.5 - 1 tonne per acre (1.1 - 2.2 tonnes per ha).

**How much** Depends on soil pH and requirements as discussed above. 1 tonne of Superlime 'Complete' per acre will provide 60 units of potassium and phosphorus.

**Other** Superlime is supplied as a powder of ground rock in 25 kg and 500 kg bags. It is also available in bulk. Keep under cover if possible.

**Supplier** Glenside Organics Ltd Tel 0786 816655
Price on application to supplier.

**Accepted** All

**Use**

Fertilisers

# SUPER-SPUD

Super-Spud is for use as a general fertiliser for use on potatoes. It contains 10% nitrogen, 10.9% total phosphates and 18% potash. Trace elements are also added to promote strong, healthy growth. Super-Spud increases microbial activity in the soil and makes nutrients more available to the plant.

**How to use** Apply through standard applicators.
**How much** Amount to apply will depend on the number of applications to be made and the time of sowing and harvesting.
**Other** Super-Spud is supplied as a granule.
**Supplier** Tony Ashmore Ltd Tel 0270 586671
Price on application to supplier.
**Accepted** GCFP

**Use**

# TIMAC

Timac is a phosphate fertiliser suitable for use on all soils particularly in alkaline soils as it contains no calcium and will not affect pH.
Timac contains 27% $P_2O_5$ and will give a slow release of phosphate that can be held in the soil.

**How to use** Apply through standard spreader.

**How much** An application of 3 - 7 cwt (150 - 350 kg) per acre is recommended. Requirements will vary depending on the current soil reserves and the crop grown. As the phosphate will be slowly released from the rock and can be held in the soil application need only be repeated every three years.

**Other info** Timac G27 is available in 50 kg or 500 kg bags.

**Supplier** Organic Farmers and Growers Ltd Tel 0449 720838
Price for 1 tonne in 50 kg bags - £111.00
Price for 1 tonne in 100 kg bags - £108.00
Delivery is charged extra on these prices.

**Accepted** All

**Use**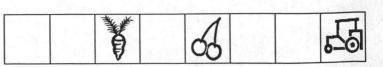

Fertilisers

# TRIPLE SLAG

Triple Slag is for use as a phosphorus fertiliser for grass either for grazing or cutting. It will sweeten pastures, improve herbage, clovers and palatability.
   Triple slag contains 30.5% total phosphates which promotes growth of clover in the sward. Clover is very palatable to stock and increases the amount of organic nitrogen available to the grasses and so improves growth of the sward.

**How to use**  Apply through standard applicators.
**How much**  For grass apply 5 bags per acre every three years.
**Other**  Triple Slag is supplied in bags.
**Supplier**  Tony Ashmore Ltd Tel 0270 586671
   Price on application to supplier.
**Accepted**  GCFP

**Use**

# Uza Frenly

> Uza Frenly is a relatively new product used to feed and condition the soil. It is suitable for use on most garden plants, fruit, vegetables and lawns but should not be used for acid loving plants. The product is noted for its sweet smell.
>
> Uza Frenly contains composted duck manure and straw. It supplies useful quantities of the major plant nutrients and has an NPK analysis of 1.98:1.48:2.27 and also supplies trace elements.

**How to use** Sprinkle over the required area and hoe or fork into the top soil.

**How much** Apply at a rate of 4 - 12 oz per square yard depending on plant species and soil status.

**Other info** Uza Frenly is supplied as a sweet smelling powder in 5 litre packs.

**Supplier** HDRA Sales Ltd Tel 0203 303517 HDRA shop only

Price for 5 litres from HDRA shop - £6.99 (1990 price)

**Accepted** All

**Use**

# WORM CASTS

Worm Casts is for use as a plant reviver and to give seedlings and young plants a good start. Worm Casts comes from a company called 'Turning Worms'.

Worm Casts contains the casts of worm breeding beds where the main source of food is seaweed so the casts are full of humus and trace elements which promote healthy plant growth.

**How to use** For putting life into jaded pot plants, tubs or window boxes top up the container with a thin layer of worm casts every couple of months. To give seedlings and young plants a good start sprinkle worm casts along the sowing drill or onto the area where plants will be transplanted.

**How much** Apply 3 oz per square yard.

**Other info** Worm casts are supplied as a powder in 2 litre packs.

**Supplier** HDRA Sales Ltd Tel 0203 303517 Ryton shop only
Price for 2 litres from HDRA shop - £1.45 (1990 price)

**Accepted** All

**Use**

# BIO FRIENDLY COMPOST MAKER

> Bio Friendly Compost Maker is a product by Pan Britannica Industries Ltd which is claimed to be 100% organic but the actual contents of this product are not listed on the product information. This product is a natural source of energy for millions of bacteria which abound in green material and soil. The rapid development of these bacteria produces heat, and this turns the plant waste into compost.

**How to use** Sprinkle required amount onto the greenery and leave as directed.

**How much** Application will vary depending on the quantity and the type of green material used.

**Other** Bio Friendly Compost Maker is available in a standard No.1 size shaker pack.

**Supplier** Pan Britannica Industries Limited  Tel 0992 23691
Price for a No.1 size shaker pack - £1.45 (1990 Price)

**Accepted** All

**Use**

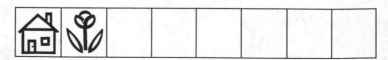

# BIOSTORE

Biostore is for use as a preservant for feed grain. It allows grain to be stored at higher moisture levels without spoilage. Biostore treated grain, unlike grain treated with propionic acid, can be sold at any time during the season.
Biostore contains two strains of the bacteria *Peddiocuccus pentosaceus*. The bacteria compete very efficiently with moulds and fungi for any available fermentable nutrients and so limits the growth of these spoilage organisms. Heating of the stored crop is also reduced.

**How to use** Mix Biostore with water and spray onto the grain by mounting a spray nozzle at the base of the auger so that the mixing action of the grain allows an even coating to be applied to each grain. After application aerate the grain to dry it down to 18% moisture content.

**How much** One sachet will treat 20 tonnes of grain. Mix 100 grams with 20 litres of water and apply 1 litre per tonne.

**Other** Biostore is supplied as a powder in 100 gram sachets. Store in a cool place but do not freeze.

**Supplier** Biotal Ltd 0222 766716 and also from
Axis Agricultural Ltd Tel 0785 850941
Price on application and will depend on quantity.

**Use**

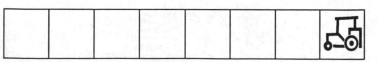

# BUMBLE BEES

Bumble Bees are for use as an aid to pollination of outdoor and protected crops. It is suitable for use with all crops where dependance on natural rates of pollination may reduce crop yields.

The Bumble Bees used are *Bombus terrestris* and being fairly large visit more flowers in a single flight and so are particularly useful in aiding cross pollination.

**How to use** Release the bumble bees into the crop as soon as flowering begins.

**How much** Number of bees to introduce will depend on the crop being treated.

**Other** Bumble Bees are supplied as a colony of bumble bees in a stypopore box measuring 37 x 25 x 25 cm.

**Supplier** Bunting Biological Controls Ltd Tel 0206 271300 and from Brinkman UK Tel 0243 531666 (South) or 0482 42123 (North) Price on application to supplier.

**Accepted** All

**Use**

# CODACIDE OIL

> Codacide Oil is used to increasing the efficiency of spraying and allow a reduction in the amount of pesticide needed to be effective. It is suitable for use on all crops.
> Codacide Oil contains 95% British grown rape seed oil and 5% formulating agents. The oil encapsulates (surrounds) the pesticide molecules to form microcapsules which form a controlled emulsion when mixed with water.

**How to use**  Mix with diluted pesticide. Timing of application will depend on the pesticide being used and the crop plant treated.

**How much**  If pesticide requirement is less than 1.75 pints per acre or 2.5 litres per hectare mix required amount per acre with 1.75 pints Codacide. Otherwise mix on a ratio of 11 by volume. 1 drum will treat 25 acres (minimum) or 10 ha.

**Other**  Codacide Oil is supplied as a liquid in 25 litre containers.

**Supplier**  Microcide Ltd Tel 0359 51077 and also from Organic Farmers and Growers Ltd Tel
Price for 25 litre drum - £30.00

**Accepted**  OFG GCFP

**Use**

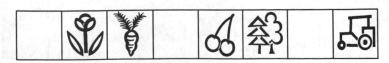

# FERTOSAN COMPOST MAKER

**G**

Fertosan Compost Maker is a compost accelerator and activator. Depending on the mix of vegetation the compost will be formed in approximately 6 weeks when temperatures are above 15°C. In cooler weather it may take 2 - 4 months to fully degrade the material. It can be used to help rot down all waste vegetation except ivy and yew leaves. Well rotten Fertosan compost is dark brown, friable and with the appearance of soil rich in organic matter.

Fertosan Compost Maker contains seaweed, rye flour and comfrey which encourage growth of bacteria in the compost that breakdown the plant material and supply trace elements that might otherwise limit microbial activity. However the rate of breakdown of the waste material will depend largely on the ratio of carbon to nitrogen in the material. Leaves and soft vegetation contain more nitrogen and less carbon and therefore rot more quickly.

**How to use** Mix the contents of a 15 gram sachet with 750 ml of water. It is best to keep the solution for 2 -3 days at a warm temperature. Build the compost heap in layers of garden waste to a depth of about 25 cm (10 inches). Sprinkle the prepared solution or powder over each layer and add a handful of fine soil if available. Ensure that the compost heap does not dry out.

**How much** For a heap 1.5 m$^2$ apply approximately 25 grams of compost maker.

**Other** Fertosan Compost Maker is supplied as a powder concentrate for mixing with water in 15 gram sachets and as a powder for direct application in 250 gram packs.

**Supplier** Ferosan Products Tel 051 632 6641 and from HDRA Sales Ltd Tel 0203 303517 and from Gala Brokers Ltd Tel 0244 390712
Price for 15 g sachet of concentrate - £0.65.
Price for 250 gram powder pack - £0.75.
Price for 2 ton (treats 2 - 3 cubic yards) from HDRA - £0.92

**Accepted** All

**Use**

| | 🌷 | 🥕 | | | | |
|---|---|---|---|---|---|---|
| | | | | | | |

# ORIGINS ORGANIC COMPOST MAKER

Origins Organic Compost Maker is a new product from Fisons which is a completely organic product containing micro organisms as the active ingredients. It also contains organic nutrients and is used for home composting. This product is effective when used on compost such as vegetable peelings, leaves, lawn clippings and green prunings but avoid woody materials and meat waste.

Origins Organic Compost Maker contains organic material that stimulates microbial activity and supplies trace elements that could other wise limit the rate of microbial breakdown in the compost heap.

**How to use** As the compost heap is built up lightly sprinkle the compost maker on with every 6 -9 inches added.

**How much** The correct application rate is 5 g per sq foot of surface area.

**Other** Origins Organic compost Maker is available in a 350 g shaker bottle. There is also an Origins Compost Bin System available.

**Supplier** Fisons plc  Tel 0473 830492 and also supplied by most garden centres or department stores.
Price for 350 g shaker bottle - £2.49 including VAT.
Price for the Origins Bin System  - £25.99 including VAT.

**Accepted** **All, is approved by the** Draft European Community Directive on producing organic food.

**Use**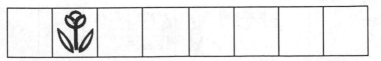

# NATUPOL

> Natupol is for use as an aid to natural pollination in tomatoes in greenhouses to achieve good flower setting and increase yields. It can be used to replace labour intensive mechanical "buzzing". not surprisingly Natupol comes from a dutch company, Koppert.
> Natupol contains the black and white/yellow bumble bee *Bombus terrestris* which is a very effective pollinator of the tomato plant. Due to their large size they visit more flowers on each flight and more flowers per minute and brush the stigmas and stamens more frequently and effectively. They will be active even at low temperatures and light intensities.

**How to use**    Simply position the hive in the crop and release the bees. The hives are supported by special poles and once positioned in the crop should not be moved so that the bees can find their way back to their own hive. The hive should be checked regularly to ensure there is an adequate supply of sugar water and flowers should be checked for pollination. A brown colouration will be apparent on pollinated flowers. The bumble bees can be used throughout the growing season.

**How much**    Initially establish two hives per acre in the crop. To maintain good pollination the hives should be replaced at regular intervals.

**Other**    The bumble bees are supplied as colonies in special hives. Use immediately upon receipt.

**Supplier**    Koppert (UK) Ltd Tel 0892 884411
Price on application to supplier.

**Accepted**    All

**Use**

# POLSEM

---

Polsem is used to aid pollination in protected crops and has been tested on onions and peppers with good results.

Polsem contains calliforid diptera (beetles) which visit the flowers to feed and as they move from flower to flower and plant to plant are effective pollinators. These pronube diptera are fairly easily reared on artificial diets and are harmless to man.

---

**How to use**    Release the diptera into the crop at the beginning of flowering. they will automatically begin to pollinate the flowers.

**How much**    The number of diptera to release will depend on the crop grown.

**Other**    Polsem is supplied as adult diptera.

**Supplier**    Urbio UK Tel 0734 661243

Price on application to supplier.

**Accepted**    All

**Use**

# QR (QUICK RETURN) COMPOST ACTIVATOR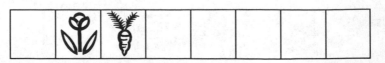

QR Compost Activator is used to increase the turn around rate of composted material and to control odours and flies in barns.
QR Compost Activator contains a herbal mix that encourages microbial activity and so speeds up the process of turning waste materials into useable compost.

**How to use** Dilute with water and apply to the material to be composted.

**How much** Details of dilution and application rates will be supplied with the product. A small pack will treat 2 cubic yards. A large pack will treat 10 cubic yards and a 4 oz pack will treat 100 cubic yards.

**Other** QR Compost Activator is supplied as a powder in three pack sizes, small, large and 4 oz.

**Supplier** HDRA Sales Ltd Tel 0203 303517
Price for small pack - £0.95
Price for large pack - £2.15
Price for 4 oz drum - £6.15

**Accepted** All

**Use**

## SEED TREATMENT FOR CEREALS

Seed Treatment for Cereals is used to improve establishment of new leys of the cereal crop, increase yields and improve crop quality. It will maximise root development which increases resistance to stress and disease. Trials show increased yields for treated crops compared to an untreated control.

Seed Treatment for Cereals contains specific growth promoters that have a direct effect on growth and hydrolysed protein complexes that provide amino acid nutrients to the seedling. Selected enzymes are included to breakdown compounds in the soil that inhibit germination.

**How to use** Coat the seeds with the seed treatment and sow as normal.
**How much** Amounts to apply will depend on the crop and seeding rate.
**Other** Seed Treatment for Grass and Clover is supplied as dry powder.
**Supplier** Cytozyme (UK) Ltd 0733 238545
Price on application to supplier. Cost of treatment is £2.50 per acre (£6.25 per hectare).

**Use**

# SEED TREATMENT FOR GRASS & CLOVERS G

Seed Treatment for Grass and Clovers is used to improve establishment of new leys of grass and clover. It will maximise root development which allows regrowth after cutting to be more vigorous and increases resistance to stress and disease.

Seed Treatment for Grass and Clover contains specific growth promoters that have a direct effect on growth and hydrolysed protein complexes that provide amino acid nutrients to the seedling. Selected enzymes are included to breakdown compounds in the soil that inhibit germination.

**How to use** Coat the seeds with the seed treatment and sow as normal.
**How much** Amounts to apply are not stated in the literature.
**Other** Seed Treatment for Grass and Clover is supplied as dry powder.
**Supplier** Cytozyme (UK) Ltd 0733 238545
Price on application to supplier. Cost of treatment is £2 per acre (£5 per hectare) maximum.

**Use**

# SEPTICO COMPOST MAKER

Septico Compost Maker is used for accelerating vegetable matter composting. It is suitable for use on all vegetable waste material including chopped woody material.
Septico Compost Maker is a herbal preparation that encourages microbial activity and so speeds up the process of turning waste materials into useable compost.

**How to use**  Sprinkle the powder in to the material to be composted. Alternatively mix with water and apply as a liquid, this will also provide moisture for the microbes to use.

**How much**  Amount to use will depend on the amount of material to be composted.

**Other**  Septico Compost Maker is supplied as a powder in 250 gram containers. It will keep indefinitely.

**Supplier**  Cumulus Organics Ltd Tel 0452 305814
Price for 250 grams - £1.95 (+ carriage)
Price on application to supplier.

**Accepted**  All

**Use**

# STUBBLE DIGESTER EXTRA

Stubble Digester Extra is used to speed up the processes involved in incorporation of straw to avoid problems such as toxin build up and soil nitrogen lock up.
Stubble Digester Extra contains hydrolysed protein complexes that provide amino acid nutrients to the soil microbes. The inclusion of selected enzymes opens up the straw structure allowing the mibrobes more access to the nutrients available in the straw. Provision of protein and energy allows the microbes to rapidly breakdown the straw. Once the microbes run out of food they will die and the nutrients they utilised will become available to the new crop.

**How to use** Chop the straw to increase the number of possible entry points for the microbes. Pre treat the straw with Stubble Digester Extra and incorporate the treated straw into the soil. Allow as much time as possible before sowing the next crop. For treatment dilute the requird amount of digester with 175 - 300 litres of water and spray on to the straw.

**How much** For whole crop treatment apply 425 - 575 ml per ha. For standing stubble and chaff apply 300 ml per ha. If nitrogen is added levels can be reduced.

**Other** Stubble Digester Extra is supplied as a liquid in bottles to treat 2 ha.

**Supplier** Cytozyme (UK) Ltd 0733 238545
Price on application to supplier. Cost is approximately #6 per acre.

**Accepted** GCFP

**Use**

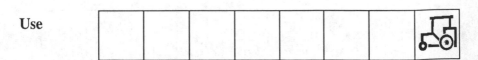

# AQUILITE SULPHUR

Aquilite sulphur is a liquid formulation of sulphur for use as a fungicide and disease preventative in cereals, oil-seed rape, sugar beet, fodder brassicas and soft fruit. This product can also be used as a foliar feed so an application can have two benefits for the crop.

Aquilite sulphur contains 90% sulphur (weight / volume). Although described in The UK Pesticide Guide as "a broad spectrum inorganic protectant fungicide" sulphur is permitted in Organic and Conservation Grade standards as it has a long history of use and has no detrimental effect on the environment.

Sulphur is not suitable for use on certain plant cultivars, for example, strawberries and some apple and gooseberry strains and it is best to consult the supplier or product label for further details.

**How to use** Aquilite sulphur can be applied through standard spraying equipment, including aerial spraying. It is best to use sulphur as soon as the disease first appears and repeat at 2 - 3 weekly intervals. Treatment is unlikely to be effective if the disease is already well established in the crop.
Certain people are sensitive to sulphur and protective clothing should be worn during application.

**How much** For arable crops apply 2 litres per acre. Recommendations for other crops is not given in the product information sheets. Consult the product label or supplier for further details.

**Other** Aquilite sulphur is supplied in 5 litre containers.

**Supplier** Organic Farmers and Growers Ltd Tel 0449 720838
Price for 5 litre container - £10.25
Delivery is charged extra to this price.

**Accepted** OFG

**Use**

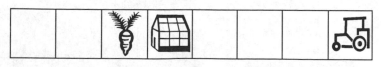

# BIG BALE SILAGE 2000

H

> Big Bale Silage 2000 is specifically designed for use on big bale silage in bags, wraps or clamps. Big bale silage is prone to aerobic spoilage as compared to clamp silage as there is a much larger surface area of crop exposed to possible air infiltration and elimination of air from the crop is less complete. Big Bale Silage 2000 will reduce spoilage of the crop by moulds and reduces the risk of listeriosis in sheep fed big bale silage.
> Big Bale Silage 2000 contains propionic and acrylic acids, mould inhibitors and surfactants that combine to give a broad spectrum control of yeasts, moulds and bacteria in the crop.

**How to use** Apply directly to the crop during bailing. It can also be used as a surface treatment prior to wrapping to give extra protection against moulds on the bale surface.

**How much** Apply 1 to 2 litres per tonne of fresh crop. Amount required will depend on conditions and crop ensiled.

**Other** Big Bale Silage 2000 is supplied as a liquid in 22.7 litre and 200 litre drums.

**Supplier:** Agil Ltd Tel 0734 785531
Price available on request from supplier.

**Use**

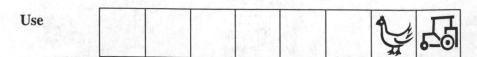

# BIO FRIENDLY ANTI-ANT DUSTER

---

Bio Friendly Anti-Ant Duster is a new product from Pan Britannica Industries Ltd which is claimed to be 100% organic but the actual ingredients are not listed on the product information. The active ingredient of this product is pyrethrum which is a natural insecticide obtained from a type of daisy.

Bio Friendly Anti-Ant Duster is a ready to use formulation which can be used inside the house and in the garden and it controls all types and species of ants.

---

**How to use** Dust liberally along runs and in crevices where ants congregate.

**How much** Apply when ants are seen and repeat as necessary. Use indoors, outdoors and dust around plants to protect them.

**Other** Bio Friendly Anti-Ant Duster is available in a standard one size puffer pack.

**Supplier** Pan Britannica Industries Limited  Tel 0992 23691
Price for a No. 1 size pack - £0.95 (1990 Price)

**Use**

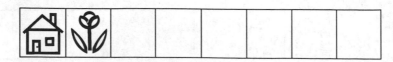

# BIO FRIENDLY INSECT SPRAY

---

Bio Friendly Insect Spray is a product by Pan Britannica Industries Ltd which is claimed to be 100% organic insecticides but the actual ingredients are not listed on the product information. The active ingredients of this product are derris (in the form of rotenone) and quassia which are both plant extracts.

Bio Friendly Insect Spray is available in a concentrated liquid insecticide which controls pests such as greenfly, blackfly and caterpillars.

---

**How to use**  Spray at own discretion.

**How much**  Application will depend on pest species and level of infestation. One standard bottle will dilute to 40 pints of spray.

**Other**  Bio Friendly Insect Spray is available in a standard 100 ml size bottle.

**Supplier**  Pan Britannica Industries Limited  Tel 0992 23691
Price for 100 ml bottle - £1.25 (1990 Price)

**Accepted**  This product should be acceptable to green growers

**Use**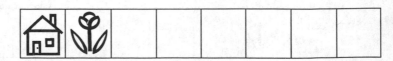

# BIO FRIENDLY PEST AND DISEASE DUSTER

Bio Friendly Pest and Disease Duster is a product by Pan Britannica Industries Ltd which is claimed to be 100% natural ingredients but the actual contents of this product are not listed on the product information. The active ingredients of this product are derris (in the form of rotenone) and sulphur. This ready to use treatment contains an organic insecticide and a natural fungicide which is suitable for all round the garden.
Bio Friendly Pest and Disease Duster controls pests such as greenfly, blackfly and caterpillars and many other garden troubles.

**How to use** Use only as a garden insecticide and apply when required.
**How much** Application will depend on pest species and level of infestation.
**Other** Bio Friendly Pest and Disease Duster is available in a standard No.1 size puffer pack.
**Supplier** Pan Britannica Industries Limited  Tel 0992 23691
Price for a No.1 size puffer pack - £1.35 (1990 Price)

**Use**

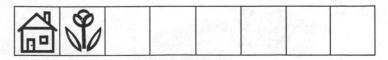

# BIO FRIENDLY PEST PISTOL

Bio Friendly Pest Pistol is a product by Pan Britannica Industries Ltd which is claimed to be 100% natural but the actual ingredients are not listed on the product information. The active ingredient of this product is soap made from fatty acids which occur naturally in plants. These fatty acids are selected for their insect-killing efficiency.

Bio Friendly Pest Pistol is a ready to use insecticide that does not kill ladybirds when used as directed but controls pests such as whitefly, greenfly, blackfly, red spider mite and scale.

**How to use** Use on outdoor plants. Spray as directed onto flowers, fruits, vegetables and shrubs.

**How much** Application will depend on pest species and level of infestation.

**Other** Bio Friendly Pest Pistol is available in a standard 500 ml size spray gun.

**Supplier** Pan Britannica Industries Limited  Tel 0992 23691
Price for 500 ml spray gun - £2.60 (1990 Price)

**Accepted** Fatty acids would probably be acceptable for most Green Growers

**Use**

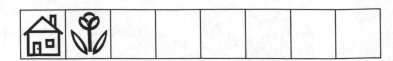

# BORDEAUX POWDER

H

> Bordeaux Powder is a traditional copper-based mix used as a contact fungicide either as a dust or mixed with water and sprayed onto the crop. Bordeaux powder contains a mix of copper sulphate and slaked lime and despite being inorganic in formula it is accepted under the Organic and Conservation Grade standards as it has a long history of use and is assumed to have no harmful effect on wildlife or the environment. Copper sulphate is toxic to livestock and causes irritation to eyes, skin and respiratory systems in man. Use in organic production under Soil Association standards requires permission from the Certification Committee and in all systems prevention by use of crop rotations, use of resistant cultivars and crop nutrition is promoted.

**How to use** Bordeaux powder can be applied as a dust or mixed with water and applied through a sprayer. Use of only freshly prepared solutions is recommended ensuring that the mix is agitated to ensure the mix stays suspended in the water.

Spray potatoes before the crop meets in the row and repeat every 7 - 14 days depending on disease pressure. To control canker in apples, cherries and plums spray monthly from August to October. For leaf spot and rust in blackcurrant, celery and gooseberry spray at first sign of attack and repeat at intervals of 14 - 21 days.

**How much** The mix should be applied at a rate of 11 kg per acre.

**Other info** Bordeaux powder is supplied in 25 kg bags.

**Supplier** Organic Farmers and Growers Ltd Tel 0449 720838
Price for 25 kg bag - £25.50
Delivery is charged extra to this price.

**Accepted** OFG SA GCFP UKROFS

**Use**

# BORDEAUX POWDER

> Bordeaux Powder is a traditional copper-based mix used as a contact fungicide either as a dust or mixed with water and sprayed onto the crop. Bordeaux powder contains a mix of copper sulphate and slaked lime and despite being inorganic in formula it is accepted under the Organic and Conservation Grade standards as it has a long history of use and is assumed to have no harmful effect on wildlife or the environment. Copper sulphate is toxic to livestock and causes irritation to eyes, skin and respiratory systems in man. Use in organic production under Soil Association standards requires permission from the Certification Committee and in all systems prevention by use of crop rotations, use of resistant cultivars and crop nutrition is promoted.

**How to use** Bordeaux powder can be applied as a dust or mixed with water and applied through a sprayer. Use of only freshly prepared solutions is recommended ensuring that the mix is agitated to ensure the mix stays suspended in the water.

Spray potatoes before the crop meets in the row and repeat every 7 - 14 days depending on disease pressure. To control canker in apples, cherries and plums spray monthly from August to October. For leaf spot and rust in blackcurrant, celery and gooseberry spray at first sign of attack and repeat at intervals of 14 - 21 days.

**How much** The mix should be applied at a rate of 11 kg per acre.

**Other info** Bordeaux powder is supplied a powder in a 112 gram tub or 225 gram tin from HDRA Sales and in a 175 gram container from Suffolk Herbs.

**Supplier** HDRA Sales Ltd Tel 0203 303517 and from
Suffolk Herbs Ltd Tel 0787 227358
Price for 112 gram tub from HDRA - £1.85
Price for 225 gram tin from HDRA - £2.55
Price for 175 gram container from Suffolk Herbs - £2.60

**Accepted** OFG SA GCFP UKROFS

**Use**

# BRIMSTONE PLUS

Brimstone Plus is for use against glume blotch, leaf spot, botrytis, fusarium, net blotch, cladosporium, yellow and brown rusts in cereals. The product comes from Mandops who have furthered their commitment to the green cause by donating 5 pence to each of: British Trust for Conservation Volunteers; British Trust for Ornithology; and The Farming and Wildlife Trust Limited; for every 5 acre pack of Brimstone Plus sold. Brimstone Plus contains three active ingredients: sodium metabisulphite, sodium propionate and potassium sorbate that combine to give effective control of fungal diseases with a minimal risk of resistance developing. Two of the ingredients are naturally found in cheese and berries and the third gives rise to sodium sulphate that can act as a source of sulphur for the plant. All three are widely used as food additives. Brimstone Plus is not systemic but can be used to protect sprayed ears for up to 6 weeks. Di-l-p-methene is included as an adjuvant to increase the effectiveness of the active ingredients.

**How to use** Brimstone Plus can be applied through standard spraying equipment. It can be used on its own or in a tank mixture with other products. A coating surfactant is included in the mix making the performance and rain proofing of the pesticide(s) more effective.

**How much** 1 pack will treat 5 acres.

**Other** Brimstone Plus is supplied as a liquid in plastic containers.

**Supplier** Mandops Tel 0703 641826
Price on application to supplier. Cost per acre is approximately £4.50.

**Accepted** GCFP

**Use**

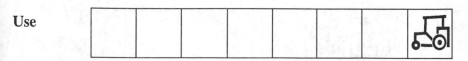

# CAT OFF

> CAT OFF is used to repel cats harmlessly and stops them digging and fouling gardens, tearing rubbish bags, damaging plants, etc.
>
> CAT OFF contains Quassia, a naturally occurring plant extract with natural hysteria producing properties. When cats move amongst the treated plants they become uneasy and move elsewhere.

**How to use** Spray onto any loosened soil patches, for example after digging, planting, seeding or weeding has been carried out.

**How much** The amount to be used will depend on the area to be covered and the persistence of the cat or cats.

**Other** CAT OFF is supplied ready to use.

**Supplier** Nilco Chemical Co. Ltd Tel 0256 474661
Price on application to supplier.

**Accepted** OFG SA UKROFS GCFP

**Use**

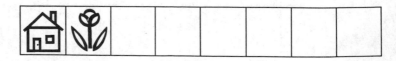

# CHEMPAK SLUG AND SNAIL KILLER

> Chempak Slug and Snail Killer kills slugs and snails on contact. It is harmless to humans, birds, livestock and earthworms but can be harmful to plants.
> Chempak Slug and Snail Killer contains aluminium sulphate which is accepted for use under SA standards. It will kill slugs on the surface and eggs within the soil.

**How to use**  Sprinkle onto the area to be protected and onto slugs and snails.

**How much**  Amount used will vary depending on severity of attack.

**Other**  Chempak Slug and Snail Killer is supplied in 250 gram containers.

**Supplier**  Chempak Products Tel 0992 441888
Price for 250 grams - £1.75
Price for 4 x 250 gram packs - £6.25

**Accepted**  SA

**Use**

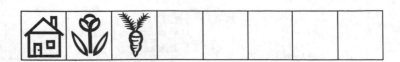

# DERRIS DUST

> Derris dust is suitable for use against aphid and caterpillar pests in fruit, vegetable and arable crops. It can also be used against flea beetle, red spider mite, thrips and other pests. It is listed as harmless to wildlife and has a low persistency making it relatively safe.
>
> Derris dust is derived from the roots of the derris plant and contains rotenone at a rate of 5 grams per kg. Rotenone is a highly flammable, highly powerful insecticide but is of low persistence. Particular care should be taken to avoid contamination of ponds or water way as rotenone is toxic to fish.

**How to use** The product is formulated for dry application as a dust.

**How much** In fruit crops and hops use 50 kg (2 bags) per acre. For other crops apply 20 kg per acre (5 bags per 6 acres).

**Other** Derris dust is supplied as a dry powder in 225 gram packs for gardening from HDRA and in 25 kg bags for the commercial grower from Organic Farmers and Growers Ltd.

**Supplier** Organic Farmers and Growers Ltd Tel 0449 720838 and from HDRA Sales Ltd Tel 0203 303517 and from
Suffolk Herbs Ltd Tel 0787 227247
Price for 25 kg bag from OFG Ltd - £25.00 delivery charged extra
Price for 225 gram pack from HDRA Sales - £1.60
Price for 225 gram pack from Suffolk Herbs - £2.60 (inc P&P)

**Accepted** OFG  SA

**Use**

# DERRIS LIQUID

> Derris liquid is suitable for use against aphid and caterpillar pests in fruit, vegetable and arable crops. It can also be used against flea beetle, red spider mite, thrips and other pests. Organic Farmers and Growers recommend the use of Derris liquid to knock down pest species that have multiplied more rapidly than their predators.
>
> Derris dust is derived from the roots of the derris plant and contains rotenone at a rate of 50 grams per litre. Rotenone is a highly flammable, highly powerful contact insecticide but is of low persistence. Particular care should be taken to avoid contamination of ponds or water way as rotenone is toxic to fish.

**How to use** The product is formulated for easy liquid application.

**How much** For field crops mix 125 ml in 100 litres (22 gallons) of water. Apply 100 litres of the mix per acre. In fruit crops use the same dilution and apply sufficient volume of the mix to drench the plants.

**Other** Derris liquid is supplied in two sizes of container for commercial use, 1 litre and 5 litre. 200 ml and 300 ml containers are available for use in the garden.

**Supplier:** Organic Farmers and Growers Ltd Tel 0449 720838 and from
HDRA Sales Ltd Tel 0203 303517 and from
Suffolk Herbs Ltd Tel 0787 227247
Price for 1 litre container from OFG Ltd - £12.30
Price for 5 litre container from OFG Ltd - £58.55
Price for 200 ml container from HDRA Sales - £2.75
Price for 300 ml from Suffolk Herbs - £4.40 (inc P&P)
Delivery is charged extra on both sizes of container.

**Accepted** OFG

**Use**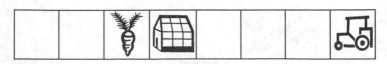

# DOG OFF

---

DOG OFF repels dogs harmlessly and keeps paths, walls, gate posts, pavements, lawns, etc free from fouling.

DOG OFF contains Quassia, a naturally occurring plant extract with natural hysteria producing properties. When dogs move amongst the treated plants or sites they become uneasy and move elsewhere.

---

**How to use** Spray onto all sniffing and marking points at the entrance to gardens, thus forming a barrier.

**How much** The amount to be used will depend on the area to be covered and the persistence of the dog or dogs.

**Other** DOG OFF is supplied ready to use.

**Supplier** Nilco Chemical Co. Ltd Tel 0256 474661
Price available on request to supplier.

**Accepted** OFG SA UKROFS GCFP

Use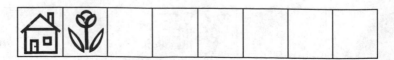

# FERTOSAN SLUG AND SNAIL KILLER

> Fertosan slug and snail killer is a contact slug killer which is harmless to worms, microbes and earthworms. However this product can be damaging to the plant. It contains aluminium sulphate and is allowed under SA standards.

**How to use** Apply to the affected area as required. Avoid any harm to plants by avoiding watering onto seedlings, and keep off lettuce leaves in dry weather.

**How much** Apply as directed on packet.

**Other** Fertosan slug and snail killer is supplied as a powder in 250 gram, 500 gram and 2.5 kg packs.

**Supplier** HDRA Sales Ltd Tel 0203 303517 and from
Suffolk Herbs Ltd Tel 0787 227247
Price for 250 grams from HDRA - £1.95
Price for 250 grams from Suffolk Herbs - £2.65 (inc P&P)
Price for 500 grams from HDRA - £3.30
Price for 500 grams from Suffolk Herbs - £4.20 (inc P&P)
Price for 2.5 kg - £10.15

**Accepted** SA

**Use**

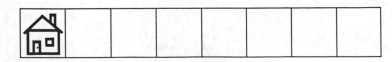

# FLOWERS OF SULPHUR

Flowers of sulphur is a powder formulation of pure sulphur for use as a fungicide and disease preventative in cereals, oil-seed rape, sugar beet, fodder brassicas and soft fruit. It is also suitable for control of small scale outbreaks of disease where localised treatment only is required, for example mildew in vegetables. This product can also be used as a nutrient to correct sulphur deficiency in the soil and can also help acidify alkaline soils.

Although described in The UK Pesticide Guide as "a broad spectrum inorganic protectant fungicide" sulphur is permitted in Organic and Conservation Grade standards as it has a long history of use and has no detrimental effect on the environment.

Sulphur is not suitable for use on certain plant cultivars for example strawberries and some apple and gooseberry strains and it is best to consult the supplier or product label for further details.

**How to use** Flowers of sulphur can be sprinkled onto the infected parts of the plant to control localised outbreaks of disease. Application to the soil is by *ad lib* dusting. It is best to use sulphur as soon as the disease first appears and repeat at 2-3 weekly intervals. Treatment is unlikely to be effective if the disease is already well established in the crop.

Certain people are sensitive to sulphur and protective clothing should be worn during application.

**How much** The amount to use will depend on the level of the problem and application to the soil will depend on the reserves of sulphur in the soil. No specific recommendations are given in the product information sheets. Please refer to product label or supplier.

**Other** Flowers of sulphur is supplied in 25 kg bags.

**Supplier** Organic Farmers and Growers Ltd Tel 0449 720838
Price for 25 kg bag - £16.00
Delivery is charged extra to this price.

**Accepted** OFG

**Use**

# HOPPIT

H

---

Hoppit is a safe, non-toxic, non-tainting systemic repellent designed to protect growing plants, shrubs and trees against predator attack.

Hoppit is based on Quassia, with natural hysteria producing properties, plus wetters and synergists which, together, induce strong revulsion in birds and animals. Hoppit enters the sap system where it is distributed throughout the plant. When predators move amongst the treated plants they become uneasy. If they try to eat the plants they experience a bitter taste plus an unpleasant smell. This, coupled with the feeling of insecurity, causes them to leave the area with any 'food imprint' related to the plants erased.

---

**How to use** It is best sprayed when the plants are growing freely and are not under stress. Hoppit should be sprayed when the field is under minimum attack. This normally occurs in the evening when the birds are going to roost and before the nocturnal animals are fully active. Row crops can be band sprayed where economy of chemical is desired. It can be used on ground crops, forestry, orchards and fruit and small plots.

**How much** For ground crops apply 2 litres in 450 litres of water per hectare (through normal sprayer). For forestry apply 3 litres in 450 litres of water (through knapsack sprayer). For orchards, small plots and fruit apply 0.25 litres in 35 litres of water. Apply 72 ml in 10 litres of water for every 10m².

**Other** Supplied in a liquid form.

**Supplier** Nilco Chemical Co. Ltd Tel 0256 474661
Price on application to supplier.

**Accepted** OFG SA UKROFS GCFP

**Use**

# LIQUID DERRIS

H

> Liquid Derris is a product by Pan Britannica Industries Ltd which is claimed to be a natural insecticide formulation. It based on rotenone which is a natural insecticide extracted from tropical plant roots.
>
> Liquid Derris is a traditional insecticide which controls pests such as greenfly, blackfly, gooseberry sawfly, thrips red spider mite and so on.

**How to use** Spray plants thoroughly using a clean garden sprayer onto all garden and greenhouse plants as soon as the pests are seen. For raspberry beetle, spray when the fruit turns pink.

**How much** For use against greenfly, blackfly and gooseberry sawfly use 5 ml in half a pint of water. For use against thrips, red spider mite, small caterpillars, raspberry beetle grubs and rose saw fly (slug worm) use 10 ml in half a pint. Repeat application as necessary.

**Other** Liquid Derris is supplied in two sizes; 100 ml which makes a volume of 5 - 10 pints and 200 ml which makes 10 - 20 pints.

**Supplier** Pan Britannica Industries Limited  Tel 0992 23691
Price on application.

**Accepted** All

**Use**

# MAIZE 2000

Maize 2000 is used to promote a strong lactic acid fermentation of the maize and to minimise aerobic spoilage to produce a stable, palatable silage.

Maize 2000 contains a blend of organic acids including acrylic acid which has a very low corrosion index. The acids low the crop pH inhibiting the growth of spoilage microbes such as clostridia. However stabilising of the clamp pH will be dependant on bacteria naturally present on the grass. Maize silage has a high sugar content making it prone to aerobic spoilage. THe combination of organic acids and a preservative is effective at preventing aerobic spoilage.

**How to use** Apply through any standard silage additive aplicator mounted onto the forage harvester.

**How much** Apply 1 - 2 litres per tonne of fresh forage depending on the dry matter content. For dry matter content below 20% apply 2 litres per tonne. For dry matter contents of 20 - 35% apply 1 litre per tonne.

**Other** Maize 2000 is supplied as a liquid in 22.7 litre and 200 litre packs.

**Supplier** Agil Ltd Tel 0734 785531
Price on application to supplier.

**Use**

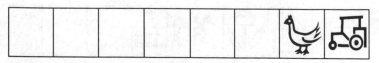

# Murphy Derris Dust

> Murphy Derris Dust product from Fisons which contains rotenone, a natural insecticide extracted from the roots of the Derris plant. It is used for the organic control of raspberry beetle, wasps, caterpillars, and flea beetle on plants.
>
> Murphy Derris Dust contains rotenone which in pure form is highly flammable. It is a highly powerful insecticide but is of low persistence. Particular care should be taken to avoid contamination of ponds and water ways as rotenone is toxic to fish.

**How to use**   Shake pack before use, Remove the cap and apply by puffing action  pointing the pack slightly downwards.  Coat both upper and lower leaf surfaces.

**How much**   Use when pests are first seen and apply to plants or wasp nests. To use for flea beetle on turnip, radish or cabbage apply as soon as seedlings appear and repeat twice at 4 day intervals. For use to control the raspberry and loganberry beetle apply just before flowers open and repeat 10 - 14 days after full bloom. For the prevention of caterpillars on vegetables, garden and greenhouse plants, apply early while caterpillars are small. Repeat as necessary. For use against wasps , unscrew the complete lid and apply dust liberally at entrance to the nest. Repeat after 7 days if necessary.

**Other**   Murphy Derris Dust is supplied in a puffer pack and has two size packs, 150 g  or 300 g.

**Supplier**   Fisons plc  Tel 0473 830492
Also supplied by most garden centres or departments.
Price for 150 g pack - £1.39.
Price for 300 g pack - £2.09.

**Accepted**   All, it is approved by the Draft European Community Directive on producing organic food.

**Use**

# NATURAL GARDEN FUNGICIDE

Natural Garden Fungicide is a mild form of sulphur combined with potassium salts, gum and water manufactured by Phostrogen Safer and is for use against fungus and mildews. It is effective against powdery mildews on fruit, vegetables and ornamental; scab on apples and pears; blackspot and rust on roses. Some varieties of fruit can be damaged by sulphur. It can also be used as an insecticide but is harmful to beneficial mites and parasitic wasps so should be used with great care where biological controls are being used.

**How to use** Spray directly on to the affected area.
**How much** Amount to use will depend on the level of infestation.
**Other** Phostrogen Safer's Natural Garden Fungicide is available in a ready to use 500 ml spray gun.
**Supplier** Phostrogen Ltd Tel 0490 2662 and from
HDRA Sales Ltd Tel 0203 303517 and also from
Suffolk Herbs Ltd Tel 0787 227247
Price for 500 ml spray gun from HDRA - £3.80
Price for 500 ml sprat gun from Suffolk Herbs - £4.45
**Accepted** OFG SA UKROFS

**Use**

# NATURAL INSECTICIDE (NATURAL SOAPS)

Natural Insecticide products are a range of insecticidal soaps made by Phostrogen Safer. The products are suitable for use against aphids, red spider mites and other pest mites, leaf hopper, thrips, soft scale and whitefly. The range includes a product for use on each of the three following plant categories: roses and flowers, fruit and vegetables, and house plants.

The insecticidal soaps are made from fatty acids of plant and animal origin and are in this sense organic. The fatty acids kill the insects on contact and will kill some species of beneficial insect if sprayed. The soaps are of low persistency and are safe to humans, pets and most wildlife.

**How to use** The products are applied by spraying directly on to the infested area of the crop or plant. Use the appropriate product for the crop or plant.

**How Much** Amount to spray will depend on the level of infestation.

**Other** Phostrogen Safer's Insecticidal Soap are available as a liquid in an easy to use spray gun.

**Supplier** Phostrogen Ltd Tel 0490 2662 and from
HDRA Sales Ltd Tel 0203 303517
Price for Natural Rose and Flower Insecticide 500 ml from HDRA - £3.80
Price for Natural Fruit and Vegetable Insecticide 500 ml from HDRA - £3.80
Price for Natural House Plant Insecticide 300 ml from HDRA - £2.75

**Accepted** OFG  SA  UKROFS

**Use**

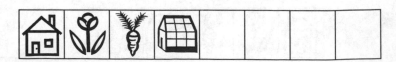

# NATURELL

> Naturell is for use against a wide range of pest insects and is suitable for use on vegetables, fruit trees and shrubs and has recently been shown to be very effective against balsam wooly aphid in forestry. It is safe to beneficial insects, wildlife and humans.
>
> Naturell contains specially formulated salts of fatty acids that kill the insects on contact. Unlike other fatty acid products currently on the market this product can be supplied with a special additional agent that allow use in hard water areas without any problems.

**How to use** Make a solution in water by placing the desired amount of water into the sprayer tank and add the Naturell to it. Mix thoroughly but gently to avoid foaming. Spray onto the leaf surfaces with standard spraying equipment.

**How much** For use against whitefly make a solution of 1% by putting 1 litre of Naturell in 100 litres of water. For treatment of aphids, thrips and scale insects use a solution of 2%.

**Other** Naturell is supplied as a liquid in 1 litre and 5 litre plastic containers.

**Supplier** Technoverde Ltd Tel 0734 661243 or 0860 327831
Price on application to supplier.

**Accepted** OFG SA UKROFS

**Use**

# NATURE'S ANSWER

> Nature's Answer to Insect Pests is a new product from Fisons. It is a natural insecticide for the protection of flowers, fruit and vegetables from greenfly, blackfly, whitefly, caterpillar, capsid and red spider mite.
> Nature's Answer contains natural pyrethrum extracted from the flowers of the chrysanthemum plant. Although pyrethrum is non persistent and is not toxic to humans or animals it causes irritation to eyes, skin and respiratory systems. Pyrethrum is toxic to bees (and beneficial insects) so measures should be taken to avoid spraying on flowering plants during the day.

**How to use** Spray evenly onto plant. On mature plants apply evenly to both upper and lower surfaces of leaves but use sparingly on younger plants to avoid damage.

**How much** Use as often as required.

**Other** Nature's Answer to Insect pests must not be used in direct sunlight or sprayed directly onto flowers. Food crops may be harvested the day after treatment if required. Available in a standard size of a 500 ml in a ready to use spray bottle.

**Supplier** Fisons plc  Tel 0473 830492
Also supplied by most garden centres or departments.
Price on application.

**Accepted** **All, is approved by the** Draft European Community Directive on producing organic food.

**Use**

# PY POWDER AND PY SPRAY

> Py Powder and Py Spray are contact insecticides for use against pests such as aphids, thrips, sawfly, weevils, leaf hoppers, flea beetles and capsids. Py Powder and Py Spray contain pyrethrum extracted from *Chrysanthemum cinerifolium* so comes from an organic source. Although pyrethrum is non-persistent and is not toxic to humans or animals it causes irritation to eyes, skin and respiratory systems. Pyrethrum is toxic to bees (and beneficial insects) so measures should be taken to avoid spraying on flowering plants during the day.

**How to use** Py Powder should be applied as dry directly to the infested plant. Py Spray should be sprayed directly on to the infested crop. For flowering plants apply at dusk to avoid uptake by bees.

**How much** Amount to apply will depend on the level of infestation and the pest species present.

**Other** Py Powder is supplied in a 175 gram puffer pack. Py Spray is supplied in a 125 ml pack ready to use.

**Supplier** Suffolk Herbs Ltd Tel 0787 227247
Price for 175 gram powder - £2.55 (inc P&P)
Price for 125 ml spray - £3.15 (inc P&P)

**Accepted** OFG SA UKROFS GCFP

**Use**

# SAVONA

---

Savona is a contact insecticide for use against aphids, thrips, mealybugs, whitefly and other insect pests on vegetables, fruit and ornamental crops. It is suitable as a corrective measure when biological controls are in use and insect infestations are high. For example it can be used to kill adult whitefly by spraying the top of the plant leaving the larvae on the lower plant to be attacked by biological controls.

Savona contains a mixture of natural fatty acids (potassium salt soap) that kill the insect on contact. It is completely biodegradable and so leaves no reside on the crop or in the soil.

---

**How to use** Dilute 1 part with 49 parts of soft or rain water and apply as a spray to the appropriate parts of the plant. If the water is too hard the solution will turn cloudy. When using a biological control agent check with Koppert (or other supplier) about the sensitivity of the species and if necessary be careful to avoid spraying the parts of the plant where the control agents are present. Savona will not affect pets, ladybird or bees.

**How much** Amount applied will depend on the level of infestation of the pest, the pest species, size of the crop plant and so on. Consult the product label or supplier for details.

**Other** Savona is supplied as a liquid concentrate in 1 litre and 5 litre plastic containers.

**Supplier** Koppert (UK) Ltd Tel 0892 884411 and from
Suffolk Herbs Tel 0787 227247
Prices available from Koppert on request. Suffolk Herbs sell the 1 litre size for £5.95 + P&P.

**Accepted** OFG SA UKROFS

**Use**

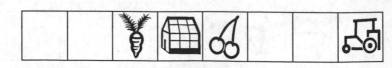

400

# SEPTICO SLUG KILLER

**H**

> Septico Slug Killer is a herbal preparation that kills slugs on contact. It is harmless to humans, birds, livestock and earthworms but van be harmful to plants.
> Septico Slug Killer contains aluminium sulphate.

**How to use**  Apply to the affected area as required. Avoid any harm to plants by avoiding watering onto seedlings, and keep off lettuce leaves in dry weather.

**How much**  Apply as directed on packet.

**Other**  Septico Slug Killer is supplied as a powder in 250 gram containers.

**Supplier**  Suffolk Herbs Ltd Tel 0787 227247
Price for 250 grams - £3.30 (inc P&P)

**Accepted**  SA

**Use**

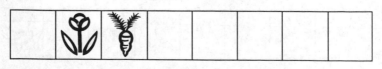

# SILAGE 2000

Silage 2000 is used to promote a strong lactic acid fermentation of the grass and to X aerobic spoilage to produce a stable, palatable silage.

Silage 2000 contains a blend of organic acids including acrylic acid which has a very low corrosion index. The acids low the crop pH inhibiting the growth of spoilage microbes such as clostridia. However stabilising of the clamp pH will be dependant on bacteria naturally present on the grass. Organic acids are effective at preventing aerobic spoilage which can occur at fed out.

**How to use** Apply through any standard silage additive aplicator mounted onto the forage harvester.

**How much** Apply 1 - 2 litres per tonne of fresh forage depending on the dry matter content. For 20 - 25% dry matter apply 2 litres per tonne. For dry matter contents above 25% apply 1 litre per tonne.

**Other** Silage 2000 is supplied as a liquid ready to use.

**Supplier** Agil Ltd Tel 0734 785531

Price on application to supplier.

**Use**

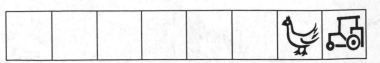

# SOFT SOAP

> Soft soap is for use as a wetting agent to make other pesticide sprays more effective. It can be used with most pesticides but always read the pesticide label carefully to check compatibility.
>
> Soft soap, when dissolved in water, reduces the surface tension making the pesticide spray cover more of the leaf surface in a thin film and preventing the pesticide from rolling off the plant. By increasing the amount of pesticide held on the plant where it can be effective allow a reduction in the amount of pesticide applied.

**How to use**  Dissolve the soft soap in a little warm water. It is best to use soft water or rain water. Mix with the pesticide as directed on the label.

**How much**  Dissolve 25 grams (1 oz) in a little warm water and make up to 3 litres (5 pints).

**Other**  Soft soap is supplied as a solid in 450 gram packs.

**Supplier**  HDRA Sales Ltd Tel 0203 303517
Price for 450 grams - £3.85

**Accepted**  OFG  SA  UKROFS

**Use**

403

# SPRAYFAST

> Sprayfast is a multi-purpose adjuvant for use in combination with almost all sprayed pesticide products on all crops to increase the performance of the pesticide.
>
> Sprayfast contains Di-1-p-menthene which increases the uptake of the pesticide by the crop, reduces spray drift and foam and improves the resistance of the pesticide to removal by rain. By making the pesticide more effective a reduced amount of pesticide can be used.

**How to use**  Mix Sprayfast with the pesticide in the sprayer tank and apply through standard spraying equipment.

**How much**  For standard ground spraying use 1 litre per 4 ha (10 acres). For aerial or low volume spraying use 1 litre per 8 ha (20 acres). For low rate glyphosate applications (other than MAFF 03176) use 1 litre per 2 ha (5 acres).

**Other**  Sprayfast is supplied as a liquid in plastic containers, and is unaffected by storage at -15°C.

**Supplier**  Mandops Tel 0703 641826
Price on application to supplier.

**Use**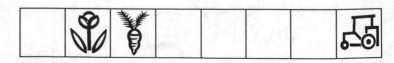

# TOP SILE

Top Sile is used to promote a strong lactic acid fermentation of the grass and to minimise aerobic spoilage to produce a stable, palatable silage. It contains a blend of propionic acid and sodium propionate for use on the clamp face to prevent aerobic spoilage at feed out. It can also be used ob big bale silage.

Propionic acid is effective at preventing aerobic spoilage which can occur at fed out and due to leakage of air under the sheeting. Dry matter losses due to aerobic spoilage can be as much as 10%. Top Sile is designed as a clamp management aid not as a replacement for a silage additive.

**How to use** Sprinkle onto the surface of the clamp before sheeting is put on. It can also be sprinkled onto the clamp face at feed out. It is advisable to wear rubber gloves as some free acid is present in the product.

**How much** Apply 0.5 kg per m².

**Other** Top Sile is supplied as a powder in 25 kg bags.

**Supplier** Agil Ltd Tel 0734 785531
Price on application to supplier.

**Use**

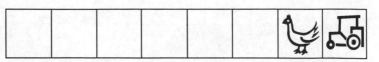

# INDEXES

## Product Use

## Manufacturers
## &
## Suppliers

# INDEX - Products by Use

# INDEX - PRODUCTS BY USE

## PRODUCTS FOR NITROGEN FIXING

## PRODUCTS FOR SILAGE MAKING

# INDEX - PRODUCTS BY USE

411

Agil Limited
Fishponds Road
Wokingham
Berkshire RG11 2QL
UK
0374 785531

Agricultural Genetics Company
(MicroBio Division)
Unit 126
Cambridge Science Park
Cambridge CB4 4FZ
0223 420262

Agrimar UK
6 Roland Gardens
London SW7 3PH
071 244 7431

AgriSense - Biological Control
Systems Limited
Treforest Industrial Estate
Pontypridd Mid Glamorgan
Wales CF37 5SU
0443 841155

Alan Haythornthwaite
Willow Lodge
Church Road
Warton
Preston
Lancs PR4 1BD
0772 634456

Alltech (UK)
16-17 Abenbury Way
Wrexham Ind Estate
Wrexham
Clwyd LL13 9UZ
0978 660198

Applied Horticulture
Toddington Lane
Littlehampton
West Sussex BN17 7PP
UK
0903 721591

Ashlade Formulations Ltd
Ness road
Slade Green
Erith
Kent DA8 2LD
0322 33671

Axis Agricultural Limited
36 High Street
Eccleshall
Staffordshire ST21 6BZ
0785 850941

B Dugdale & Son
Bellman Mill
Salthill
Clitheroe
Lancs BB7 1QW
0200 27211

Berk Limited
PO Box 56
Priestley Road
Basingstoke
Hampshire RG24 9QB
0256 29292

Betagro
Trewinnard House
Perran-ar-Worthal
Truro
Cornwall TR3 7QD
0872 865614

BINAB USA Inc
Bråtenvägen 74
S-542422
Mariestad
Sweden
010 46 501 16804

BIOCON (UK) Limited
Eardiston
Tenbury Wells
Worcs WR15 8JJ
058470 345/391

Biotal Ltd
Chiltern Close
Cardiff CF4 5DL
UK
0222 766716/747414

Brinkman (Horticultural Service)
UK Ltd
Dunswell Lane
Dunswell
Hull
N Humberside HU6 0AG
0482 842123/4/5

Brinkman (Horticultural Service)
UK Ltd
Spur Road
Quarry Lane
Chichester
W Sussex PO19 2RP
0243 531666

Britmilk
Ballantrae House
Collin
Dumfrieshire DG1 4PT
038775 459

Bunting Biological Control
Limited
The Nurseries
Great Horkesley
Colchester
Essex CO6 4AJ
0206 272001

Chapman & Frearson
Victoria Street
Grimsby DN31 1PX
0472 352321

# INDEX - Manufacturers and Suppliers

Institute of Horticultural Research
East Malling
Maidstone
Kent ME19 6BJ
0732 843833

International Pheromone Systems
Limited
Units 12 & 13 Meadow Lane
Meadow Lane Industrial Estate
Ellesmere Port
South Wirral L65 4EH
051 357 2655

J & H Bunn Ltd
Bunns Lane
Great Yarmouth
Norfolk NR31 0JD
0493 441111

Kemin UK
Waddington,
Lincoln LN5 9NT
0522 720165

Kettle Produce Ltd
Balmalcolm Farm
Cupar
Fife KY7 7TJ
0337 31000

Killgerm Chemicals
PO Box 2
Osset
West Yorkshire WF5 9BW
0924 277631

Koppert (UK) Limited
1 Wadhurst Business Park
Faircrouch Lane
Wadhurst
E Sussex TN5 6PT
0892 884411

L William Teweles
19 Main Street
Seaton
Leicestershire LE15 9HU
0572 87692

Lever Indstrial
PO Box 100
Runcorn
Cheshire WA7 3JZ
0928 719000

Mandops
Tower Industrial Estate
Chickenhall Lane
Eastleigh
Hants SO5 5NZ
0703 641826

Maxicrop International Limited
Weldon Road
Corby
Northants NN17 1US
0536 402182

May & Dawson (Agrochems) Ltd
Cranswick Ind Estate
Beverley Road, Hutton Cranswick
Driffield
E Yorks YO25 9PF
0377 70296

Microbial Developments Limited
(see Microferm)
Spring Lane North
Malvern Link
Worcester WR14 1AH
0684 568434

Microcide Ltd
Shepherds Grove
Stanton
Bury St Edmunds
Suffolk IP31 2AR
0359 51077

Milk Marketing Board
Cleeve House
Lower Wick
Worcester
Worcs WR2 4NS
0905 424940

Mydas Natural Products
The Organic Garden Centre
PO Box 544
Milton Keynes
MK6 2UR
0525 211131

Natural Pest Control Limited
Watermead
Yapton Road
Barnham
Bognor Regis
Sussex PO22 0BQ
0243 553250

Nilco Chemical Company Ltd
Kingsland Industrial Park
Basingstoke
Hampshire
0256 474661

Nutrimix
Boundry Road Industrial Estate
Boundry Road
Lytham,
Lancs FY8 5HU
0253 730888

O V Limited
(was Oxford Virology Ltd)
10 Storey's Gate
Westminster
London SW1P 3AY
071 222 3791

Organic Concentrates Ltd
Chalfont St Giles
Bucks
02404 2563

Organic Farmers and Growers Ltd
Abacus House
Station Yard
Needham Market
Ipswich
Suffolk IP6 8AT
0449 720838

Pan Britannica Industries Limited
(PBI)
Britannica House
Waltham Cross
Herts EN8 7DY
0992 23691

Pertwee Holdings Ltd
Harbour House
Colchester
Essex CO2 8JF
0206 577991

Phostrogen Ltd
Corwen
Clwyd LL21 0EE
0490 2662

Phosyn International
Manor Place
The Airfield
Pocklington
York YO4 2NR
0759 302545

RCR Layson
3 Tatton Court
Kingsland Grange
Warrington
Cheshire
WA1 4RR

Rentokil Ltd
Felcourt
East Grinstead
W Sussex
RH19 2JY
0342 327171

Rigby Taylor Ltd
Unit 7,
The RiverWay Estate
Portsmouth Road
Peasmarsh
Guildford
Surrey
GU3 1LZ
0800 424919 0483 35657

R I O
Westbourne House
Station Road
Glos

Robin Appel Ltd
The Town House
The Square
Bishop's Waltham
Southampton SO3 1AF
0489 896388

Rumenco
Stretton House
Derby Road
Burton on Trent
Staffs DE13 0DW
0283 511211

Schering Agrochemicals Ltd
Chesterford Park Research Station
Saffron Walden
Essex CB10 1XL
0799 30123

Sea Trident Ltd
Sarum House
Oak Park
Dawlish
Devon EX7 0DE
0626 862489

Shamrock
Bord na Mona
Dublin
Ireland

Shell Chemicals UK Limited
Agricultural Division
Heronshaw Ho  Ermine Bus Park
Huntingdon
Cambridgeshire
PE18 6YA
0480 414140

Sinclair Hort & Leisure Ltd
Firth Road
Lincoln LN6 7AH
0522 537561

Steel & Brodie Ltd
Stevens Drove
Houghton
Stockbridge
Hampshire
0794 388698

Suffolk Herbs Ltd
Sawyers Farm
Little Cornard
Sudbury
Suffolk CO10 0NY
0787 227247

Synchemicals Ltd
44/45 Grange Walk
London SE1 3EN

Technoverde
24 Donnington Road
Reading
Berks
RG1 5ND
0734 661243

The Fyba Pot Co  Ltd
Malvern Road
Knottingley
W  Yorks
WF11 8EG
0977 677676

Tithebarn
Tithebarn House
Weld Road
Southport
Merseyside PR8 2LY
0704 60606

Tomen UK Ltd
Tomen House
13 Charles II St
London SW1Y 4QT

Tony Ashmore Ltd
Lane End Farm
Clay Lane
Haslington
Nr Crewe
Cheshire
0270 586671

Vitrition Ltd
Ryhall Road
Stamford
Lincs PE9 1TZ
0780 55651

Vitax Ltd
Selby Place
Stanley Industrial Estate
Skelmersdale
Lancs WN8 8EF
0695 51834

W L Dingley & Co
Buckle Street
Honeybourne
Evesham
Worcs WR11 5QB
0386 830242

Xenova Ltd
545 Ipswich Road
Slough
Berks SL1 4EQ
0753 692229

# About the Authors

**Steve Lisansky** is one of the founders of the UK biopesticide business having worked on the development and marketing of products based on bacteria and fungi. He is the author of a detailed study concerning the marketing, technical and legal aspects of biopesticide manufacture and use. With more than fifteen years experience in the food and agricultural industries he has been involved in all aspects of the development of new crop protection products from research, through development to validation and marketing.

**Alison Robinson** was trained in agricultural and environmental science at Newcastle University. She has subsequent practical experience in both organic and conventional farming systems as well as having worked in marketing of animal nutritional products, including trials involving yeast cultures.

**Jim Coombs** is internationally recognised in areas of agriculture, biotechnology and alternative crop use. He has served as an expert for the Commission of the European Communities in areas of bioconversion and new uses for agricultural products. This follows industrial experience in directing agricultural research in nitrogen fixation, biological pest control and low input systems. He contributed to formulation of standards which led to the evolution of the *Conservation Grade*.